PELICAN BOOKS

A341

THE HUMAN SPECIES

ANTHONY BARNETT

ANTHONY BARNETT

THE HUMAN SPECIES

A BIOLOGY OF MAN

PENGUIN BOOKS

Penguin Books Ltd, Harmondsworth, Middlesex

CANADA: Penguin Books (Canada) Ltd, 178 Norseman Street,
Toronto 18, Ontario

AUSTRALIA: Penguin Books Pty Ltd, 762 Whitehorse Road,
Mitcham, Victoria

SOUTH AFRICA: Penguin Books (S.A.) Pty Ltd, Gibraltar House,
Regent Road, Sea Point, Cape Town

—

First published by MacGibbon and Kee in 1950
Published in Pelican Books 1957

Made and printed in Great Britain
by Butler and Tanner Ltd, Frome and London
Collogravure plates
by Harrison and Sons, Ltd

CONTENTS

PART TWO: HUMAN DIVERSITY

ILLUSTRATIONS

PLATES

DRAWINGS AND DIAGRAMS

WHAT IS BIOLOGY?

Amoeba has her picture in the book,
  Proud protozoon! – Yet beware of pride.
All she can do is fatten and divide;
  She cannot even read or sew or cook ...

JULIAN HUXLEY

BIOLOGY began when men first distinguished between useful and dangerous plants and animals. Every branch of scientific knowledge has an origin in man's attempts to satisfy his material needs; biology, the science of living things, is most closely linked to the production of food and the prevention of disease.

Accurate biological knowledge is thus very much older than civilization, but the systematic and deliberate study of plants and animals is a recent affair. Apart from rather isolated individuals, such as Aristotle in classical times, or Albertus Magnus in the middle ages, the first biologists appeared about three centuries ago, in western Europe. Interest in the variety of living things had been greatly stimulated by new discoveries abroad. New types of timber, new fur-bearing animals, new fruits and foods of all kinds made an interest in at least one aspect of biology profitable. To ensure the full benefit from these discoveries an agreed classification and system of names for all known living things were needed. As a result, in the eighteenth century, many biologists turned their attention to the classification and naming of plants and animals.

Among the new things found in different lands were unfamiliar types of men. Linnaeus, the foremost of the classifiers, nevertheless recognized that all human beings belong to one species, and named the species *Homo sapiens* – thinking man. This is the species with which this book is concerned. But although man will here be studied from the point of view of a biologist, this does not imply that human needs and desires will be ignored. Human biology is a branch of knowledge that can be of practical value to every human being. Health and disease, food, the sizes and quality of human populations, the diversity of human types and their abilities, are all topics on which knowledge is not only desirable, but, for a twentieth-century adult, necessary.

This treatment of biology, focused on man and based on the usefulness of biological knowledge, is the opposite of the conventional one. Even the relatively few, who have studied biology at school, will find most of the facts in this book unfamiliar. In the schools, we may learn in detail about a seaweed called *Fucus*, which is not even edible, let alone important; but often little is heard of man's biggest industry, agriculture, on which we depend for food. In the animal kingdom we may begin with the study of an obscure organism called *Amoeba*, but perhaps learn nothing of the related malarial parasite, although malaria is the worst of all the infectious diseases. The earthworm is studied in detail, but the part it plays in making soil fertile may go unmentioned. Among insects attention is usually concentrated on the cockroach, which happens to be a minor pest though this fact is often not to be found in the textbooks; the many serious insect pests are frequently ignored. When we come to the group to which man belongs, the vertebrates, the chosen example is commonly the frog, a vertebrate of many highly unusual characteristics, and of negligible economic importance.

Some teachers are trying to change all this, and not all biology courses ignore the practical significance of the subject; but many must leave the impression that biology is largely an academic study.

In this book the attempt is made to relate the main facts of human biology to the problems facing us in the middle of the twentieth century. The second chapter, on nature and nurture (or heredity and environment), deals with a topic which underlies much of the rest of the book. It is sometimes asserted that human nature cannot change: what this statement could mean, and whether it is true, is part of the subject matter of the chapter. The third deals in more detail with some aspects of human genetics. These two are the most difficult chapters. They are followed by one which completes the story of human reproduction and development.

After them there are six chapters on the evolution of man, and the differences between groups of men (or races) and between individual men and women today. Most people know that men are descended from ape-like ancestors; chapter five outlines the evidence for this statement, and chapter six gives some account of the evolution of man's most distinctive feature, his behaviour. Everyone knows that man exists in many shapes and colours; that some men are stupid, others intelligent; some criminal, others virtuous. In the next four chapters it is shown that these facts raise a number of urgent social problems, to some of which biological knowledge can suggest solutions. Finally, there is a series of chapters on various aspects of human populations. Like other animals man must, in order to survive, overcome the dangers of starvation and infection; at the same time he must be fertile. Four chapters therefore deal with food, disease, and the growth and decline of human populations.

This biological approach to the study of man might seem to reduce men to the status of 'mere animals'. In fact, however, as we shall find throughout the book, it enables us to see with great clarity the unique character of the human species. No apology, therefore, is offered for the objective treatment of human problems. A doctor taking the pulse-rate of a patient is making an objective measurement, in the same way as an engineer observing the revolutions of an engine, and nobody criticizes him for doing so. Human beings are very much more complex than any machine, but that need not deter us from being matter-of-fact about ourselves.

B

Part One

Heredity and Reproduction

The differences between individual human beings depend partly on what we inherit from our parents, partly on differences of environment: heredity and environment interact in complex ways to produce the end-product of the adult individual. Neither heredity nor environment can properly be said to have a greater influence in causing variation among individuals, but when we come to practical action we can influence environment, for instance nutrition or working conditions, while for man heredity has generally to be accepted.

The great variety of inherited differences is maintained by the mixing of the inherited factors, or genes, in sexual reproduction. The genes are transmitted from parent to offspring in microscopic structures, the chromosomes, which are present in the sperm and egg and also in every cell of the adult body. The regular behaviour of the chromosomes determines laws of heredity which apply to man and throughout the animal and plant kingdoms.

Sexual reproduction entails a complex development from a minute fertilized egg. In man the first forty weeks of life are spent as a parasite within the mother, and the physiological processes which take place in mother and child are now coming to be understood, with results of great importance to the individual and society.

Part One

Heredity and Reproduction

NATURE AND NURTURE

> A devil, a born devil, upon whose nature
> Nurture will never stick.
>
> WILLIAM SHAKESPEARE:
> (*The Tempest : Prospero on Caliban*)

IT is sometimes said by Europeans that all Chinese look alike. Doubtless few take this statement seriously; certainly, it is very far from the truth. In every human group individuals differ from each other both physically and in behaviour. There are two sources of this variation: in the first place individuals differ in the factors handed on from their parents, the *inherited* factors as they may be called; second, the influences that act on the individual from outside, and make up his *environment*, are highly variable. The study of these effects, that is, of variation and heredity, is called *genetics*. Human genetics is the subject of this and the next chapter.

If a child has insufficient iodine in his food he fails to grow normally and becomes a dwarf, of the type known as a cretin. This used to happen a good deal in Switzerland, and it is an example of environment influencing growth; a simple alteration in the environment, the addition of iodine to table salt, prevents the effect. But similar dwarfs occasionally appear in communities in which there is no lack of iodine, and no alteration in the amount of iodine in the food, or in any other environmental agency, affects their occurrence. In this case the condition is said to be due to heredity. These two examples show that stature can be affected by both environment and heredity.

Heredity (or 'Nature')

The word heredity is used here in a slightly unfamiliar way. If a tall father has a tall son, it is sometimes said that the son inherits his tallness from his father. We shall see later what really does happen. But the case of the dwarfism due to heredity is different, since the parents of the dwarf are themselves normal: there is no question of the dwarfism being inherited from one of the parents in the usual sense. This sort of thing is quite familiar from our experience of normal characteristics. Two brown-eyed parents may have a blue-eyed child: when this happens the parents may say the child 'inherits his eyes from his grandfather', or something of that sort.

But of course there is no direct handing on of *characteristics* from generation to generation, since all characteristics are developed anew in each individual. If one inherits a house, the house itself is actually handed over. We may recall the Wodehouse young man who, asked if he believed in heredity, replied, 'Of course, that's how I got my money.' This is legal inheritance, and it must be clearly distinguished from biological inheritance. The material passed on to us from our parents, and responsible for biological inheritance, is microscopic: it is contained in an egg-cell (produced by the mother) and a sperm (produced by the father). The two unite, and the fertilized egg so produced develops into the new individual with his or her own particular quota of 'characters'. The production of sperms and eggs is further described in chapter 4.

From the difference in size between egg and sperm it might be thought that the mother must have more effect on a child's characteristics than the father. This is not the case. In general, inherited effects are equal from both parents. There are minor exceptions to this rule, but few have anything to do with the fact that a human egg is about 85,000 times as large as a sperm.

Egg and Sperm. Human egg-cell, with sperm-cell drawn to scale

The Chromosomes and Heredity

The reason for the equal part played by egg and sperm is that each has a complete set of structures called chromosomes, and it is the chromosomes that carry the genetic factors, or *genes*. To appreciate the part played by chromosomes in heredity we must understand something of the microscopic structure of the tissues of the body. If small fragments, or very thin slices, of animal or plant tissues are examined under a microscope they are seen to be divided into exceedingly small compartments, the cells. Tissues grow by the increase in the size of the cells, followed by division of the cells into two. Cells vary a great deal in shape and function, but nearly all have a nucleus. Ordinarily a nucleus is a nearly spherical object without any obvious internal structure, but when a cell divides most of the nuclear material condenses, to form objects resembling minute rods or threads. These are *chromosomes*, and their number varies with the species of animal or plant; in man there are 48, forming 24 pairs. Each chromosome can be seen, soon after it appears, to be already split along its length; later, the halves of each chromosome separate, and two complete sets, each of 48 chromosomes, are formed. The cell then divides into two, and each newly-formed cell

Division of the Nucleus of an Egg-cell (*Mitosis*). The nucleus, when not dividing, appears as a structureless, roughly spherical object. When division begins the chromosomes become visible as double threads; the members of each pair separate, and two daughter-nuclei are formed, each with the same number of chromosomes as the parent nucleus. The whole cell then divides, and each daughter cell gets one nucleus. This happens throughout the body in the cells of growing tissues. The number of chromosomes is here shown as only one pair, for simplicity: man has 24 pairs

Chromosomes of Egg and Sperm. When egg and sperm-cells (gametes) are formed, in the ovaries and testes respectively, a special type of nuclear division (meiosis) takes place: the result is that, in man, the nucleus of an egg or sperm has only 24 chromosomes, instead of 24 pairs. At fertilization the full number of 48 is restored. Here only one pair is drawn, and a single parent cell is shown giving rise to four sperm cells, each with the half-number of chromosomes (haploid)

takes one set. However many times cell division takes place, each cell has a nucleus made up of the full complement of 24 pairs of chromosomes. This process is illustrated on page 10.

An important exception to this rule is provided by the germ cells – the egg-cells of the female and the sperm-cells of the male. When the germ cells are produced, in the ovaries and testes respectively, the chromosomes behave differently: each egg or sperm receives only 24 chromosomes, or one of each pair present in an ordinary cell. When an egg is fertilized by a sperm the two half-sets of chromosomes come together, and so in the fertilized egg the full number of 48 is restored, as shown on page 11.

This is the mechanism by which each parent contributes equally, on the average, to a child's constitution. The expression 'on the average' has to be put in, because, if a single person is studied, it often seems that resemblance to one parent is much more marked than to the other. This is not because there has been any abnormality in the chromosome mechanism: it is often because some of the genes carried by the chromosomes of one parent may mask the effects of the corresponding ones on the other set of chromosomes. Examples of how some of these genes operate are given in the next chapter.

The chromosome mechanism ensures that the genetic factors are distributed throughout the body. The fertilized egg is itself a cell, and all the cells of the body are derived from it by a series of repeated divisions. And we have already seen that, after division, each cell has a full complement of chromosomes.

If, then, a child has hair similar to that of its parents, it is not because the hair is handed on in any material sense, like a wig, but because the parents' chromosomes, carrying genetic factors which bring about the development of that particular kind of hair, are passed on, and are present in the cells of the skin from which the hair grows. (The example of hair is taken because hair characters are relatively little affected by environment. In general it is of course true

Human Chromosomes. Above, the 24 pairs drawn in a row; below, as they are seen in a cell during division of a nucleus

that part of our resemblance to our parents is due to sharing a common environment with them: for example, we grow up in the same country, and so learn the same language.)

It can now be seen why in biology the words 'heredity' and 'inherited' are often avoided. As Helen Spurway has said: 'Everyday speech perpetuates archaic concepts. It is still literate to say I inherit my father's nose, his surname, and his watch!' Very often therefore a difference between two individuals is said to be 'genetically determined'; this means that it is due to the action of the genetic factors, or genes, carried by the chromosomes and transmitted in the way described. One of the pioneers of genetics, Francis Galton, preferred to speak of *nature* and *nurture*, instead of heredity and environment.

Now that the machinery of transmission from parent to offspring has been established it is possible to be clear about what the often misused words *familial, congenital, constitutional*, and *idiopathic* signify. A disease is sometimes said to be familial when it occurs in several members of the same family or group of related families. By itself, this tells us nothing about its causes. A familial disease may be largely due to the transmission of a particular gene, or it may be caused by some environmental influence that acts on many members of the family. Tuberculosis, for example, is particularly common among people, such as those of the mining communities of South Wales, who do exhausting work in conditions that encourage its appearance. If several members of the same family get tuberculosis it may be because they all suffer these conditions, or because one infects others. However, there may be a genetic factor *as well*. People vary a great deal in their resistance to tuberculosis, and part of the variation is genetically determined. It follows that there may be families of persons all with a lower resistance than the average, because they all possess a particular set of genes.

This is far from saying that tuberculosis is an 'inherited disease'. The immediate cause of tuberculosis is infection with a particular kind of microbe, the tubercle bacillus, or T.B., together with a certain degree of susceptibility in the infected person. The infection itself is an environmental effect, arising usually from the presence of the microbe in the air or in milk. But susceptibility is affected both by other environmental influences, such as housing, and by genetic factors.

The word familial thus covers a complex set of possibilities. The same applies to the word congenital. A congenital condition is, strictly speaking, one present in the new-born child. The word thus refers to the time of appearance of the condition, and not to its cause. The cause may be genetical, at least in part, but sometimes it is wholly environmental. For instance, congenital syphilis is due to infection of the child by the mother shortly before birth – a purely 'environmental' effect. By contrast, 'lobster claw', an abnormality of the hands and feet, appears, as far as we know, in all individuals with a particular rare gene. On the other hand there is a rare condition called Mongolian idiocy which again is probably due to a single gene: unless a person has one or more genes of this particular kind, he cannot be a Mongolian idiot. The condition might consequently be said to be genetically determined. But there is a complication: not all people with the gene are Mongolian idiots; Mongolian idiocy is more likely to appear among the children of relatively old mothers, and especially of those who are over the age of forty when they have a child. (Even among such children it is rare.) It seems therefore that conditions in the womb influence its appearance: in other words the environment of the unborn child also plays a part. So in this instance both genetical and environmental differences are important.

The other two words, constitutional and idiopathic, are used principally by medical writers. Like the first two, they are often employed loosely, with a meaning (if any can be discerned) rather like that of congenital. They tend to imply that the condition described is 'inborn' or genetically determined, but often they signify little more than that the causes of the condition are obscure. It would be an aid to clear thinking if both terms were discarded.

One further expression, of a rather different kind, should certainly be given up. This is the word 'blood', used in the sense of 'heredity'. Expressions such as 'royal blood' are firmly rooted in our language, but obviously have no literal validity. They are based partly on the erroneous belief that the mother's blood flows directly into the blood vessels of the embryo. But the notion that a person is of 'noble stock' or has 'good blood' involves also the confusion of legal with biological inheritance which has already been mentioned. Royalty, nobility, 'family' in general, depend on the inheritance of name, title or estates or other property. Commonly, the inheritance is in the male line, and takes no account of the many ancestors not in that line. Some personage may be able, perhaps, to trace his ancestry back to William the Conqueror. So, probably, could every English person living today, if the records had been preserved. If we do not allow for the marriage of relatives, the number of our ancestors living in the eleventh century works out at many millions more than the total population of England at that time. Thus we are, not only all descended from William the Conqueror, but also from all of his contemporaries who have left descendants. This is a general consequence of sexual reproduction in the absence of rigid restrictions on mating. Indeed, if we could trace our descent far enough back, we should find that every living person today has a single origin in a pair – an 'Adam and Eve' – who lived some tens of thousands of years ago.

Environment (or 'Nurture')

It will be evident, from the discussion above, that the term environment, like heredity, is here being used in a sense rather different from the usual one. Environment is used in this book to refer to every influence that acts on the individual from outside, from conception (or fertilization) onwards.

The environmental influences that first act on a human being are those of the womb (or uterus). We have, in Mongolian idiocy, had one example of their importance, and there are plenty of others. The nutrition of the unborn child depends on the food materials carried in the mother's blood. This blood circulates in the tissues of the womb, and some of the materials dissolved in it diffuse into the blood stream of the embryo, which is separated from it only by a very thin membrane. If the mother herself is receiving a poor diet, the child too will suffer: deficiency of calcium in the mother's food may be responsible for defective bones in the child.

A mother's 'mental' state may also affect an unborn child. It has been suggested, for instance, that a recent increase in pyloric stenosis in infants reflected the increase in mental strain due to war. Pyloric stenosis is a narrowing of the exit of the stomach, causing vomiting of a peculiar kind and inability to take food normally. It is thought that mental disturbance in a mother causes an alteration in the contents of her blood, and that this in turn affects the blood of the embryo and brings about an abnormal growth of certain tissues.

If this is true, the psychological state of the mother, in this example, affects the child through a change in her blood, and this change does not give rise to the same state in the infant. There is nothing here in common with the belief that what a mother sees or thinks during pregnancy directly affects the appearance or thoughts of the child after it is born. There is no support for the belief that, if a pregnant woman sees strawberries, her child will have a 'strawberry mark'. In a novel published shortly before the first world war a child is described as being born 'hating his father', as a result of the feelings of his mother towards her husband. A new-born infant could not hate in this fashion, because it lacks a sufficiently developed nervous system. Only later can a child be induced to hate. The influence of the thoughts of a pregnant mother on her child is through such prosaic matters as the blood supply to the womb. She cannot ensure that her child will have a placid temperament by being calm herself, or that it will appreciate the arts as a result of her visits to picture galleries and concerts during pregnancy.

Once a child is born the environmental influences acting on him become much more complex. His parents form a most important part of the environment, but there are also other people, the climate, food, disease germs in the air and elsewhere, and many more subtle influences.

Lamarck and Lysenko

The importance of environmental influences is indeed obvious, and there are plenty of further examples in later chapters. There is however one supposed action of the environment which has caused violent controversy. It is commonly thought that if, let us say, a man becomes by training skilled in a particular trade, his children are likely to inherit some of this acquired skill. (Of course, many children learn their father's trade as they grow up, but *learning* from one's father is for our present purpose no different from learning from a school teacher: heredity is not involved in any biological sense.)

This doctrine, misleadingly called 'the inheritance of acquired characters', is associated with the name of Lamarck, an eighteenth-century biologist. And so we sometimes speak of *Lamarckism*. It is a doctrine that has long been in disrepute with biologists, but lately the controversy has been revived in a new form.

According to Lamarck, and to many other biologists of his time and later, various effects operating during the life of an individual influence the character of the individual's offspring: the most important are use and disuse, and Lamarck considered that the will or desire of an organism to perform an act was also important. Lamarck was unusual for his time in being an evolutionist: he was convinced that (as is now generally agreed) species are not immutable, but undergo a slow process of change; change, he thought, was brought about by the influence of the environment on successive generations, and their efforts to adapt themselves to it. The present theory of evolution is described in chapter 5. Our concern here is with the question whether Lamarckian transmission of environmental effects can be found anywhere, and if so the extent to which it is important.

One of the reasons for doubting the Lamarckian theory is our knowledge of the chromosomes and genes, and of the part they play in heredity. If the theory were true, we should have to suppose that a process, such as learning to be a good pianist, caused changes in a person's genes, or other transmitted material, so that children subsequently conceived would be capable of becoming pianists without training, or with less training. There is no known way in which this could occur, and what we know of the ways in which genes change is against it.

However, the apparently impossible sometimes turns out to be true, and many experiments have been devised to test the theory. Most of these experiments have failed to give acceptable evidence of a Lamarckian effect: the genes seem for the most part to be remarkably stable, and unaffected by ordinary environmental changes. Thus the effect of disuse was tested when flies were bred in the dark for 69 generations; at the end their eyes were unaffected, and they reacted normally to light. Further, in some experiments, it has been possible to show that the Lamarckian effect does not occur where, if the theory were true, it would be expected to do so. The best known of these experiments were on beans. The plants were self-fertilized, and the progeny selected for size of seed. It was found that if, in each generation, the largest seeds are selected for planting, the average size of seed, as might be expected, increases. This process does not, however, continue indefinitely: after a number of generations the *average* size reaches a constant figure – or, if it shows variation, there is no steady trend up or down. And no further selection makes any difference. (Strictly, a qualification is needed here: eventually, mutation, which is discussed in the next chapter, will enable selection to act.)

On each bean plant there is still some variation in the size of the seeds, because size depends partly on position in the pod: if a seed is in an unfavourable position its growth is less than that of others. Nevertheless, even if the smallest seeds are now chosen for further breeding, the seeds on the plants which grow from them show the same average size as those grown from large seeds. The explanation is that selection combined with self-fertilization has led to the production of a strain of plants in which there is *no genetical variation*: all individuals have the same genetic constitution,

The Effect of Selection over many Generations. Maize plants were selected (a) for high protein content of seed (upper line) and (b) for low protein content. At first, selection had a marked effect, but after 6–8 years approximate stability was reached: the small annual variation was probably due to weather differences, and might be up or down. This is an example of selection producing pure lines, in which there is no genetic variability on which selection can act further and variation between them, if it is observed, can be due only to environment. Variation in the sizes of the seeds is due to the environmental effect of a different food supply in different positions.

For the Lamarckian theory the importance of these experiments is that here is an environmental effect – position in the pod – which is well marked in each generation, but which has no effect on later generations. However carefully large or small seeds are selected for further breeding, the average size of seed on the new plants remains constant. If there were a Lamarckian effect, selection of the largest beans would lead to further increase in size in later generations, or of the smallest to a decrease. In such a case the *genotype*, or genetical constitution, is the same for each seed, but the *phenotype*, or visible characters, vary. This phenotypic variation occurs without alteration of the genotype.

A strain of plants or animals, in which breeding has eliminated genetical variation, is called a *pure line*. In animals, something very close to a pure line can be got by brother and sister mating for thirty or more generations, and this has often been done with quickly breeding species such as certain flies, and even with rats and mice. Pure lines are of great value for some types of research. If, for instance, the effects on growth of two different diets are to be compared, it is desirable to give the diets to two groups of animals, each as nearly as possible genetically identical: it is then probable that any differences observed between the groups are not genetically determined, and a possible source of error is avoided. Inbred stocks, as we shall see in chapter 12, are also of great importance in agriculture and stock-breeding.

These facts are important also for human biology. If two human groups, such as the inhabitants of Japan and of Scotland, are compared in respect of a character such as height or fertility, both of which can be measured, the averages may be found to differ. The two groups certainly have different environments, and doubtless also differ genetically. The difficulty is to find out the extent to which environmental and genetic differences influence the observed variation in height or fertility. In later chapters we shall see that, despite the difficulties, it is possible to reach some conclusions in problems of this kind. It is however essential to realize that the difficulties exist.

If we return now to Lamarckism, we can sum up the conventional view of the theory, as it is found in most text-books, by saying that it is held to be without experimental foundation, and contrary to everything we know of the mechanism of heredity. It is now however realized that this outright rejection, of all transmission of environmental effects, is too sweeping. Although what has been said above is true as far as it goes, there is much more to be said. The criticism of the conventional view is today associated particularly with the work of a Russian biologist, Lysenko. But, although his views have received more public notice in the western Press than those of almost any British or American scientist, there has been less discussion of the biological issues involved than might be thought.

Lysenko has long been known for his studies of the development of plants from the seed, and in particular for treatments which make it possible for seed to be sown successfully in cold climates. He and his colleagues have also investigated the grafting of fruit trees. In all their work they have been concerned with the urgent problems of raising agricultural yields. They now assert that altering the environment of the growing plant can, in certain conditions, not only influence the growth of the plant itself, but also exert a persistent effect on the progeny of the plant: for instance, once a winter wheat has been converted to a spring wheat (that is, one that will develop as soon as it is sown without a dormant period in the soil), the wheat plants of subsequent generations retain this character. Another example, from grafting experiments, concerns tomato plants: it is reported that seeds taken from grafts may grow into plants with some of the characters of the *host* plant – that is, not of the parent plant but of the plant on to which the parent plant had been grafted.

Claims of this sort might seem to conflict with the apparently stable character of the genes referred to earlier, but they are not on that account rejected by geneticists. Similar phenomena have been observed in a number of species beside those studied in the U.S.S.R., and some have been given a tentative explanation. Although most genetical transmission is a function of the chromosomes of the cell nucleus, it has long been known that some genetic effects are due to factors outside the nucleus; these factors are passed on in the egg-cell, which has a considerable mass of non-nuclear material (cytoplasm), but not in the sperm. It follows that they are transmitted only by the mother and not by the father. It is held that factors of this sort are more easily influenced by environmental effects, and that they are involved in phenomena such as those of the grafted tomatoes.

The most striking examples of apparent 'Lamarckian' transmission, of effects due to environmental action, have been observed in micro-organisms – Bacteria and Protozoa. It is now accepted that, in certain of these, a change in the environment can produce a changed organism which then passes on its new character to later generations. An important and unresolved question is whether comparable effects can occur in larger, many-celled organisms.

It is clear that not all heredity can be explained on the basis of the simple, conventional scheme based entirely on nuclear inheritance. Most geneticists, however, consider that the main body of genetical theory still stands, but that some anomalous effects must be accounted for by new mechanisms, possibly involving the cytoplasm.

Lysenko and his followers do not deny the rôle of the chromosomes in heredity, but they criticize emphasis on the *unchanging* nature of the genes. This criticism follows naturally from their belief that they can alter the genetic characters of organisms by altering their environment. The orthodox view is that genes do change, but only rarely. Examples of such changes, or *mutations*, are given in chapters 3 and 9; the nearest we get to mutation in everyday experience is perhaps the occurrence of a 'sport' (or *mutant*) in a garden plant: the sudden appearance of an oddity among normal plants may be due to a mutation of some kind. The rate at which mutation occurs can be increased by the use of radiation, such as X-rays: suitable doses directed towards the egg-cells of fruit-flies, for instance, have greatly increased the number of abnormal types in later generations; and these abnormalities are inherited. (If atomic bombs were ever used again in war similar effects would be observed in any surviving human populations, as they already have been observed in Japan.) The abnormalities are of the same kinds as those observed in untreated flies, but are much more numerous. Mutations have also been induced in many organisms by various sorts of chemical treatment; sometimes mutant plants produce larger fruits, and so are useful.

The claims of the Lysenko school go further: according to them, particular inheritable changes can be induced by special treatment, and in this way new types of plants and animals, useful to agriculture, can be deliberately created. Linked to this is an emphasis on the view that the chromosomes should be regarded, not as entities somehow set apart from the ordinary life of the cell, but as material taking an active part in cell metabolism, and influenced by the rest of the cell as well as acting on it. This conception, though glossed over in elementary texts, is however that of most geneticists. The Lysenko group holds further that productive research has been held up by conventional genetics, which has made little contribution to agricultural practice.

The last statement is certainly true, in the sense that most of the practical breeding done would be just as effective if formal genetics were unknown. There are, however, clear instances of the usefulness of 'Mendelism' in practical plant breeding. The production of wheat resistant to rust disease has made a major contribution to wheat farming in vast areas of the world; another instance is the hybrid maize which has raised corn production in the United States by

at least 20 per cent. Other examples concern disease-resist-
ant sugar cane, and the production of penicillin from *Peni-
cillium* mould.

Nevertheless, controversy will certainly continue, and it
is possible to hope that it will be carried on rationally and
without abuse on either side. More important, we may
expect that new knowledge will rapidly accumulate. C. H.
Waddington has recently described novel experiments with
a bearing on the problem. Populations of fruit flies (*Drosophila*), selected for a particular wing character in an unusual environment, produce a genetical type which breeds
true even when the flies are returned to their normal
laboratory environment. This at first sight might appear
to be a 'Lamarckian' transmission of an environmental
effect, but in fact it seems that something rather different
has happened: the strange environment allowed the new
wing character to appear in some of the flies, because these
flies had a particular genotype conducive to the production
of the abnormal character. Selection of these flies over
several generations accumulated genes which tended to produce this character, until eventually the accumulation of
genes was so great that the character appeared even when
the flies were back in their ordinary conditions (which are
relatively unfavourable for the appearance of the character).
In this case, therefore, the suggested explanation involves a new effect within the framework of conventional
genetics.

It seems likely that other lines of study, especially biochemical studies of the cell nucleus, and of the interaction
of the nuclear material with the rest of the cell, will soon
reveal further effects – perhaps of far-reaching importance.

This topic has been discussed at length, and rather technically, less because it is topical than because it is of
fundamental importance. The connexion between the
agents of heredity, and the process of development from
egg-cell to adult, is one of the central topics of biology, as
well as one of the most difficult. Further research will certainly yield results of both practical and theoretical interest.

Twins and Heredity

There remains a good deal more, of a less controversial kind, to say on the subject of disentangling the effects of nature and nurture. One of the great problems, as we have seen, is to determine *how much* variation in a given character, such as stature, is due to heredity, and how much to environment. There are certain human beings who provide us with a special opportunity for answering such questions. They are the so-called identical twins.

Human twins are of two kinds. About two pairs in every three are the result of the presence, when insemination occurs, of two egg-cells instead of only one. (This ratio applies to Europeans but not to all other groups.) Both are fertilized, and they grow side-by-side in the womb. Small mammals such as cats, dogs, rats, and rabbits, and some larger ones such as pigs, lions, and tigers, produce several young at birth in this way. Human twins of this sort are called binovular, or two-egg, twins, and they can be and often are very different from each other; they may of course differ in sex. Twins of the other type develop from a single fertilized egg which gives rise to two separate individuals. Twins of this sort are genetically identical: since they both originate from the same fertilized egg-cell, the chromosomes in the nuclei of the cells in all parts of their bodies are derived from the single set of chromosomes originally present in the egg. Such twins often show remarkable resemblances, not only in appearance but also in emotional and intellectual characteristics. They are always of the same sex.

But the important fact about them is that they are never quite identical. Most are brought up together, and so have very similar environments as well as identical genetical factors. Nevertheless, even then, differences can be detected, though they are much less, on the average, than those between ordinary brothers or sisters, or between binovular twins. For example, they differ in their scores in intelligence tests, on the average, by about 9 points. Ordinary brothers and sisters show an average difference of about 16 points.

The ways in which marked differences can arise between uniovular twins are very complex. An example concerns a woman who suffered from high blood pressure (arterial hypertension) for eight years. This woman was lighter at birth than her twin, showed slower growth, and was always behind her twin in physical and intellectual development: she also had more infectious illness. The healthy twin never developed high blood pressure, but tests showed that she was *potentially* hypertensive; possibly, had she suffered severe stress at any time, she would have developed hypertension, like her sister. In this instance it seems that the initial poor start, presumably resulting from conditions in the uterus, led to an accumulation of disadvantages for the weaker twin: as a result, her development in *every* respect – intellectual and emotional as well as 'physical' – was influenced.

Important studies have been made of twin pairs that have been separated early and brought up by different guardians and in very different conditions. It is common to hear of such pairs that they remain remarkably similar. Often, this is true: there are instances of separated pairs being reunited as adults, as a result of one being mistaken for the other. It is also true that similarity between uniovular twins, whether separated or not, extends to the most extraordinary details: for instance, the distribution of decay in the teeth is often the same. Sometimes the similarity is of medical importance. One of a pair of uniovular twins living in Oxford died of an inoperable cancer of the stomach. The survivor was X-rayed, but no trouble could be detected. X-raying was repeated at three-monthly intervals, and after a year there appeared a slight indication of a growth in the stomach wall. The surgeon consulted held that the X-ray evidence alone was insufficient to justify operation, but he operated nevertheless, and duly removed a very early cancer of the type of which the first twin had died. The patient recovered.

To return to the pairs that have been separated in infancy, we do not invariably find that they are strikingly similar. One pair of boys, born in Glasgow, was separated at three years: one remained in a working-class quarter of the city, the other went to live in a village outside Glasgow. At sixteen, when they were compared, it was found that both were above the average in their score in intelligence tests, but that the city child scored 125 to the other's 106. Both were good at football, but the country-bred one was physically superior; in particular, he was an inch taller; he also showed more mechanical ability.

Cases like this illustrate how environment can affect both intellectual achievement and physical development. Even more marked emotional differences are sometimes shown. Two American girls, uniovular twins, were separated in infancy. One lived with a comfortable middle-class family with many social contacts and able to provide a good education. The other was looked after by a couple in poor circumstances and the general education she received was not so good. At twenty the first girl was a cheerful, sociable individual, clearly enjoying life and without any evident psychological difficulties. The other was moody, shy, diffident, and depressed, and spoke with a lisp.

The Interaction of Nature and Nurture

It is sometimes asked: which is the more important, heredity or environment? There is no simple answer to this question. If the question means, which has the greater *effect*? no general answer is possible, but only a number of particular answers. For instance, individual differences in eye-colour are mainly determined genetically, and so for this particular characteristic heredity may be said to be the more important. At the other extreme, infection with measles, for example, is mainly dependent on the presence in the environment of a sufficiently heavy concentration of the germs that cause measles.

Between the two extremes come characters such as

stature. There is no doubt that heredity plays a part in determining a person's height: if you have tall parents you are *more likely* to be tall than short. On the other hand, growth is certainly affected by environmental influences such as nutrition. In England, before 1940, boys who went to schools at which heavy fees were charged ('public' schools) were on the average about four inches taller than the children of poorer parents who could afford to send their children only to free schools. This by itself proves nothing: the poor might conceivably be genetically incapable of growing to the stature of the rich. However, experiment has also shown that if the children of the poor receive a diet more like that of the more fortunate children, they approach more and more closely to them in height and weight. This effect was observed on a very large scale during the second world war, when rationing and price control made possible a great improvement in the food eaten by most people in Britain.

The height of any one person is, then, an expression of the combined effects of his genetic make-up and his environment. We cannot properly say that one has a greater effect than the other. This interaction of nature and nurture has often been illustrated by experiments on animals. It is possible to isolate pure strains of mice with different capacities for growth. When this is done it is found that different strains grow best in different conditions: there is no single environment that is best for all kinds of mice. We can reasonably suspect that the same applies to man. So the adage that one man's meat is another's poison expresses a very general and important biological principle.

Despite these facts, there are still those who attach more weight to nature than to nurture, and others who insist that nurture is all-important. Those who put the emphasis on nature, or heredity, we shall mention again, in chapter 8. Meanwhile it is as well to consider what is meant by those who lay especial emphasis on environment. So far, in answer to the question: Which is the more important? we have given only the sort of non-committal and rather irritating response that often comes from scientists. Neither nature or nurture, we have said, can reasonably be regarded as having a greater effect than the other.

But it is possible to improve on this answer. If the question is considered from a practical point of view, from the point of view of getting something useful achieved, then the answer must put the emphasis on environment. This, of course, applies only when man is being considered. We can, and do, improve our livestock and our cultivated plants by breeding: in doing so we may kill the young that do not please us, permit only a selected few to breed, and perhaps derive much of our stock from artificial insemination or hand pollination. Before doing so, we have to decide on the precise environment for which we are breeding: an animal bred for one set of conditions may do very badly in another. But in man selective breeding of this sort is rarely proposed. We must, with a few possible minor exceptions, accept the genetic constitutions of existing populations, and try to adjust the environment to them. If coal-miners dislike coal-mining, and if they are also liable to get serious diseases in the pursuit of their calling, there is no question of breeding a strain of men that will react differently. The problem is to alter the conditions of coal-mining. Later chapters will provide much more evidence in support of this conclusion.

3

MENDELISM AND MAN

There are many laws regulating variation, some few of which can be dimly seen and will be hereafter briefly mentioned.

CHARLES DARWIN

ALTHOUGH we can do nothing to alter our own genetic constitutions, and though few of us would alter our plans for marriage on genetic grounds, it is nevertheless worth while to know all we can about human genetics. The principles of genetics have mostly been worked out from experiments on plants that can be artificially pollinated, and on quickly breeding animals, such as the famous fruit fly, *Drosophila*. The first man to publish an accurate account of the way in which what we now call genes determine differences between individuals of the same species was an Austrian priest, Gregor Mendel. Mendel used sweet peas for his experiments. It is an extraordinary fact that, although the journal in which he published was available in London and other centres in 1866, it was completely ignored.

In 1900 two Germans, Correns and Tschermak, and a Dutchman, de Vries, independently published papers confirming Mendel's observations. Since then an enormous mass of research has been done on the subject, but Mendel's priority is still acknowledged in the name 'Mendelism'.

Mendelian Heredity and Chromosomes

It is possible to give examples of 'Mendelian heredity' from man. Let us suppose that a woman with bright red hair marries a man with black hair; and that all their offspring have black hair. (This will happen if the man is not carrying a single gene for red hair: in other words if he is, as an animal breeder would say, pure bred for black hair.) The black-haired state thus masks red hair, and is referred to as *dominant* to red hair; red hair is said to be *recessive*. Let us now suppose that one of the children of this couple marries the child of a similar couple, and that they in turn have a large family: say, twelve children. Although they themselves have black hair, one in four of their children, on the average, will have red hair: that is, the most probable number of red-haired children out of twelve will be three.

Characteristics are sometimes said to skip a generation, and this is an example. The next question is: what is the explanation? In the previous chapter we saw that every individual receives one set of chromosomes from each parent; the chromosomes are themselves the bearers of the genetic factors, the genes. Bright red hair depends on the presence of a gene which we may represent as r, and red hair occurs only in individuals (of either sex) who have received r from both parents. Red-haired people therefore have the constitution rr. In the case described above the woman in the first couple was of this constitution. Her husband, on the other hand, had no r gene. In him, the corresponding genes were for black hair, and his constitution may be represented as RR. Capital letters indicate dominance.

Each of the children of this couple received r from the mother and R from the father. Their constitution was thus Rr, and their hair black, since R always causes black hair even if r is present. The next step was the marriage of two persons with the constitution Rr. Their children may be RR, Rr, or rr, and the *average* proportions of black to red will be 3 : 1. This three-to-one ratio is of course observable only if large numbers are studied: it cannot be established from observation of one or two families, even if they are exceptionally large. In fact, as we have already seen, ratios of this kind were first worked out on plants, and then on insects, before they were demonstrated in man. To observe a Mendelian effect it is necessary to breed plants or animals for two generations, and to study the proportions in which

Inheritance of Red Hair in Man. Bright red hair is due to a recessive gene, that is, one of which the effect is seen only if it is present with another gene of the same kind. 'G' stands for 'gene'

the characters occur in large numbers of individuals. By no means all characteristics are inherited in this simple fashion, and the early workers had to hit on ones that are.

One of the results of the new genetics was that it showed that heredity is not a blending process. In the past it had been thought that each individual was a blend of the characteristics of his parents, just as orange-coloured paint can be made by blending yellow and red. In the example of hair-colour we see that red hair appears in undiluted form in the second generation. We therefore attribute its appearance to genes that are transmitted intact from generation to generation.

A consequence of this individuality of the genes is that characteristics may appear in new combinations as a result of marriage between persons carrying different sets of genes. In one instance, in South Africa, a Griqua woman married a Scot, and their daughter married a 'white' man of mixed parentage. The latter couple had four sons: one was very tall, almost white, but had brown eyes and frizzy hair; one was of medium height, had a darker skin, brown eyes but straight, black hair; the third was also of medium height and rather darker than the second, with brown eyes and

Kaffir-type hair; the fourth, again of medium height and coloration, had brown eyes and brown-black Hottentot-type hair. Thus in this family (illustrated in plate 2) various features appear in unfamiliar combination: in the first son, for instance, Negro-type hair with a light skin.

It is clear that if characteristics are determined by genes on different chromosomes they must be expected to *segregate* in this way. Each chromosome that an individual receives from his father may have come from either of his father's parents; and each chromosome from his mother, from either of her parents. Different children of the same family will receive different combinations of chromosomes, and so may display different combinations of grandparental charac-teristics. The appearance of these different combinations of characters shows that no blending occurs.

But each chromosome carries many genes, and so it might be expected that instances would be discovered of charac-ters that did not segregate or separate in this way, but re-mained together. *Linkage* of characters is indeed well known to occur in many animals and plants, but there are not many examples from man. For our present purpose it is not of great importance, since linkage is very rarely complete. The reason for the failure of linkage is shown in the diagram on page 11: the cause of it is an exchange of material between pairs of chromosomes during the formation of the eggs and sperm. This exchange of material inevitably breaks the linkage between genes on the chromosomes.

The general conclusion then is that genetic effects are determined by individual particles, the genes, and that the genes may appear in any combination in different indi-viduals. This recombination is the origin of much of the variation between people that we see around us. Even a group of people living in a small community and with very similar environments may show great variation in appear-ance and in other characters. Though part of the variation may be due to small environmental differences, a great deal comes from the mixing and reshuffling of the genes in each generation.

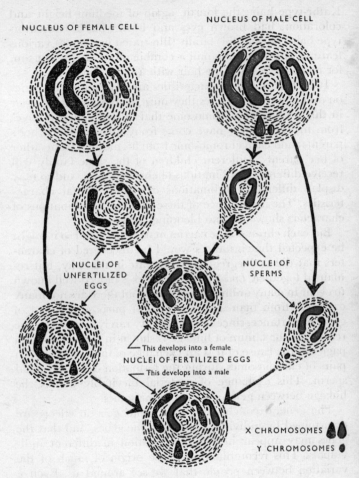

NUCLEUS OF FEMALE CELL NUCLEUS OF MALE CELL

NUCLEI OF UNFERTILIZED EGGS

NUCLEI OF SPERMS

← This develops into a female

NUCLEI OF FERTILIZED EGGS

← This develops into a male

X CHROMOSOMES

Y CHROMOSOMES

Sex Determination. Sex is determined at the moment of fertilization, and depends on the sperm: eggs fertilized by a sperm with an X-chromosome become females; those fertilized by one with a Y-chromosome become males. Certain genes, such as the one causing haemophilia, are on the X-chromosome and are said to be sex-linked

Sex Determination

One of the most obvious of the characteristics that can be
said to be inherited, is sex. It is true that environmental
agencies can interfere with the development of sex characteristics: in some mammals the presence of a twin of opposite sex in the womb may cause the development of a mixture of male and female organs; in other words, the
production of an intersex. But this, though it exemplifies
once again the intermingling of the effects of heredity and
environment, is not of significance for our present purpose.

In normal development sex is determined by the chromosomes by a simple mechanism, shown opposite. We
have already seen that there are twenty-four pairs of
chromosomes in man. One pair plays a special part in sex
determination. In a woman's cells the members of this pair
are identical, as far as can be seen with a microscope; both
are called X-chromosomes. In a man's cells there is only
one X-chromosome; with it is a smaller one, the Y-chromosome. Now consider what happens when the germ-cells are
produced, each with a half-set of chromosomes. Each egg-
cell gets one X-chromosome, but a sperm-cell may have
either an X-chromosome or a Y. There are consequently
two kinds of sperm. If an egg is fertilized by a sperm with an
X-chromosome the fertilized egg (with its full set of chromosomes) will have two X-chromosomes and will develop
into a female; but if a Y-bearing sperm fertilizes it there will
be one X and one Y and so development will be into a male.

One of the first questions arising from this is: can we
control sex in man, or in other animals, by allowing only
X-bearing, or only Y-bearing, sperm to reach the egg? At
present, in 1957, the answer is, no; attempts have been
made but so far none has been entirely successful. It is,
however, possible that in normal conditions the Y-bearing
sperm have a better chance of fertilizing an egg than those
with an X-chromosome. It is well known that rather more
boys are born than girls: in Britain about 105 boys are born

C

for every 100 girls. This is what is meant when it is said that the sex ratio at birth is 105. We do not know what the sex ratio is at conception; it has been said that more male foetuses die than female, but recent work suggests that this is not the case. It is however certain that more males are conceived than females. This is not what would be expected from a knowledge of the sex-determining mechanism: female-producing sperm (X) and male-producing sperm (Y) are produced in equal numbers, and if the two types have equal chances of successful fertilization the sex ratio at conception should be 100. The fact that it is higher suggests that Y-bearing sperm have an advantage.

It is clear that the possibility of different behaviour by the two types of sperm is important. Quite apart from the control of sex in man it would be of great value if it could be arranged that the great majority of calves born in dairy herds were female; similarly, on poultry farms, it would be an advantage if most chicks hatched were female. Artificial insemination is already well established. It is possible that eventually it will be possible to treat sperm, collected for artificial insemination, so that only one kind of sperm remains active.

It is a remarkable fact that the high initial sex ratio, combined with the higher mortality among males, gives a sex ratio of about 100 at puberty; youths of each sex are in approximately equal numbers. But in advanced countries the lower death rate among women continues, and at 85 the sex ratio is about 55: nearly two women to each man. The greater survival of women is not fully understood; occupational hazards play some part in it, but it is doubtful whether they are the only cause.

One consequence of the sex-determining mechanism is that recessive genes carried on the X-chromosome may take effect in males owing to the absence of any corresponding gene on the Y-chromosome. (In a female the other X-chromosome will usually carry a dominant counterpart of the recessive gene.) The best-known example is the gene responsible for the disease haemophilia, in which the blood

MALE
FEMALE
AFFECTED MALE

Haemophilia. Pedigree illustrating origin by mutation, or sudden change, in a normal gene, occurring in a family with no previous history of haemophilia

clots only very slowly, if at all. Haemophilics have a very low expectation of life, since they may bleed to death from a small cut, or through internal haemorrhage. Haemophilia is known only in males. The gene responsible is recessive, and a man gets the disease as a result of receiving from his mother an X-chromosome which carries the gene. The mother, having another X-chromosome carrying a dominant gene which enables blood to clot in the normal way, is not a haemophilic. Thus haemophilia is almost always transmitted by a normal woman carrying, unknown to herself, a gene that is likely to kill half of her sons. Only half the

sons, on the average, will be affected; the others will have
received the other, normal X-chromosome. Theoretically
a woman could have two haemophilia genes, and so have
the disease. Only one such case is known, perhaps because
the possession of the two genes usually kills the foetus.

One of the women known to have been carriers of haemophilia was Queen Victoria of England: one of her sons, at
least three grandsons and six great-grandsons have been
haemophilics, including members of the ruling families of

Sex-linked Inheritance. A pedigree of red blindness due to a sex-linked
gene: the effects of a sex-linked gene are shown more often in males than
in females, since in the latter a normal gene on one of the X-chromosomes usually masks the effect of the recessive mutant gene on the other.
In a male there is no second X-chromosome and there is no masking

Inheritance of Red Blindness. See previous figure

Spain and Tsarist Russia; but the members of the present British royal house have escaped the offending gene.

Genes carried on the X-chromosome are said to be *sex-linked*, and several are known in human beings. A common sex-linked recessive gene is responsible for the most frequently found type of colour-blindness, in which red and green are confused. This condition occurs much more frequently in men than in women, because a woman must have two of the appropriate kind of gene, and this combination can occur only rarely.

Mendelism in Practice

The obvious places for attempting the application of Mendelian genetics are the farm and the garden. In man there is less scope, but it has nevertheless some potential importance. Sometimes a man or woman about to marry wishes to know whether there is danger that children of the marriage will display some undesirable characteristic. In the previous chapter we saw, for example, that both tuberculosis and at

least some types of cancer are influenced by genetic constitution. But with both diseases the genetic effect is too
small to be taken into account when marriage is considered. If, for instance, a near relative has died of one of
these diseases there is no cause for alarm, nor any reason
for avoiding marriage. This type of genetical transmission
is discussed further at the end of the chapter.

Some diseases, however, are determined genetically in a
quite straightforward way. Haemophilia, as we have seen, is
one example, and others are given in chapter 8. There is,
in fact, a considerable mass of knowledge on the genetics of
human defects, and an authority on human genetics can
occasionally give useful information to couples who wish to
have children. It is, however, not possible to give this information in a short, non-technical book.

A special case is that of marriage between cousins. The
effects of cousin marriage can be considered from the point
of view of the individual, or of the community. The individual wishes to know what is the chance of producing
defective children. It is impossible to answer this for particular cases: the danger comes from recessive genes, and
we cannot say what recessive genes are present as a rule,
since a recessive gene, unless sex-linked, exerts (by definition) no effect unless it is present in company with another,
similar gene. If both cousins carry the same recessive gene
for a particular defect, then it is most likely that the proportion of their children showing the defect will be one in four,
or 25 per cent.

It must be emphasized that the great majority of cousin
marriages do not produce defective children at all. However, there are recessive genes in man which cause the
development of defects; and two first cousins are more likely
both to carry the same recessive genes than are two individuals taken at random from the population. It follows
that the chance of two first cousins having defective children
is slightly higher than that of an unrelated pair.

This fact does not, and need not, deter first cousins from
marrying. The exceptions are cousins with relations who

have developed any of the defects known to be determined by recessive genes: these include a fatal skin disease called xeroderma pigmentosum, a form of idiocy (juvenile amaurotic) and a form of deaf mutism; all are rare diseases.

○ FEMALE　▧ MALE　● AFFECTED

Transmission of a Recessive Character. Pedigree of a condition (blistering of the skin) produced by a recessive gene. In three instances the marriage of cousins led to the production of children with the condition, though the parents were normal. (This sort of thing happens in only a small proportion of cousin marriages.) By chance, only females were affected in this example

On the other hand, from the point of view of the community, it can be claimed that cousin marriage is undesirable. If the marriage of first cousins ceased, there would be a fall in the incidence of the three conditions just mentioned: this is because, although only a small proportion of cousin marriages produce them, the number so produced is large relative to the total number of sufferers. However, the total genetic effect of forbidding cousin marriages would be quite trivial, and it would be difficult to justify the consequent interference with individual happiness.

Cousin marriage is one form of inbreeding. The most intense form possible in man is pairing between parent and offspring, or between sibs (that is, brothers and sisters). Such inbreeding is of great value in plant and animal husbandry, but it is forbidden in most human communities. Close inbreeding was customary among the rulers of Egypt during a period in the second millennium B.C., and some of the Pharaohs born of marriages between sibs seem to have been persons of very great gifts. Perhaps the Pharaohs of the eighteenth dynasty were exceptionally free from deleterious recessives. Ordinarily, however, the danger of producing defective children is a good deal greater from 'incestuous' marriage than from marriage of first cousins. Apart from obvious defect, there is evidence that close inbreeding in man may lead to lowered fertility.

Some Limitations of Mendelism

From the foregoing it might be thought that all heredity would be found to conform to Mendel's comparatively simple rules. This is far from true. We have indeed already mentioned one comparatively minor modification of Mendel's laws: this is sex-linked inheritance, exemplified by haemophilia and red-green colour-blindness.

Many other cases to which Mendelian laws do not apply provide examples of the fact that the genes do not act in isolation, but function as parts of a complex whole. Although the chromosome mechanism is operating, characters such as height and weight, which show 'continuous variation' (illustrated on page 44), are influenced, not by one or two genes only, with the rest neutral in their effects, but by many. In most adult human populations every height, to the nearest one-twentieth of an inch or smaller, is represented, between something less than five feet and something more than six. Of course, a good deal of this variation (as we saw in chapter 2) reflects differences of environment. But insofar as it is genetically determined, the genes responsible are probably to be numbered in hundreds, and each one has only a small effect. The total number of genes, in one half-set of human chromosomes, is believed to be about 20,000; hence there is plenty of scope for complexity.

This sort of thing is very important when characters such as 'intelligence' are considered. Although there is a correlation between the degree of intelligence shown by parents and children (even when the children are separated from their parents) there is no simple transmission of intelligence, however the latter is measured or defined, as there is of red hair.

Further reference will be made to 'intelligence testing' and its implications in later chapters. Meanwhile, the same principles can be applied to many pathological conditions. It is sometimes asked: Is insanity inherited? Since definitions and diagnoses of 'insanity' vary, this would in any case be difficult to answer. But various inquiries have been made on the incidence of diagnosed psychosis in the families of known psychotics. The sort of conclusion which has been reached, so far, is that, if a person becomes psychotic, the chance of any one of his brothers or sisters also becoming insane is about one in twenty; whereas the figure for the population as a whole is about one in a hundred. (These figures apply, approximately, to the white population of the United States.) Thus there is evidently a genetical element in the development of psychosis. The current view among many psychiatrists is that psychosis, such as schizophrenia, arises when a person with a certain kind of genetic constitution grows up in a particular sort of

PERCENTAGE FREQUENCIES FOR SUB RANGES OF HEIGHT

POPULATION A	0·08	0·18	0·89	3·26	8·35	15·72	21·57	21·57	15·72	8·35	3·26	0·89	0·18
POPULATION B	0·18	0·89	3·26	8·35	15·72	21·57	21·57	15·72	8·35	3·26	0·89	0·18	0·03

ARBITRARY SCALE OF FREQUENCY

POPULATION B

POPULATION A

4 CMS

CENTIMETRES HIGH   150   160   170   180   190

4

Variability in a Measurable Character. If the height is taken of every person in, say, a large town, the number of persons at each height, to the nearest inch, can be shown in a series of rectangles, as in the first figure. The modal or most 'popular' height would perhaps be 5 ft. 7½ in., with the numbers falling off progressively on each side of the mode. The smooth curve in the first figure is another way of presenting the same facts. The curves shown are of the type called 'normal' or 'Gaussian'. When we study genetical variations due to differences in many genes, and not just one or two, this is approximately the sort of variation which is often found.

When two large groups of people are *compared* in regard to a measurable character, such as strength or fertility or mathematical ability, the two distribution curves may differ both in shape and in the position of the mode, as shown in the other figures. See also the actual examples on pages 141, 142, and 177.

Comparisons of this kind illustrate that great overlaps can occur, even when averages are different. It *may* be true that women, on the average, are genetically inferior to men in mathematical ability, but it does not follow that no women can excel in mathematics, and in fact some do. Sometimes, as Haldane has pointed out, we know nothing about average differences, but only the performances of champions. For example, Negroes often excel at sprinting, Finns at long-distance running; nevertheless, as recent events have shown, other countries can produce champions in both

unfavourable environment. An important aspect of a person's environment is, of course, the relatives with whom he grows up. It is possible that some people have genetic constitutions which, in unfavourable conditions, lead them to behave so that they make *other* members of their family psychotic. It seems likely, in fact, that the causation of these conditions is highly complex, and involves most intricate interactions of nature and nurture.

Studies on this kind of problem are done, where possible, on twins, and the twin method has been used in psychiatric investigations. It has also been employed in work on susceptibility to infectious disease. A notable example is tuberculosis. If one of a pair of uniovular twins has tuberculosis, it is highly probable that the other will have it too; with binovular twins (who are not genetically identical) the concordance is much lower. Here, therefore, we find clear

evidence of genetical variation in susceptibility to tuberculosis. The practical implications, apart from the obvious
one of avoiding infection, are that especial care is desirable
for adolescents and young adults with tuberculous relatives;
and that people with tuberculosis in the family should not
be employed in work, such as nursing, in which the incidence of the disease tends to be high. It must be emphasized
that, as we shall see further in chapter 14, the most important causes of tuberculosis are environmental; the discovery
that some people are genetically more susceptible than
others does not alter this fact.

The general conclusion here is that most important human
characteristics, being influenced by many genes (as well
as by the environment), fall outside any simple Mendelian
scheme. Their incidence in the population must be described in terms of frequency distributions (as on page 44
and below); and predictions about *particular individuals* are
of little use. It is not of much practical value to be told, for
instance, that the chances are about one in seventeen that
one will die of a particular disease before the age of sixty;

Distribution of Heights of British Men. A histogram illustrating the distribution of a measurable character influenced both by many genes and
by the environment. See also pages 44 and 143

nor is it really valuable to know that about one in a hundred of one's children is likely to be mentally deficient. On the other hand, statistical facts of this sort are of great importance in such matters as the planning of health services for large populations.

Mutation

The most drastic exceptions to Mendel's laws are still to be described. So far in this chapter genes have been treated as fixed. This is quite justifiable for many purposes, and their normal constancy from generation to generation was mentioned in chapter 2. But sometimes, as we have seen, they change, or mutate: it appears that, on occasion, during nuclear division, a gene is not reproduced exactly, and the new gene is similar to the old but not identical with it. Thus the gene that causes haemophilia may be regarded as an inexact copy of a normal gene that enables blood to clot at a normal rate.

The rate of mutation in nature is always very low. It has been calculated that the haemophilia mutation occurs at a rate of one in 50,000, and this is probably an exceptionally high rate. Nevertheless mutation is very important. If genes were absolutely fixed there would be only a limited (though large) number of possible genetic constitutions: beyond these, no new types could be produced, and the evolution of animals and plants could not take place.

FROM EGG TO ADULT

> O why did God,
> Creator wise, that peopl'd highest Heav'n
> With Spirits Masculine, create at last
> This noveltie on Earth, this fair defect
> Of Nature, and not fill the World at once
> With Men as Angels without Feminine,
> Or find some other way to generate
> Mankind?
>
> JOHN MILTON

THE study of heredity is perforce a study for the most part of 'characters', such as stature or musical ability, and it is easy to think of these characters mechanically, as if they were unchanging units. Actually, as we have seen, everything about us is a product of development: the genes exert their influence, tempered by that of the environment, on *processes*, and the processes go on throughout life at different rates, most of them especially rapidly in early development. We know rather little of the chemical actions by which the genes influence particular processes, such as growth, and nothing which is worth putting in this book. But there is plenty of useful information on the stages of human development and the bodily machinery concerned in reproduction. In this chapter therefore we turn aside from the main theme of human diversity (to which we shall return in the next chapter), to discuss some aspects of reproduction and development.

Sperm and Egg

In some mammals sperm are produced during only one part of the year, the rutting season, and only at this time does the male display interest in the female; but in man the production of sperm is continuous, and if there is any seasonal variation it is not of practical significance.

A special feature of the testes of most mammals is their presence in a sac of skin, the scrotum, outside the cavity of the abdomen. When there is a breeding season they may descend into the scrotum from the abdomen only during

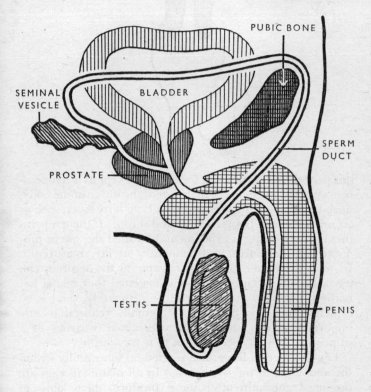

Male Reproductive Organs. Sperm are produced in the testes, and pass along the sperm ducts which join to form the urethra – the tube which carries both sperm and urine through the penis to the outside. The prostate is one of the glands of which the secretions make up the seminal fluid in which the sperm are suspended. The two seminal vesicles are branches of the sperm ducts, and they store sperm

TUBE

UTERUS

OVARY

VAGINA

Female Reproductive Organs

this period. In this position the testes are kept at a temperature several degrees lower than that of the inside of the body,
since they have only a thin skin, with no fatty layer, such as
occurs elsewhere, between them and the air. If the temperature of the scrotum is experimentally raised the sperm produced are ineffective, and temporary sterility may result.
In man the application of hot water to the scrotum can
have this effect, and it has been suggested that taking hot
baths at night may reduce fertility; fortunately, there is no
evidence that this possibility is actually realized to any
important extent, though the continuous wearing of a
suspensory belt has been known to cause sterility.

Egg-production however is carried on successfully within
the abdomen, in the two ovaries. In all mammals eggs are
produced intermittently: some produce them only in
spring, others at regular intervals throughout most or all of
the year. In those that have litters several eggs ripen at
once, some coming from each ovary. A woman is usually
fertile between the ages of fifteen and forty-five, though
exceptionally the fertile period may be much longer.

During this period one egg develops every 28 days, approximately, in alternate ovaries, except during pregnancy (and to some extent lactation) when no eggs ripen. A few women produce more than one egg at a time and so, as we saw in chapter 2, may give birth to two or more children at once. An advantage in producing only one child at each birth is that a human child has a long period of slow development, during which parental care is vitally important, and parental care would be less effective if several young were born together.

The Menstrual Cycle

The childbearing period in a woman is marked by the 'monthly period': at fairly regular intervals there is a loss of blood and other matter from the vagina, lasting for about four days; the commonest interval between the beginning of one period and the beginning of the next is 28 days. The correct name for this event is menstruation. What is the connexion between menstruation and the monthly ripening of an egg-cell? The answer to this is complex, and, before giving it, it will be convenient first to describe in more detail how the ovary produces eggs.

A cell destined to become an egg first becomes conspicuously different from the others by enlarging; it also comes to be surrounded by a mass of smaller cells, in the midst of which appears a space full of liquid into which the egg projects. The space, with its surrounding cells, is called a follicle, and the follicle enlarges and protrudes on to the surface of the ovary. Eventually it bursts and discharges the egg, which enters the tube leading from the ovary to the uterus (or womb).

While this ripening has been going on a change has been taking place in the uterus. The inner lining grows thicker, and its blood supply is increased by enlargement of the blood vessels. By the time the egg is liberated the growth is completed and *the wall of the uterus is now in a state in which it can receive a fertilized egg and allow it to develop*. It remains in

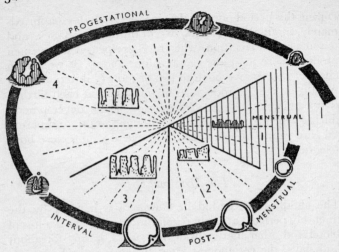

Menstrual Cycle. The stages through which the ovary and uterus go during the menstrual cycle. The outer rim shows the changes in an egg follicle in the ovary: at the beginning of stage 4 the egg is discharged, and if the egg is fertilized the uterine wall (shown within) is ready to receive it. If pregnancy does not begin, the uterine wall breaks down and produces the menstrual flow (stage 1)

this state for about fourteen days, and then, if the egg is not fertilized, quite suddenly it breaks down: much of the thickened tissue of the inner lining comes away in fragments and, since this tissue contains enlarged blood vessels, some blood is lost too. This is the material lost in menstruation. After menstruation the whole cycle begins again: there are a few days of inactivity and then the lining of the uterus again begins to thicken; meanwhile another egg (usually in the ovary of the opposite side) is ripening.

Menstruation therefore occurs roughly half-way between the liberation of one egg and the next. If the cycle always lasted exactly 28 days, its most usual length, it would be possible to date the time of egg production with some accuracy: it would probably be 14 days after the first day of menstruation. However, many women have cycles of

The Ovum and the Menstrual Cycle. On the left the egg-cell is shown in successive positions after its discharge from the ovary, when fertilization does not take place. On the right successive stages of implantation are shown, after fertilization in the tube which leads from the ovary to the uterus

average length as low as twenty-five days or as high as thirty. Moreover it is not usual for a woman to have consistently the same interval from one period to the next. So although the ovary, with its regular production of eggs, has been called a time-piece, it is not a reliable one. This is of practical importance, both to couples who wish to make sure of having a child and to those who wish to avoid one. Coitus can lead to pregnancy only if a ripe egg-cell is available. We do not know exactly how long the unfertilized human egg survives, but in the rabbit the time is about six hours. Rabbit sperms last about thirty hours. The figures for human eggs and sperms may well be different, but it has been shown that coitus is most likely to cause pregnancy if it takes place about half-way between menstruations. This fact is the basis of the 'safe-period' method of contraception. Some people, especially Catholics, are adjured on religious grounds not to use any of the efficient contraceptive methods, but are not prevented from avoiding coitus at the time when the woman is presumed to be most fertile. Unfortunately the 'safe' periods are by no means wholly safe, since instances are known where coitus just before or just after menstruation was followed by conception. However, if only the two periods of seven days immediately before and after menstruation are used, the chances of conception are materially reduced, and so this is a real, though unreliable, method of family limitation.

An interesting question is, what is the function of the menstrual cycle? All mammals have a cycle of some sort: what use is it? A partial answer to this can be given for most mammals. Eggs are produced only intermittently, sometimes seasonally, and the uterus must be enlarged to receive them; at the time when eggs and uterus are ready the behaviour of the female changes: she is said to be *on heat*, or *in oestrus*, and she is willing to receive the male. At other times the male is repulsed, and coitus is impossible. It is said that the only animals in which rape, or coitus with an unwilling female, is known, are human beings and white mice. (Heat, or oestrus, in other animals does *not* correspond to menstruation in a woman, but to the time when an egg is liberated.) It seems that while in most mammals the cycle – the oestrous cycle as it is called – synchronizes the activities of the male with the internal changes in the female, in the human species it has lost this function. Nevertheless the cycle remains, though in altered form.

While most mammals have an oestrous cycle, only a few menstruate: they are certain monkeys, the apes, and ourselves. A few others, including the bitch, have a show of blood at certain times, but this is not due to breakdown of the inner lining of the uterus.

The Sex Hormones

The cyclical changes so far described are anatomical changes. In laboratory animals they can be observed by dissection, and by microscopic examination of the various organs; in human beings they have to be studied for the most part in post mortem material, for instance in the organs of people killed in accidents. This sort of study does not tell us how the changes are brought about: how, for instance, the uterus becomes ready for the early embryo at just the time of the liberation of an egg from the ovary.

The menstrual cycle, and other features of our reproductive physiology, are dependent on the endocrine, or ductless, glands. The most familiar sort of gland is that exemplified by sweat glands, or by the salivary glands which produce spittle: they are organs which secrete a liquid with a special function and pass it out through fine tubes, or ducts; the tubes of the sweat glands end on the skin surface, those of the salivary glands in the mouth. There are many other such glands, for instance those which discharge digestive juices into the stomach and intestines. The endocrine glands, on the other hand, pass their secretions directly into the blood, and have no ducts to lead the secretion away.

An example of an endocrine gland is the *pituitary*, a small organ lying in a pit in the bone below the brain and above the roof of the mouth. Removal of this gland, or indeed of the anterior part of it, from a male rat stops sperm production in the testes; but extracts can be made which, injected into the animal, restore sperm production to normal. These extracts evidently contain a substance – a *hormone* – which the intact gland passes into the blood and which stimulates the sperm-producing tissues of the testes. In mammals in which sexual activity is seasonal, sperms ripen only in the breeding season; this ripening is dependent on the pituitary, which produces the testis-stimulating hormone only at this time. Probably, the pituitary is in turn stimulated by the brain, and in particular by the hypothalamus, which lies just above the pituitary and is connected to it. (What stimulates the hypothalamus is for most species not known; but in some it is the increase in the amount of daylight in spring.)

The pituitary has many other functions besides stimulating the testes, and it produces several hormones, but here we are concerned only with the part it plays in reproduction. In a woman it has a function similar to that in a man: it stimulates the ovaries to go through their regular cycle of changes, and the whole of the menstrual cycle depends on it. The action of the pituitary on the ovaries is in the first place to stimulate egg-production; but it has other actions, and to understand these we must go further into the way in which the ovaries work. We have seen how the cycle of egg-production in the ovaries is paralleled by a series of changes in the uterus; if both ovaries are experimentally removed, say, from a rat, the changes in the uterus stop. Clearly the ovaries in some way control the uterine changes; how they do it has been shown by further experiment. Extracts of ovary can be made (just as with the pituitary) which induce growth of the inner wall of the uterus; this is the same as the growth which occurs in the normal cycle before an egg ripens. The ovary is, in fact, an endocrine organ as well as a source of eggs. The hormone which brings about growth of the uterus is called the *oestrogenic hormone*, or oestrogen.

But it is not the only hormone produced by the ovary. When a ripe egg is discharged it leaves, in the ovary, the tissues of the follicle in which it has developed. These tissues grow, to form what is called a *yellow body* (or, more usually, a *corpus luteum*). This structure secretes a hormone (called *progesterone*) which is necessary for the further development of the lining of the uterus. The production of this too is stimulated by a pituitary hormone. After about fourteen days, if there is no pregnancy, the yellow body collapses, and so does the inner lining of the uterus. The changes of the menstrual cycle are therefore dependent on hormones from the pituitary and from the ovary.

If however the egg is fertilized, and burrows into the wall of the uterus to begin development, the yellow body remains, and grows still further. And if, early in pregnancy, the yellow body is removed, abortion takes place: the uterine wall collapses and the embryo dies. (Actually, this has been observed mainly in experimental animals which have litters: in them there are several yellow bodies in each ovary, one for each egg liberated; and all the yellow bodies have to be cut out for abortion to occur.)

The reproductive hormones are therefore the means by which the changes in the reproductive organs are synchronized. In particular, in a woman, they accurately dovetail events in the ovaries and the uterus. This is the practical significance of the menstrual cycle in women.

This is not, however, the only function of these hormones: they play an essential part also in the control of the *development* of the reproductive organs. Consider first the development of the male at the time of puberty, usually between the ages of thirteen and sixteen: not only does sperm production begin, but the penis enlarges; hair appears on various parts of the body; and growth of the larynx causes the voice to deepen. If the testes are removed before puberty, these changes do not take place. This operation, castration, is commonly practised on domestic animals: male cattle become bullocks, horses geldings, and so on. It has also been extensively used in the past on human beings: eunuchs were castrated slaves who could be trusted with a man's

The Gonads in Development. In the embryo the gonads (ovaries or testes) develop far forward in the abdominal cavity. In both sexes they descend during development, and in the male they eventually pass through the abdominal wall into the scrotum. The differences in physique between male and female (further mentioned in chapter 10) depend on the secretion of hormones by the gonads wives: and to provide cathedral choirs with trebles and altos promising choirboys were emasculated so that their voices should remain high. The effects of castration on general development can be prevented by the use of a hormone found in the testes: the testes, in fact, like the ovaries, are endocrine organs, secreting a hormone which plays an essential part in sexual development. Descent of the testes themselves into the scrotum, like sperm production, depends on the pituitary; it occasionally happens that a young man has testes which fail to descend, and preparations which have an effect like that of one of the pituitary hormones can sometimes remedy the defect.

In the development of a woman the oestrogenic hormone of the ovary does work similar to that of the testis hormone in a man. The initial stimulus comes again from the pituitary, which, generally between the ages of twelve and fifteen, stimulates the ovaries to begin the secretion of oestrogen. This evokes a general growth of the accessory reproductive organs, the uterus, vagina and the breasts; the menstrual cycle is set going; and hair appears in the arm-pits and in the pubic region.

In both sexes the distinctive male and female physique (mentioned further in chapter 10), and sexual behaviour, are partly dependent on the action of the hormones.

The reproductive hormones, then, by their many actions on different parts of the body, ensure that the organs of reproduction both *develop* and *function* in unison. Our knowledge of the way in which they work is far from complete, but the chemical nature of some of them is known, and some use has been made of them in medicine. The example of undescended testes has already been mentioned. As another we may take the common complaint of dysmenorrhea, or pain during menstruation. The origin of this pain is far from fully known, but it is sometimes at least an accompaniment of cramps or contractions of the uterine muscles – the muscles which are largely responsible for expulsion of a child when it is born. It is sometimes possible to treat this complaint successfully with hormone preparations.

This example has been taken because it illustrates very well the state of our knowledge of reproductive physiology. A very great deal has been learnt, mainly during the twentieth century, and the new knowledge has valuable applications; but the knowledge is exceedingly incomplete, and the application has often to be tentative and cautious. The hormonal treatment of dysmenorrhea was based on the experimental study, often on laboratory animals, of the effects on various organs of administering the hormone in various dosages. It was, in fact, an application of knowledge carefully and laboriously acquired. It contrasts with some other treatments that at one time had a good deal of notoriety but which lacked sound physiological foundation. The most publicized was the operation in which monkey testes (called 'monkey glands', evidently to preserve the proprieties) were grafted into old men to rejuvenate them. Leaving other objections on one side, this operation is unsound because such grafts cannot survive: the grafted tissues rapidly degenerate and disappear. The operation soon became a joke, but premature attempts to make use, not of glands themselves, but of glandular extracts, have had more serious and lasting influence. G. W. Corner describes

the exploitation of endocrine preparations in the drug trade ahead of scientific knowledge. . . . Barrelfuls of extracts and millions of tablets have been fed and injected into human patients, with uncritical optimism, before the chemists and physiologists could learn the facts. The benefits of endocrine research on the reproductive glands have been almost stifled by this exploitation. Even today the practising physician finds it difficult to distinguish what is sound and practical amid the flood of well advertised endocrine drugs.

Sexual Behaviour

The need for properly established facts has recently become obvious also in the field of sexual *behaviour*. Most people know what they themselves, and probably a few friends, do;

many assume that theirs is the 'normal' and 'natural' way of behaving, and that any other sorts of behaviour should be despised or condemned. Others, in ignorance of what their fellows do, may believe themselves abnormal, sometimes because they have been taught to look on sexual functions as to some extent disgusting. The various possible attitudes are all products of the particular teachings of some section of our own society. Studies of other societies, and of the different strata within a society, have shown that there is infinite variety in the accepted codes and practices. In many communities sexual relationships between young children are taken for granted; in others, extra-marital relationships are part of the conventional pattern of behaviour; in yet others, open homosexual behaviour has been usual. These facts exemplify the general plasticity of human behaviour which we discuss further in chapter 6. General statements in this section apply primarily to the behaviour of people in Western civilizations today.

Recently, scientific scrutiny has been applied, not only to groups remote from Western civilization, but to the populations of countries such as Britain and the United States. The researches of the team headed by A. C. Kinsey are the most extensive, and the most discussed, of such studies. Research on the sexual behaviour of people in advanced societies has generally been inspired by the known frequency of sexual difficulties within marriage – often, it is believed, due to ignorance, and by the need for a sound basis of information for advice to the married or to the young.

It is clearly established that small children are capable of sexual behaviour, and all go through an early phase of touching and exploring their genitals. It is doubtful whether there is any period in childhood in which sexual responsiveness is wholly absent, but it is, of course, at puberty, when a new hormonal balance develops, that the need for sexual activity becomes strong.

In the male such activity reaches its maximum very early, around the ages sixteen to twenty; thereafter it declines, at first very gradually and always slowly, without any sudden change in later life. The form sexual activity takes varies a great deal between individuals: masturbation, nocturnal emissions (in which ejaculation takes place during sleep), and homosexual relationships are all common, as well as the biologically 'normal' heterosexual coitus. Masturbation is, indeed, almost universal. These facts indicate that accepted custom in our society, to say nothing of the law, is ill adapted to human needs. It must be emphasized that no physiological harm need arise from any of these types of sexual behaviour; harm can, and often does, arise, however, if feelings of shame or guilt are engendered in children or adolescents. One obvious conclusion which might be drawn is the desirability of early marriage.

In the female the pattern of sexual development is different. Young girls, like boys, are capable of erotic arousal at an early age, but far fewer have much sexual experience before maturity. Sexual activity includes masturbation and homosexual relationships; in women, unlike men, the latter do not come under the condemnation of the law in Western countries. According to Kinsey and his colleagues early sexual experience, of whatever kind, helps to ensure the attainment of sexual satisfaction in marriage. These authors point out that the failure to recognize the sexual capacities and needs of teen-agers is quite recent: Juliet, for instance, was fourteen when Romeo made love to her. These two, Daphnis and Chloë, and many others 'would be

Scrotum and Clitoris. In the embryo the genital organs of both sexes are represented. In the adult the clitoris of the female (sensory in function) corresponds to the male penis, and the labia majora to the male scrotum

looked on as immature adolescents and identified as
juvenile delinquents if they were living today'.

Although the two sexes are alike in the early development
of sexual capacities, women do not reach their highest level
of sexual activity until much later than men – commonly,
it seems, in the thirties; later in life they are potentially
more active than men. On the other hand, many women,
but few men, seem able to live contentedly for long periods
with little or no sexual outlet. Another difference is that
most men are easily stimulated by sexual associations –
hence the pin-up girl and the leg show; while women, on
the whole, tend to be less aroused by associations, and more
exclusively by direct contact. This difference is often not
known to married couples, and may lead to mutual misunderstanding.

It is commonly said that, among the differences between
the sexes, is a profound contrast in the nature of the orgasm
attained at the climax of coitus. In a man orgasm is marked
by the ejaculation of semen, and this of course has no
counterpart in a woman. However, the few physiological
studies which have been made indicate that orgasm in the
two sexes is less unlike than had been thought. In both there
are rhythmic movements, accompanied by raised pulse and
respiratory rates and blood pressure; and in both, the
phenomenon of tumescence, or swelling of certain tissues
due to increase in the blood supply, occurs; in a man the
principal tissues concerned are those of the penis, in which
the swelling causes erection; in a woman the clitoris (which
is the small analogue of the penis) and the labia minora,
similarly swell; in both, the breast nipples and the internal
tissues of the nose also become engorged. After orgasm,
there is a rapid decline in tumescence, and a general and
pleasurable relaxation throughout the body. Apart from
ejaculation, the main difference is that a man rarely enters
coitus without reaching orgasm, while women often do so.
There is very great variation in the ability of women to
attain a climax; the explanation of this is not clear, but the
inhibition of sexual responses in childhood may play a part.

Fertilization

Now that we have surveyed the organs of reproduction and their mode of functioning, we come to the *raison d'être* of the whole complex system. We are all forty weeks older than we acknowledge, and it is the events of this neglected period that now concern us.

The egg, on discharge from the ovary, enters the mouth of the tube which leads to the uterus. Fertilization usually takes place in the tube: sperms, discharged into the vagina, make their way into the uterus and so into the tubes, and if an egg has recently ripened one of the sperms fertilizes it. Sometimes a fertilized egg remains in the tube instead of moving down into the uterus. After a few weeks' development internal bleeding results from rupture of the tube, and an operation becomes necessary. Fortunately this happens only in about one in three hundred pregnancies. Although only one sperm fertilizes each egg, a vast number are present in each ejaculation. About a teaspoonful of semen is discharged in each coitus, perhaps 240m.* sperms. There is evidence that the presence of many sperms is needed to ensure fertilization, and it is likely that they help to create the necessary chemical conditions in vagina, uterus, and tubes. When infertility in a married couple is investigated it is often found that the husband's emissions consistently contain a much smaller number of active sperms than the normal; and, although many millions of sperms are present, they are evidently not enough for normal fertility.

The study of the chemistry of seminal fluid, and of the numbers and behaviour of sperms, has been stimulated by the use of *artificial insemination* in stockbreeding. By collecting the semen of a selected male a breeder can use the male to serve many more females than would normally be possible, and so can more rapidly improve the genetical qualities of his herd. In man artificial insemination is now being used for a different purpose. It is sometimes

* Throughout the book 'm.' stands for 'million'.

impossible for a married couple to have children, even though the woman is normal. If the difficulty is due to the husband's impotence, but his semen is normal, the semen can be collected artificially and injected into the wife's vagina. When the defect is in the husband's semen a physician may use that of an anonymous donor.

The controversy that this practice has aroused illustrates the way in which social problems spring from human applications of biological knowledge. Artificial insemination has been attacked on religious and moral grounds, and complaints have been made that it raises grave legal difficulties. It has been said that the use of a donor's semen is adultery, and it is further condemned (absurdly) because the production of donor semen involves masturbation; and it has been complained that a child produced by artificial insemination is legally 'illegitimate', and this leads to various difficulties, especially over the inheritance of property.

The supporters of artificial insemination hold that it should be regarded as yet another example of technical advances giving us further control over nature; that if it is applied with the consent of both man and wife it can give, and has given, the greatest satisfaction to both; and that although it does raise moral and legal problems, they can be solved. It has further been claimed that the religious objections are in much the same terms as those in which the churches opposed the use of anaesthesia in childbirth a century ago.

The history of other advances in human biology and medicine suggests that artificial insemination will continue to cause controversy, but that it will nevertheless be used, and its use will increase.

Ourselves Unborn

The timetable of pregnancy, and of the growth of the child, is conveniently reckoned not from fertilization, but from the beginning of the last menstrual period. On this scheme the

WEEK after last men-struation	TIMETABLE OF DEVELOPMENT
2 (end)	Fertilization
3	Egg travels down tube into uterus; begins to divide
4	Implantation in wall of uterus
5	Early stages of skeleton and nervous system
6	Head, heart and tail visible; gill pouch rudiments present; rudiments of arms and legs. Length about 6 mm. ($\frac{1}{4}$ inch)
7	Chest and abdomen formed; fingers and toes appear; eyes developing. About 12 mm. ($\frac{1}{2}$ inch)
8	Face, features and external ears developing; gill rudiments disappearing. About 21 mm. ($\frac{7}{8}$ inch), weight 1 g. ($\frac{1}{28}$ oz.)
9	Face completely developed; now resembles a human child. Length 30 mm. (1·2 inch), weight 2 g. ($\frac{1}{14}$ oz.). From now on embryo usually called a *foetus*
14	Limbs, including fingers and toes and nails, fully formed; external genital organs developed. Sex can be determined by trained person without microscopic examination. 77 mm. (3 inches), 30 g. (1 oz.)
18	Movements (quickening) begin; heart can be heard; hair all over body; eyebrows and eyelashes. 190 mm. ($8\frac{1}{2}$ inches), 180 g. ($6\frac{1}{2}$ oz.)
23	Head hair appears. 300 mm. (12 inches), 450 g. (16 oz.)
27	Eyes open. 350 mm. (14 inches), 875 g. (31 oz.)
32	400 mm. (16 inches), 1425 g. (3 lb. 2 oz.). If born now can survive, given special care
36	450 mm. (18 inches), 2375 g. (5 lb. 4 oz.). Better chance of survival now, in eighth month, than in seventh (contrary to commonly held belief)
40	Full term. Skin covered with cheese-like material. Head hair typically 1 inch long; may be other hair on shoulders, but soon disappears. Head still very large relative to body. 500 mm. (20 inches), 3250 g. (7 lb. 4 oz.). *All measurements are averages, and there are many wide departures from them, especially in the later months*

most probable time of fertilization is the end of the second week. The fertilized egg then spends about a week travelling down the tube and floating in the uterus. During this time development begins: the egg-cell divides, and successive cell-divisions give rise to a ball of cells. (Cells have already been mentioned in chapter 2.) The earliest stages of human development are not known, owing to the difficulty of getting material, but those of other mammals, including one species of monkey, have been fully studied. It is known that the embryo becomes implanted in the inner wall of the uterus (already, as we have seen, prepared to receive it) after a number of divisions of the cells have taken place. Soon after implantation it becomes completely embedded in the uterine tissues. The presence of the embryo prevents menstruation when it is next due, and this is usually the first indication to a woman that she is pregnant. Rarely, a loss of blood resembling that of menstruation occurs, sometimes more than once, at the times when the period would have been expected.

When implantation has taken place the uterus continues to grow and to increase its blood supply. On the average the uterus increases in weight thirty times during the first pregnancy.

During the first weeks the embryo undergoes very rapid development and shows a number of striking anatomical

5½   7   8   9   10   18 WEEKS

Human Embryos. The umbilical cord is shown in the three largest changes, some of which will be mentioned later. In this early phase the embryo's hold on life is relatively precarious, and spontaneous abortion is common: the embryo dies, becomes detached from the uterus and passes out of the vagina, probably with blood and other debris. Very early unplanned abortion (in the first six weeks or so) is often painless and harmless, and probably occurs in at least one out of five pregnancies; the proportion has been estimated to be even as high as one in three. Other mammals, such as the rabbit and the sow, also suffer a similar proportion of early, harmless abortions. In the human species, however, the majority occur in the period from the eighth to the twelfth week. It is possible that many of the aborted embryos are defective, and could never have become normal individuals. If so, their early elimination can be regarded as a natural economy, but the mother may feel very ill for some time after it has happened.

Recapitulation of Ancestral Characters

A feature of early development, much discussed but not often well understood, is the so-called recapitulation of ancestral stages. It is sometimes said that we go through a fish stage representing the fish stage of our evolution, and it is even said that we 'climb our family tree' during our embryonic existence. Neither of these statements is quite true. What actually happens does indeed reflect our evolutionary history, but the details are complex.

The evolution of the human species is discussed more fully in the next chapter; here we need say only that about 300m. years ago our ancestors were certainly some kind of primitive fish, and that on land the stages in our ancestry included a cold-blooded reptilian phase and, later, warm-blooded primitive mammals with hair instead of scales and young which were born in an active state instead of hatched from eggs.

What traces of this evolutionary history can we find in individual development? The most obvious are found about

D

four weeks after fertilization (week 6 in the table). Extern-
ally the embryo seems to have rudimentary gills (though
actually they never fully develop); it has a tail, of considerable length relative to the whole body; and in general it
resembles, not a fish, but a *fish embryo*. Internally the resemblance is carried further: for instance, the arrangement
of the blood vessels is fish-like, and the principal muscles of
the body are divided into segments which in a fish become
those we can easily see when we eat, say, cod or salmon.
All these structures undergo a rapid and complex transformation, and within a few weeks there is little obvious
trace of them. This transformation is, on the whole, directly
into the structural arrangement typical of the human being:
it is not possible to discern, for instance, a phase in embryonic development corresponding to the reptilian stage in
evolution, although certain parts of the body do show
temporary arrangements which resemble those in a reptile.
Actually, it is possible to find traces of our pre-human
ancestry at every stage in development, including the adult:
there are, for instance, the much commented-on muscles
which a few gifted people can use to waggle their ears, but
which in most of us are ineffective; most mammals can
move their ears in the direction of particular sounds, and in
us these muscles are a vestige reminding us of a mobile-
eared ancestry.

We can see, then, traces of our evolutionary history in our
development, but the study of embryology by no means
saves us the trouble of trying to work out how we evolved
by other methods, such as those described in the next chapter. There are other examples of the ways in which development fails to reflect evolution. Take, for example, the shape
of the face. In most mammals there is a prominent snout,
but in man the face is flat. If there were a straightforward
recapitulation of ancestral characters, we should expect that
the human embryo would develop a snout and then lose it.
In fact, no snout ever appears in human development. In
mammals which have snouts, the forward growth of the face
occurs relatively late; all early mammalian embryos are

flat-faced. Thus the shape of the face in man is an embryonic characteristic retained in the adult. This is the opposite of what would be expected if the simple idea of recapitulation were true. Even more obvious is the *placenta*, or after-birth, the structure which enabled us to draw nourishment from the maternal blood stream. This large organ develops partly from embryonic tissues, but it does not represent any stage in our evolutionary history. It is an embryonic modification characteristic of mammals.

To sum up, we can find indications of our ancestry at every stage of our development, including the adult, but there is no simple recapitulation. It is not only the adult structure that undergoes evolutionary change: the whole of our life-history has been subject to change; at some stages, however, the difference from the ancestral arrangement is rather less than at others.

Pregnancy and the Placenta

The most obvious of the evolutionary changes undergone by mammalian embryos are those connected with development in the mother's uterus, instead of from an egg laid outside the body. The egg of a reptile, like that of a bird, has a large yolk which provides the food on which the embryo lives until it hatches. In a mammal there is no yolk at all: all food is supplied by the mother, and the structure of the embryo is adapted to this parasitic mode of life. At implantation the egg, as we have seen, is already divided into a number of cells. Not all these cells are destined to form the child: some of them form what are called *extra-embryonic* tissues – a term which means simply that they are outside the embryo. The embryo is completely surrounded by these tissues and, once implantation is complete, the tissues in turn are surrounded by those of the uterine wall.

The extra-embryonic tissues thrust minute, finger-like processes into the uterine tissues, and so greatly increase the area over which food material can diffuse into the embryo. This is the beginning of the formation of the placenta

Enlargement of the Uterus in Pregnancy. The virgin uterus, on the left, compared with the uterus at full term

already mentioned, the organ of interchange between mother and child. It is constituted partly by embryonic and partly by maternal tissues, and is eventually shed as the *after-birth* soon after the child is born. The placenta grows rapidly in the early stages, and by full term it weighs about 450 g. (1 lb.). After the first few weeks it becomes localized on one side of the embryo, and connected to the embryo only by the umbilical cord. The cord contains blood vessels which carry blood in both directions between the placenta and the child, and it has to be cut when the child is born. The navel is the scar marking the junction of the cord with the belly.

The blood and blood vessels in the umbilical cord are all part of the embryonic system: the mother's blood does not mingle with that of the child, though in the placenta they are separated only by exceedingly fine membranes. Across these membranes pass the substances exchanged: oxygen and food from mother to child, carbon dioxide and other waste products in the opposite direction.

The demands of the embryo for certain foodstuffs put a strain on the mother which may injure her if she is inadequately fed or otherwise in poor health. It is not the general demand for food that is important: it is a fallacy that a pregnant woman needs a great deal of extra food. The average net gain in weight during a first pregnancy is about

Full Term Human Foetus

23 lb., and during later pregnancies about 21 lb. The child accounts for about one-third of the gain, the rest being due to the enlarged uterus, increase in body fat, the placenta, and the 'bag of waters' which surrounds the embryo and protects it from injury. The whole of the gain in weight takes place after the sixteenth week; before then there is no gain, and there may be a loss. But a gain of 23 lb. in 34 weeks is not very much, and the extra daily intake of food required is quite small.

In Western countries, where there is little gross under-nutrition or malnutrition, the nutritional difficulties of preg-nancy are due to special shortages. The old maxim 'a tooth for every child' is based on the fact that calcium deficiency is common in mothers. A pregnant woman who gets too little calcium in her food transfers calcium from her bones and teeth to the embryo; as a result, her skeleton and teeth may be weakened; the effect on the child is thus reduced. Similarly, according to one investigation, anaemia due to iron shortage occurs in at least one American woman in three in the last three months of pregnancy, owing to the demands of the embryo for iron. Deficiency of calcium, iron, and other dietary essentials, notably vitamins, can be avoided by giving pregnant women a good diet, as we shall see in chapter 13.

Some other problems of pregnancy are not so easily solved. Strangely, predicting its duration is one. The birth of a child is predicted on the assumption that it will take place 280 days, or forty weeks, after the first day of the last menstruation. 280 days is indeed approximately the mean duration of pregnancy, found from studies of large numbers of normal births; but, as most parents know, there are many wide departures from it. In one study of 537 white American women, all of whom bore living children, the results were as follows:

	per cent
before 266th day	12·7
2nd week before (days 266–272)	12·3
1st week before (days 273–279)	22·0
on 280th day	3·7
1st week after (days 281–287)	24·2
2nd week after (days 288–294)	15·6
after 294th day	9·4

If the percentage for each day is taken it is found to be highest for the 280th day, and to fall away slowly both before and after; thus 280 days is the mode as well as the mean length of pregnancy; but it will be seen how impossible it is to predict accurately in any particular case.

It is comparatively easy to make statistical studies such as the above, given secretarial help and a punched-card system; but other problems of pregnancy require more elaborate study. The most obvious are the so-called *toxaemias* of pregnancy – an expression based on the belief that they are due to 'poisons in the blood'. The toxaemia of early pregnancy is pernicious vomiting, an exaggeration of the common morning sickness. Some nausea or vomiting is exceedingly common early in pregnancy: according to Guttmacher it is severe in about one-third of all cases and mild in a third; the rest are entirely free. 'Many an ink-well has been drained dry over the cause of vomiting in pregnancy, but we are only slightly wiser than when the first quill scratched about it.' In the mild cases it disappears about the twelfth week, but the most severe cases, which are rare, require special treatment. The toxaemias of late pregnancy are all accompanied by high blood pressure, and usually by a disturbance of the chemistry of the body which causes an excessive retention of water. In an extreme case, now very rare when there is good ante-natal care, convulsions develop.

It is general ante-natal care that is most effective in countering these dangers, and where it is practised it has already greatly reduced the incidence of serious cases. But the causes of the toxaemias of pregnancy are still unknown, and since about one pregnancy in fifteen, in an advanced country such as the United States, is complicated by one of them, they would repay extensive research.

Much the same applies to childbirth itself, the aspect of pregnancy which probably looms largest in most minds. The pangs of childbirth seem to have been taken for granted throughout history, and when, a century ago, anaesthesia was invented, its use in childbirth was condemned as 'unnatural' and 'immoral'. Actually, the most obvious objection to anaesthesia (which causes unconsciousness) is that it is not safe; it also deprives the mother of the unique pleasure felt on holding her new-born child. Today the emphasis is rather on analgesia, which is the relief of pain without loss of consciousness. Quite recently new and better analgesics have been found, and they are coming to be widely applied. It is however claimed that pain can be largely prevented without the use of drugs, by instruction of the mother in the nature of pregnancy and in what is required of her during the actual birth. This instruction includes lessons in the technique of muscular relaxation – a means of reducing harmful tension, due to fear. Fear of pregnancy, largely due to ignorance, is common, and is considered to contribute a great deal to the discomforts of childbirth. Once again, therefore, the importance of ante-natal care and instruction is evident.

More research, and wider application of what is known by means of improved health services, are needed along all these lines: improvement of ante-natal care, psychological preparation of the mother, and analgesia. Meanwhile important facts have been brought out by an entirely different approach. In a primitive community nearly all women begin to bear children soon after puberty: the average age of the mother at the first birth is perhaps seventeen. In advanced communities, especially today, the age is much greater. Statistical studies of maternal and infant mortality have shown that both tend to rise in proportion to the age of the mother, as does the incidence of abnormal babies; probably, the best age for having a first child is twenty-two. Further inquiry has suggested that subsequent children should be born at intervals of about 24 months.

It is important to be clear on exactly what this signifies. It is not that a married couple should despair of bringing up a family if the woman has, say, reached her thirties without having a child. Ante-natal and obstetric care has advanced so far today that, even when the mother is over forty, the successful birth of a first child is no longer a matter for astonishment. Certainly, if early child-bearing is practicable, it should be encouraged, but the significance of the figures quoted in the previous paragraph is for society as a whole, rather than for the individual. The reasons for late marriage and delayed maternity are mostly economic. (We have already seen that there are good psychological grounds for supporting early marriages.) If social organization obliges women to delay child-bearing to the detriment of their health and that of their children, the obvious conclusion is that the social organization should be changed. These points will be further discussed in chapter 15.

'This Fair Defect of Nature'

The study of human reproduction and of early development is obviously worth while, for it tells us how to improve the lot of parents and children. This has been a main theme of the present chapter. To end it we may turn to the much more general question asked, with some humour, by Milton in the passage quoted at the chapter head. Even if we do not agree that the division of humanity into two sexes is a defect in nature, or that of the two sexes the 'feminine' can be more easily dispensed with, we may still be curious to know what is the biological significance of sexual reproduction and development from an egg.

This type of reproduction is usual throughout the animal kingdom, and is quite general also among plants. Many plants, and some animals, can reproduce by division or budding; the offspring are then already highly differentiated, and there is no need for a long and complex development from a single cell. Yet the fact that this asexual process is relatively rare suggests that the sexual process has some advantage over it.

The explanation seems to lie in the fact that all living things undergo evolution, and the advantage of sexual reproduction is that each individual so produced has a combination of genes from two individuals. We have seen that each parent contributes one half-set of chromosomes, and so of genes, to each offspring. In practice, this means that each individual (apart from uniovular twins) is genetically unique, and that there is always a good deal of genetical variation in any population of any species. Hence advantageous genes (which may have arisen separately by mutation) can become associated in one individual, and new and more effective combinations of genes can appear. This variability (as we shall further see in chapter 5) makes possible greater adaptability in a species, especially in relation to new conditions, and enables it to evolve comparatively rapidly.

Consequently, to get the advantages of sexual reproduction, even the largest animals and plants retain a stage in their life history of microscopic size, namely, the fertilized egg. Fertilization is thus primarily a means by which genes are brought together in new groupings; but it also, necessarily, in all large organisms, is the starting point for a complex development.

We end this chapter, therefore, by emphasizing that man is a product of evolution; in the next, the evidence for this statement is more fully set forth, and the course of human evolution is outlined.

Part Two

Human Diversity

Man is a product of evolution. The main features which distinguish him from his nearest living relatives, the apes, are his large brain, manual dexterity, and the power of speech: these, with other special characters, make possible man's unique form of social organization. His brain, in particular, is so organized that his behaviour is free from the rigidity of the 'instinctive' activities of most animals, and is consequently highly flexible and adaptable to new conditions.

Only one human species exists today, and the physical differences, such as skin colour, by which human types are classified, are of only trivial significance, although for social or political reasons they are sometimes given a spurious importance. All human groups or 'races' include individuals of a wide range of ability and social worth; there is no justification for saying that one group is innately inferior to another, and the social achievements of each group depend largely on the natural resources and amenities available. Theories of the inferiority or criminality of particular groups often arise from the political needs of a dominant group, such as foreign conquerors or employers of cheap labour. Much ability is wasted and injustice caused by the inferior position which the colonial and other backward peoples occupy. Similar waste and injustice occur within each country in which there are large unprivileged classes of poor people. In most countries women form an unprivileged class.

5

FROM APE TO MAN

> We must, however, acknowledge, as it seems to me, that man with all his noble qualities ... still bears in his bodily frame the indelible stamp of his lowly origin.
>
> CHARLES DARWIN

GENETICS, our main topic so far, is a study of differences between individuals. We come now, in this and the next five chapters, to differences between large groups. Today few dispute that men, like other animals and plants and indeed the earth, the sun, and the stars, are a product of evolution. The present chapter deals with the stages of the evolution of men from primitive apes, and the variety of human types that have existed in the last million years.

The Evidence of Rocks and Fossils

The main evidence that the animals and plants of today have evolved from very different previous forms is based on our knowledge of the changes that have occurred in the earth's crust. For at least the past 500m. years ice, wind, and rain have been eroding the surface of the earth, while in other parts rivers and sea have been depositing layers of new rock made up largely of the eroded particles. If we dig deep into the earth we find that the rocks are arranged in layers, and where there has been no violent disturbance such as those due to volcanoes or earthquakes the older rocks are the deeper. Sorting out the different types of rock, and determining their origin, which is a part of the science of geology, is not easy; but it has been successfully done in many parts of the world.

Each type of rock that has been laid down by sea or river water contains its own characteristic fossils; so does the coal-bearing rock formed from primeval forests. Fossils are the traces of plants and animals: as a rule only the hard parts, such as bones, are preserved, and they undergo a chemical change in which the organic material is replaced by rock substance, without alteration of the original structure. The skeletons of giant 'dinosaurs' that one sees in the museums are made, not of bone, but of rock in the form of the original bony skeleton.

Not only can the order in time of the different rocks be determined; their ages also can be roughly calculated in various ways. The calculations show that the evolution both of the rocks and of living things has taken some hundreds of millions of years. The group of backboned animals (the vertebrates), to which we belong, began in the sea more than 300m. years ago, and at first the only vertebrates were fish-like animals. If the fossils of successive layers are studied it is found that some early fishes gradually developed the capacity to live on land, and so gave rise to the land verte-brates. The earliest land vertebrates were amphibians (a group now represented by frogs and newts), but for the greater part of the time after this the most prominent land vertebrates were reptiles, including the notorious dinosaurs, pterodactyls, and so forth. One branch of these reptiles de-veloped feathers, wings, and warm-bloodedness, and became birds.

Meanwhile, even before the great reptiles evolved, an entirely different branch of the reptiles specialized in a different way. The original peg-like teeth (as in a crocodile today) became more complex, as ours are: some became grinders, others came to be similar to front and eye teeth. During the period of the great reptiles some of these forms with complex teeth developed warm blood and the capacity to bear young in an active state (instead of laying eggs); we do not yet know when, because the skeletons that remain do not tell us. At all events it is certain that by the time the great reptiles perished, evidently as a result of drastic climatic changes involving the whole world, there were mammals in existence ready to take their place.

The mammals, the class of warm-blooded, furry verte-brates that includes our own species, have been the main land vertebrates for 60m. years. We have an enormous mass of fossil remains of some groups: we can trace every detail of the evolution of some modern hoofed mammals, and of large carnivores such as lions and tigers, from small, undistin-guished creatures rather like shrews. Other groups of mammals have left fewer fossil remains, because they did not live in surroundings which favoured fossilization. Among these less well-recorded orders is unfortunately that of the primates, the one that includes the monkeys, apes, and men – nearly all forest-dwellers. Moreover, the fossil record becomes exceptionally thin when we come to the precursors of man himself. This is probably because many of the ancestors of man were not only forest-dwellers but comparatively rare animals. Nevertheless it is already pos-sible to give a reasonable account of the evolution of man-kind from ape-like creatures.

The Causes of Evolution

Before we come to this account we must see something of how evolutionary change has come about. The man whose researches finally brought scientists to accept the theory of organic evolution was Charles Darwin. Among a number of evolutionists of the eighteenth and nineteenth centuries Darwin not only presented a mass of evidence for the fact of evolution: he also produced the first convincing theory of how it had occurred. At the same time as Alfred Russel Wallace he put forward the theory of *natural selection* (often miscalled the 'survival of the fittest').

Natural selection depends on two things: first, inherited variation; second, either a selective mortality, so that some types tend to live longer than others, or inherited differ-ences in fertility. *Inherited variation* has already been dis-cussed, in chapters 2 and 3. Its agents are the genes, and mutation ensures a continuous supply of new forms. For *selective mortality* we have to assume the production of off-spring in excess in each generation. In a population of constant size this excess will not survive, and with the excess will disappear certain inherited characteristics. This last assumption is perfectly justified. In every plant or animal species studied, even the least fertile such as elephants, gannets, and man, many more offspring are produced than are needed to maintain populations at a constant level. There is always a high mortality in the young and a considerable death-rate among adults. This mortality is undoubtedly one of the means by which natural selection occurs.

This account of the machinery of evolution is not just guesswork. In some instances evolutionary change has been observed while it was taking place. For example, in some species of moths black varieties have replaced paler forms in industrial areas where everything is covered with soot: the black types are less conspicuous, and so better equipped to evade their enemies. This is an example of the replacement of one *variety* by another. Darwin thought that varieties were incipient species, and today we have good evidence that he was right.

One of the most useful ways of deciding whether to call two closely related types separate species is to find out whether they can be crossed and made to yield fertile off-spring. The horse and the ass, which are different species, can be crossed, but the mule which results is sterile. In some instances crosses of this sort, between fairly widely different types, give offspring with impaired fertility. The gypsy moth, of which the Latin name is *Lymantria dispar* (indicating that only one species is involved), is found in a number of different areas, including Western Europe and Japan. Each area has its own particular 'race', and these races can be crossed; but the resulting offspring usually breed among themselves only with difficulty, if at all. Evidently the different geographical varieties of *Lymantria* are on the way to becoming distinct species, and this is another instance of evolutionary change which can be observed in progress.

It is clear that to observe evolutionary change directly, save in a fragmentary way, is impossible, because of the time-scale of the changes. Nevertheless, the evidence of the succession of rocks, with their wealth of fossil remains, together with studies of the contemporary variety of plant and animal life, give us an outline both of the course and the causes of evolution.

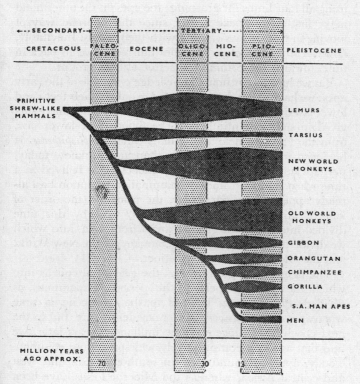

Family Tree of the Primates

Prehuman Fossils

The preliminaries to the evolution of man took place between 30 and 60m. years ago, when the tailless apes appeared as a group separate from that of the ordinary monkeys. The monkeys leap from one tree-hold to another, using all four limbs for grasping; the apes on the other hand make first-rate trapeze artists, since their normal way of moving in trees is by swinging with their hands. Inevitably, however, the distinction becomes blurred as we go back in time, towards the common ancestor of both groups.

But we have no intimate knowledge of the life of the early apes: we have as yet direct knowledge only of their teeth and lower jaws; only these, the least destructible parts, have survived in sufficient numbers to be found. One lower jaw, from the Faiyum, near the Nile, is called *Propliopithecus*. It belonged to an ape far smaller than any we know today, perhaps not more than eighteen inches high. It lived at a time when the main lines of mammalian evolution had already appeared; in particular, the primates (the order of lemurs, tarsiers, monkeys, and apes) were by this time divided into the main groups, apart from man, into which we divide them today, with the monkeys of the New World and the Old World already distinct.

The figure on page 83 shows the geological epochs into which the Tertiary period, the period of mammals, is divided. *Propliopithecus* belongs to the Oligocene, a time when apes or their ancestors were evidently rare. But in the next epoch, the Miocene, some millions of years later, we find that apes are comparatively widespread and common. Today, apes are found only in south-east Asia and west and central Africa, whereas the Miocene fossils have been found also in North and East Africa, and widely dispersed in Europe and Asia.

These Miocene apes belong to a group called the Dryopithecinae. They include a considerable variety of types, ranging in size from that of a small gibbon to something like

DRYOPITHECUS   MAN-APE   GORILLA   HOMO SAPIENS

Upper Jaws and Teeth. Dryopithecus has a dental arch like that of a modern ape, i.e. 'square'; *Plesianthropus*, one of the South African man-apes, has the curved, human type. Note the massive canine in the gorilla, not found in the others

that of a gorilla. *Dryopithecus*, a large European and Asian type which has been known for some time from its jaws and teeth, has grinding teeth showing resemblances both to those of the chimpanzee and gorilla, and to our own. A similar form, first found in India, is assigned to the genus *Sivapithecus*. We have only a few fragments of the rest of the skeleton of either of these, but other Dryopithecine fossils found recently, in Kenya, provide a more complete picture of the group. Among them is *Proconsul*, a large form something like a chimpanzee. The skull of *Proconsul* is lightly constructed compared with that of modern apes, and it lacks their heavy brow ridges and very projecting muzzle; in certain respects it has more in common with monkeys than it has with modern apes. A number of limb bones, belonging to various Dryopithecine types, have also been found in Kenya. The thigh and arm bones are relatively slender, and, relative to the body, the arms are shorter and the legs longer than are those of present-day apes. Thus the proportions are half-way between those of apes and men. The structure of these bones indicates that their owners are not tree-living: they did not leap from branch to branch, like monkeys, nor swing like gibbons, but lived on the ground; it seems that they were active, agile creatures, able to run and jump.

As links between men and apes, another group of recently discovered African fossils are even more important. They are called collectively the Australopithecinae, but here we shall refer to them as the South African man-apes. (They have nothing to do with Australia.) These forms have been given a variety of generic names, such as *Australopithecus*, *Plesianthropus*, *Paranthropus*, and so on: students of human evolution are always fertile in such inventions. It would however be more reasonable, in the opinion of some authorities, to put them all in one genus: this genus would be divided into several species, each species being rather variable and including several distinct types.

The interest of these fossils depends on the facts that first, they are much more complete than any of those so far mentioned; second, they display a remarkable patchwork of human and non-human features. In general, the brain, skull, and teeth are of ape-like proportions, but the details of structure show a number of similarities to man. Like the gorilla and chimpanzee, they had brains of less than half the size of our own, and heavy protruding jaws with large teeth. The average cranial capacity of five skulls has recently been estimated at 576 cubic centimetres – rather more than that of most gorillas. The teeth are arranged in the jaw in human fashion, forming a curved arch; the canines (or eye-teeth) are quite small, and not tusk-like as in apes; and the grinding teeth are human in the details of their construction: these man-apes chewed their food as we do. In the skull, the margins of the nose are formed, as in apes, by a bone called the premaxilla, but the brows lack the heavy ridges above the eyes characteristic of apes, and the cheek region also is human in construction.

MAN-APE   HOMO SAPIENS   CHIMPANZEE

Skulls of Apes and Man. The South African man-ape has a cranium of similar size to that of the modern chimpanzee, but in other features is more human: note especially the teeth, and the absence of heavy ridges on the cranium

We have knowledge of the skeletons of the limbs as well as the skull. In one instance parts of two arm bones (humerus and ulna) and a skull were found together in one lump of rock, and could therefore be assigned with certainty all to the same animal. (This is important, because there have been instances of bones being found moderately close to each other and giving rise to fierce but inconclusive arguments on whether they belonged to the same individual.) The almost complete pelvic skeleton, and wrist, thigh, and ankle-bone fragments have also been found. They show that in size most of the man-apes found so far were smaller than most men, perhaps resembling human pygmies. There are, however, some very recently discovered forms which were probably above the average height of modern man. More important, the limb bones are found to be in structure (though not in size) typically human, even in detail. There is thus no doubt that the limbs of the South African man-apes resembled ours, and that these creatures walked erect as we do. The thumbs too resemble ours, and not those of modern apes, in being efficient grasping organs, probably capable of manipulating tools and weapons. The ankle bones, however, were partly ape-like, giving a greater mobility. The erect posture is confirmed also by the structure of the base of the skull, where it joins the vertebral column: the skull was held erect, like ours, not poked forward like that of an ape. The ape-men lived on the ground, on grasslands, instead of being forest-dwellers.

The general picture that emerges, then, is one of a small, man-like body, with a head more ape-like than human but having some human features. It is therefore natural to ask whether the ape-man had developed greater intelligence than true apes. In size of brain they were no different, and so it is, perhaps, unlikely for that reason alone. But it has been suggested that the man-apes used tools. Baboon skulls have been found near some of the remains, fractured as if they had been struck by a blunt instrument. Dart has consequently suggested that the man-apes were at least intelligent enough to hunt and to kill their prey with weapons.

Perhaps, soon, more evidence will be available on this point. Certainly, knowledge of the variety of man-apes is rapidly increasing, as new fossil finds are reported. If Dart's view is confirmed it may be necessary to abandon the expression 'man-ape', and to refer to the South African fossils as men.

Fossil Man

The last sentence provokes the question, where is the line drawn between man and not-man? Clearly, if we had a complete series of fossils, as we have for some other mammals, we should have to choose a quite arbitrary point in the series to mark the division. As it is, there are two possible sorts of criteria for distinguishing human from pre-human types. First, we can use anatomical features: this, indeed, is the obvious thing to do, since fossils give us direct information on structure, but only indirect knowledge of anything else. So William Howells, the anthropologist, says that 'man zoologically became man when he first walked erect on the ground, or at least developed an arch to his foot'. Second, we can say that the use of specially manufactured tools is diagnostic of man, and there is no evidence that the Australopithecines were tool-*makers*.

It is, of course, a matter of terminology – of nomenclature – whether we call the South African man-apes 'men' (more technically, Hominidae) or 'apes'. What is important is our knowledge that creatures existed with this curious combination of human-type limbs and ape-like skull. The fossils we possess probably come from the beginning of the Pleistocene, and so are earlier than the earliest known actual remains of men. It seems likely that beings of very similar structure were also ancestors of men. Even at this remote date stone balls chipped by an undoubted human agency are known from elsewhere in Africa.

By the middle Pleistocene, perhaps half-a-million years ago, several different forms of men existed in Java and China, and may have existed elsewhere. The first discovered, and among the most ancient, was the famous fossil

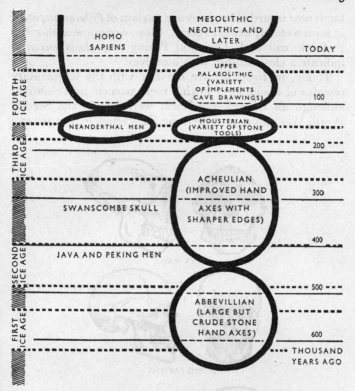

Fossil Men and their Cultures

man of Java, called *Pithecanthropus erectus* by his discoverer, Dubois. This name was at first given to nothing more than a skull cap, a thigh bone, a lower jaw, and a few teeth. From these remains the existence was inferred of an exceedingly primitive man, with a brain midway in size between a man's and a gorilla's, and teeth intermediate in structure, but with erect posture. This diagnosis has been in general confirmed, not only by further discoveries in Java, but also by much more extensive discoveries near Peking. Peking man has been called *Sinanthropus pekinensis*, but is now regarded by many as a variant of *Pithecanthropus*, or at most a closely similar species. Moreover, some authorities prefer to call both Java and Peking man *Homo erectus*, to indicate a close kinship with ourselves.

Today, in 1954, we are familiar with the fragmentary remains of about forty Peking men, women, and children, although all the original fossils were lost in the Second World War; none was anything like complete, but we can

JAVA MAN

HOMO SAPIENS

NEANDERTHAL

Human Skulls. Java man (*Pithecanthropus*) has the smallest cranial capacity of the three types, and the heaviest bony ridges. Modern man has the most lightly constructed skull, no snout, and correspondingly well-developed nose and chin be certain, not only of the similarity to the Java men, but also that the brain size on the average was greater: the males had an average brain capacity of about 1150 cubic centimetres, which is 250 above Java man and about 350 below us. (Adult male Europeans have a mean cranial capacity of about 1500 cubic centimetres.) They varied, however, from 900 to 1250. Limb bones are fully human in structure in both the Java and the Peking men. As for height, Java man seems to have resembled us (about five feet six inches), while Peking man had a height of about five feet.

The evidence for the use of tools by Java man is not complete: stone implements have been found in the same deposits as the skeletal remains, but that is not absolutely conclusive. On the other hand it is certain that Peking man used stone implements, and their structure shows that he was right-handed like us. They include heavy choppers, and smaller flaked scraping tools. They belong to the old stone age, but are not the most primitive of all known stone implements. The main food was evidently venison, to judge by the bones found in the caves, but many other species were hunted. There is evidence from the condition of the bones that Peking man also killed and ate other members of his own species: in other words, that Peking man was a cannibal. Moreover, he may have cooked his food. Certainly, there are patches of blackened earth which show that he had fire. From all this we can suspect that he also had speech, since it is probable that the construction of tools and the use of language developed together.

Other groups of men were in existence at about the time when the Java and Peking men lived. Perhaps the most notable of these is that represented by a massive jaw found in a sandpit at Mauer near Heidelberg. Heidelberg Man had no chin, but the features of his teeth and the shape of his dental arch are unmistakably human.

One of the features of early man is the thicker and heavier bone of the skull, compared with our own. This applies to the Java and Peking skulls, but even more to some more recently discovered fragments. The average thickness of the

NEANDERTHAL   HOMO SAPIENS

Skeletons. In skeletal structure we (*Homo sapiens*) show full modification for walking upright on two legs. Gorilla is not adapted for walking, but has long arms suitable for 'brachiation' in trees. *H. neanderthalensis*

bones of the brain case of Java man is about twice that of modern man, but the new specimens, though fragmentary, show an even more massive structure. The most important discoveries of these heavyweights were made, once again, in Java, and one authority believes that the complete individual must have been 'much bigger than any living gorilla'. If this is true, there were certainly giants in the earth in those days, and it is possible that some of them were among our ancestors.

Anatomically, apart from bone thickness, these men belong to the same group as the men of Java and Peking. They

GORILLA

is more ape-like than we are – a feature which he evidently developed
anew, since earlier human and prehuman types walked erect as we
do

may have been no more than a larger form of *Homo erectus*.
The search for more specimens was interrupted by war;
when it is resumed it will perhaps be possible to come to a
more definite conclusion on their significance in human
evolution.

The men of Java and Peking may have lived about half-a-
million years ago, mid-way through the Pleistocene period.
Human fossils which can be assigned to the early part of the
Pleistocene are fragmentary and difficult to interpret. We
must therefore now come to the Upper Pleistocene. During
a great part of this period most of the Old World seems to

have been inhabited by forms of man that regularly buried their dead. Like some American Indians and the Ainu today, they also left in the graves tools and sometimes animal skulls. We thus have large numbers of well-preserved specimens, together with the tools they used and the remains of animals they hunted.

These men have from the first been classified as belonging to the same genus, *Homo*, as ourselves: the Latin name of the best-known form is *Homo neanderthalensis*, from the place in Germany in which one of the first skeletons was discovered. Neanderthal man occupied parts of Europe and Asia and also North Africa. Remains of other, similar types have been found in Central and South Africa, and in Java.

We have partial skeletons of more than twenty individuals, and the fragmentary remains of very many others. It is therefore possible to see that these archaic forms of Upper Pleistocene man, like modern man, were very variable in skeletal characters.

Neanderthal men, the form in which we know them best, are distinguished by a remarkably large brain: the average cranial capacity was 1450 cubic centimetres, without distinction of sex, while the figure for the average male European today is 1500. On the other hand they had prominent brow-ridges, a receding forehead, and no chin. The teeth were larger than ours but essentially human. It is uncertain whether Neanderthal man stood perfectly erect or not, but his supposed stoop has probably been exaggerated. The average height was about five feet.

Neanderthal man, compared with modern man, was not very enterprising in his use of stone tools. He flaked stone to make scrapers and pointed implements, and simple bone tools were also used. The stone-age culture for which he was responsible was the Mousterian. He seems to have hunted mainly by means of fall-traps. It is commonly believed that Neanderthal man lived in caves, but it is perhaps more correct to say that it is the archaeologists who have the cave-dwelling habit: caves make convenient sites for archaeological study, and are places where skeletons are likely to be

preserved. It is probable that only a few of the Neanderthalers themselves lived in caves. There are no cave paint-
ings associated with Neanderthal man.

It has been held that Neanderthal was no more than a
cousin of modern man: that he evolved quite separately
from our own immediate ancestors and was later replaced
by *Homo sapiens*. This view is supported by the fact that the
early Neanderthalers are more like ourselves than the later
ones: this is evidence of evolutionary divergence from our
own line. Moreover, in Europe the Neanderthal communities were quite suddenly replaced by men of modern
type, evidently as a result of immigration by the latter. As
we dig down we find first the comparatively recent traces
of *H. sapiens*, and then, quite abruptly, an earlier deposit
with Neanderthal remains. There was no gradual change
from one type to the other.

This view of the later Neanderthal men, as sharply distinct from ourselves, may have to be modified as a result of
some remarkable discoveries in caves on Mount Carmel, in
Palestine. In one cave was found the skeleton of a woman,
mainly Neanderthal in structure but with some modern
features. In another there were several skeletons, of modern
type on the whole but with some Neanderthal characteristics. One explanation of these discoveries is that on Mount
Carmel (and doubtless elsewhere) men of modern type were
mingling with Neanderthalers, and breeding with them,
just as widely divergent human types intermarry today,
when emigration brings them together. The two types had
doubtless evolved separately, whilst parted by geographical
barriers; but they were not so different, when they met,
that they could not interbreed.

This interpretation is only a suggestion, and we shall need
many more discoveries of fossil men before everyone is satisfied. Nevertheless we can regard the Mount Carmel discoveries, tentatively, as the last stage in the series that ends
with modern man. If we recapitulate we see that the
nearest we have to primate forms ancestral both to ourselves
and to modern apes are Miocene types such as *Proconsul*.

The next stage is that of the South African man-apes,
which had already acquired the type of skeleton needed for
walking upright; but they had ape-like skulls and correspondingly small brains. Then we come to the earliest individuals known to have made tools. The men of Java and
Peking not only walked erect, but also had larger brains and
more human skulls than the man-apes. Peking man grades
off into Neanderthal man, and, as we have just seen, there
are intermediates also between early Neanderthal and ourselves. The later Neanderthalers diverged from our own
type, and were finally displaced by us throughout the world.

Complexities

It would be convenient if the story of human evolution
could be left in the form summarized in the last paragraph,
but there are various other fragments which fail to fit into
so simple a scheme.

The most famous is the *Swanscombe skull*. This skull is
known from two fragments, forming the back and base of
the brain-case and part of one side. They were found in a
gravel pit south of the Thames between Dartford and
Gravesend. Howells, the American anthropologist, remarks
on the geological appeal of the district, and refers to

the perils of any navvy who works there: the back of his neck is hot
from the breath of archaeologists, and he can hardly throw a
shovelful of gravel in any direction without hitting some tweedy
individual from a learned society.

The Swanscombe skull belonged to a woman in her early
twenties. Her skull bones were thicker than is usual in
modern skulls, but her cranial capacity seems to have been
1325 to 1350 cubic centimetres. Her importance is that she
was almost certainly a near contemporary of Java and
Peking man, and so provides fairly convincing evidence for
the existence of men of modern appearance in the Middle
Pleistocene.

It is obvious that we shall be unable to interpret these
remains finally until we have many more specimens. There

is some further fragmentary evidence of the existence of
sapiens-like individuals in the Middle and Upper Pleistocene, *before* the appearance of Neanderthal man. The Stein-
heim skull is one: this is another woman, rather like the
Swanscombe specimen but also with some distinct Neanderthal features. In time she comes later than Swanscombe,
but earlier than Neanderthal. In two further fragments,
found at Fontchevade, in the Charente district of France,
and of Upper Pleistocene date, the bones are unusually
thick, but otherwise of modern appearance and without
Neanderthal features.

Another Pleistocene skull, which has caused a good deal of
trouble, is that of *Piltdown man*, also called the Sussex woman.
The brain-case, found accidentally in a gravel pit, resembles
that of modern man in general form, but the bones are
twice as thick. It is now known, as a result of chemical
tests, to be less than one hundred thousand years old. Near
the brain-case a lower jaw was found, in circumstances that
suggested that the two fragments belonged to the same individual. This jaw-bone has no chin and resembles that of a
modern ape, and some authorities were led to believe that
the Sussex woman had a skull for the most part resembling
ours, but a jaw like that of a chimpanzee or orang-utan.
This proved too much for some palaeontologists to swallow;
and the sceptics have now at last been proved to be in the
right: refined methods of chemical analysis have shown that
the jaw is indeed that of a modern ape, skilfully faked to
make it seem to belong to the brain-case (which is a genuine
fossil). Irritation at a practical joke may be tempered by the
reflexion that this recent discovery provides a striking
vindication of the view that man is the product of an
orderly, though complex, evolutionary process, from primitive primate, through generalized human forms, to our own
species.

It is evident that from the Miocene onwards a great
variety of prehuman and human types have appeared in
different parts of the world. Their precise interrelationships
will be unravelled only when much more evidence is available.

As far as the Swanscombe and similar skulls are concerned, they indicate that men of modern type had evolved at about the same time as, if not before, Neanderthal man, forming a parallel line of development. The intermediate types, between Neanderthal and ourselves, may then represent either the results of interbreeding, or merely an early phase in the divergence of *H. neanderthalensis* from *H. sapiens*.

Nose and Chin. Outline of skulls of gorilla (left) and man (right), with nasal cavities and tongue muscles in black. In modern man the projecting nose allows the same amount of nasal cavity as in the gorilla; and the thickness of the front part of the lower jaw bone is on the outside in man, giving him a chin and making room for the tongue muscles

Modern Man

Our own type, for which the name *Homo sapiens* is usually reserved, has spread and multiplied over the whole world, largely within the past 10,000 years. In our bony structure the distinctive features include the relative lightness of the bones, brow-ridges which form no more than a pair of small bumps in the forehead, hollow cheeks, a well-developed chin and a prominent nose. The last two features are related to the disappearance of a projecting snout: without the development of a prominent nose this would have left rather little room for the nasal cavity; similarly the tongue muscles would have had to be very small but for the change in the shape of the lower jaw that gives us our chins.

It might be thought that, at this point, it would be appropriate to introduce some of those well-known portraits of long-haired, uncouth-looking individuals, which are supposed to represent the facial appearance and even the expressions of early human types. It has however been shown that it is not possible to reconstruct accurately the features of a modern man from the skull, let alone those of long extinct forms. The portraits, entertaining though they are, have therefore been omitted.

As for our teeth, we have a better record of the modifications they have undergone than of any other structure. There is an unbroken series of teeth, modern or fossil, from the completely ape to the human. We have lost both the canine tusk and the cheek teeth adapted for tearing flesh with a shear-like action; and in general our teeth are relatively small and close together. It has been suggested that the reduction in the size of the canines, and the modification of the molars for grinding only, may have taken place during a period when our ancestors were of great size, or at least had very heavy skeletons. Men of sufficient size or weight would probably have had teeth large enough to tear flesh without special modification. We are probably now undergoing evolutionary change in the direction of fewer teeth: some people fail to develop the normal number of molar teeth, and this is evidently related to the overcrowding of the teeth that has resulted from reduction of the snout. Our own teeth today are capable of dealing with a varied, but not a very tough, diet. Man is, in fact, capable of living on a far wider range of foods than most mammals: omnivorous behaviour such as we display is hardly found elsewhere except among the rats and mice that share our food.

Our hairlessness also may be a result of large size. Large mammals lose heat from the body surface less easily than small ones, since the greater their size the smaller is the ratio of surface area to volume; they are thus less likely to require hair to keep them warm. Just as elephants and other large mammals are relatively hairless, it may be that our ancestors lost their hair, as a result of an evolutionary process, when they were of great size. Today our hairless condition, like the structure of our teeth, makes us more

E

adaptable: by varying our clothes we can tolerate an exceptionally wide range of climates. Few, if any, other animal species are as widely spread over the earth as *Homo sapiens*.

But our adaptability is, more than anything else, related to the remarkable nature of our limbs and brains. The way we move about is very unusual. The apes are exceptional in having an 'upright' position whilst moving. This is related to the trapeze method of locomotion (brachiation), a mode which is most highly developed today in the gibbon, with its long arms and small legs. In men, though the arms are long for a mammal, they are shorter than in apes, and our legs are relatively very long: in us the physique of the upright apes has been rejected for walking. It is believed that the line of primates that led to man did not develop the specialized limbs needed for the tree-living as opposed to the ground-living habit. *Proconsul*, described earlier, seems in fact to have been a quadrupedal animal whose teeth had already acquired features shown by the present-day gorilla and chimpanzee.

Walking upright requires more than an enlargement of the legs. The curves of the vertebral column alter so that we are not bowed when walking as an ape is. There are also important changes in the foot. The human big toe is non-opposable: that is, we cannot use it in grasping objects as we use our thumb and as apes use both thumb and big toe. It has been remarked that man has two hands but apes have four. We still have vestiges of the muscles used for working the big toe as a thumb. Together with the reduction in the functions of the toes the mechanical arrangement of the bones of the foot is changed. Apes have a highly flexible foot, without a well-marked heel. In ours there are two fixed arches, which enable us to rise on our toes, and a well-developed heel. We are thus able to stride and to run. An ape's movement on the ground is limited much as ours is if we walk only on our heels without using the ball of the foot.

The use of the legs alone for walking, and of the arms and hands alone for other purposes, has meant a great deal in the development of man. When the walking habit evolved our ancestors had probably already a highly-developed co-ordination of movements of the hands with sight: this, at some stage in his ancestry, had been necessary for movement in the trees. With the hands released from locomotory function the hand-eye relationship came to have other uses. Hands could be used more and more for manipulation. All these changes took place over an immensely long period – probably several million years. There was no deliberate choice, by our ancestors, of the use to which they put their limbs. They were undergoing the slow process of evolutionary change which was discussed at the beginning of this chapter.

In most mammals the snout is the first part of the body that comes in contact with an object, and smell is one of the most important of the senses, usually much more important than sight. In man, as in other Primates, the hands have come to be the exploratory organs; we have no snout, our sense of smell is less acute, but our eyesight is exceptionally good. Many of our most important peculiarities, such as our eyes, our ability to breed at any season, and the muscles which enable us to make facial movements expressing emotion, are shared with the modern apes. But apes have no *speech*. Our ability to make complex sounds, and to use them to refer both to objects or processes and to ideas, is unique in nature, and with our manual dexterity makes human society possible. (The dominance of the sense of sight, by contrast with smell, we share with all the primates – the apes, monkeys, tarsiers, and lemurs.) The importance of communication between individuals is emphasized by the elaborate development of the facial muscles of expression; and, as M. Abercrombie has pointed out, by the development of the 'whites' of the eyes, which enable us to observe the direction in which a person is looking. It seems possible too that the red colour of the lips, apart from any sexual significance, aids in communication, since, however well we can hear a person, we are usually aided if we can also see his lip movements.

All these changes were accompanied by corresponding

PONGIDAE AND
NEANDERTHAL

PEKING AND
NEANDERTHAL

H SAPIENS AND PONGIDAE   PONGIDAE AND PEKING

Ranges of Brain-Case Size. For each type, the largest and smallest brain-case is shown in outline. The Pongidae are the modern apes (gorilla, orang-utan, chimpanzee, and gibbon). Modern man has a vast range, which overlaps those of Peking and Neanderthal men

changes in the structure of the brain. The part concerned with smell became much reduced, that with sight enlarged. Like the monkeys, but not other mammals, we have a specially sensitive area, the macula, near the middle of the retina of the eye; it is this area which enables you to read this page, and to distinguish colours. Our vision is also stereoscopic: that is, both eyes observe the same object, instead of looking in different directions as in most mammals; this makes possible accurate judgement of distances, and of the spatial relations between objects, and consequently the accurate control of movements, especially of the hands.

The most conspicuous difference between the brain of a man and that of an ape or any other mammal, is size. It is true that the largest mammals, the whales, and even the much smaller elephants, have bigger brains than we have; but while in man the brain constitutes about one forty-sixth of the weight of the body, in an elephant it is only about one five-hundred and sixtieth and in a large whale about one eight-thousandth. In the next chapter we consider further some features of the human brain, and of the complex behaviour which it makes possible.

6

BRAIN AND BEHAVIOUR

Man is by nature a political animal.
ARISTOTLE

THE account of human evolution, given in the last chapter, has treated of man as an animal, albeit an exceptional one. The picture so far is of an upright, hairless, ground-living ape, with a swollen head and brain, no snout, rather feeble teeth, a reduced sense of smell, excellent eyesight, remarkable dexterity, and the power of speech. These characters make possible the other unique features of man, those which are usually considered the foundation of his humanity. These unique features are the ones which make man a social animal, and in chapter 11 we continue the account of human evolution with a description of human society.

In the present chapter we are concerned with the biological foundations of individual behaviour.

The Expanding Brain

To justify the title of this chapter we must first say what is meant by behaviour, and second show that the brain is especially concerned with it. The term behaviour has a variety of meanings, but here we use it to refer to all the movements of a man or other organism. This, in man, of course includes speech, and other complex activities which we regard as a product of consciousness, as well as automatic movements such as breathing. Behaviour also includes glandular secretion, as in weeping (which involves the activity of the tear glands), or sweating. Thus the behaviour of an animal is the whole of the activities of its muscles and glands. The behaviour of an organism in this sense is indeed not sharply distinguishable from other bodily processes. Any comprehensive study of behaviour always involves also study of the sense organs, and of the nervous system which connects the sense organs to the muscles and glands.

Nowadays it is generally taken for granted that the brain is the most important of the organs influencing behaviour. This view has not always been held, as common expressions such as 'heartless' indicate. The present view is based partly on our knowledge of the effects of brain injury. We know that damage of particular parts of the brain may produce complete blindness, or deafness: that is, the inability to respond to visual or auditory stimuli; this involves of course a marked change in behaviour. Other damage may produce partial or complete paralysis. Apart from these gross effects we find also relatively minor changes in behaviour due to the removal or destruction of certain regions of the brain: in one type of instance there may be a measurable loss of 'intelligence'; in another, emotional changes are found: in one famous case, a bar of iron passed through the front part of a man's brain without killing him, and afterwards the man was described as 'not the same person', because his general behaviour towards his friends was greatly changed.

Further evidence is derived from the results of local stimulation of the brain during operations. In one region such

Three Brains. Not only is the human brain relatively and absolutely far larger than the others, but it is more complex, and large parts of the cerebrum (not black) are concerned with 'higher' intellectual processes. The drawings are not to the same scale

stimulation evokes movements, say, of the arm; in another, the patient reports a sensation in some region of the skin.

There is now much other information of this sort; and in addition there is the familiar, but less direct, evidence derived from comparative anatomy. If, for example, we compare the size of the brain, relative to body size, in a fish and a typical mammal like a rat, we find that the mammal has relatively a far larger brain. Correspondingly, we find that the complexity of the behaviour of the mammal is much greater; in particular, it can, in experimental conditions, learn more complex tasks. As we have seen in the last chapter, there is still further enlargement in the sequence from monkeys through apes to men; and indeed in men the brain is relatively vast. Corresponding to these structural differences, we find increasing complexity of behaviour.

Nearly all parts of the human brain are enlarged, relative to body size, but the most notable expansion is in parts not directly connected either with sense organs, such as eyes or ears, or with the muscles: that is, in the frontal, parietal, and temporal parts of the cerebral hemispheres. The effects of injury suggest that these regions are particularly concerned with the capacity to perform very complex tasks, which involve the solution of problems, and with memory.

We shall discuss the importance of this later, but before going on to brain function we must clear up one minor problem about brain size. There is much variation of brain size among individual men: while the average cranial capacity for males is between 1300 and 1500 cubic centimetres, normal individuals range from 1050 to 1800. It might be thought, from the facts given above, that a relation could be found between brain size and intelligence *within* the human species, but this is not found to be the case: if it were, the Eskimo would probably be the people with the highest average intelligence, since they are said to have the largest brains. As we shall see later, the question of measuring 'intelligence' is a controversial one; but studies of cranial capacity in relation to intelligence quotient (measured by intelligence tests), have shown almost no correlation.

There have been mentally deficient persons with brains above average size; and men of great intellectual ability have had relatively small brains. Moreover Neanderthal man, who seems to have had no art, and who created only primitive stone tools, had a higher average cranial capacity than we have. Knowledge of the internal structure of his brain might suggest a reason for his ultimate replacement by modern man. Certainly, together with size, the human brain has developed a very great complexity of microscopic structure, giving scope for much variation that could not be detected from an examination of externals.

The Nervous System at Work

We must now look more closely at the ways in which this complex structure operates, beginning with a simple example. If a light is shone in a person's eye, the pupil will be seen to contract. This response depends on a series of events beginning in the retina of the eye. The retina includes a layer of cells which are sensitive to changes of illumination; these cells are connected to nerve fibres which end in the brain, and which carry impulses (or 'messages') to the brain when they are stimulated. Within the brain, other cells are stimulated, and some of these have fibres which are connected to a muscle which surrounds the pupil. Impulses in these fibres cause the muscle to contract, and this contraction is responsible for the visible narrowing of the pupil.

Such a simple response is called a reflex. A reflex is carried out always by the same muscles or glands: it is in this respect quite unlike a complex, learnt activity such as playing the piano, in which the same note, for instance, may be played by any finger; it is also independent of the experience of the individual. Other familiar examples are the salivation, or mouth-watering, which occurs when food is placed on the tongue; and the tendon reflexes, such as the knee-jerk, which, like the pupillary reflex, are used by doctors during examination of a patient.

The mechanism involved in a reflex consists of a sense

SKIN
MUSCLE

SENSORY
NERVE CELLS.

MOTOR NERVE
CELLS

CONNECTING NERVE CELLS

The Mechanism of the Reflex. The diagram shows a sense organ (the skin), sensory nerve cells which influence connecting nerve cells in the central nervous system, and motor nerve cells which bring about muscle contraction. All ordinary responses involve hundreds or thousands of nerve cells at each stage, usually linked in far more complex ways than those shown·

organ or receptor (the retina in the pupillary reflex); sensory nerve fibres in which impulses travel inwards to the central nervous system; connecting nerve cells in the central nervous system; motor nerve cells, and their fibres in which impulses travel outwards; and effector organs – muscles or glands – which perform the response itself.

The mechanism of a 'simple reflex' is, in fact, quite complex, when examined in detail, but not so complex as to be incomprehensible. Our understanding of nerve function is helped by our familiarity with electrical gadgets like telephone systems, which have a superficial similarity to the nervous system. That the resemblance is only superficial can be shown by enlarging on our example of the light shone in the eye. Supposing a very brilliant light is suddenly used, the response is different: the pupil will contract as before, but in addition the eyes will be screwed up, the head perhaps turned away, and the hands may be put in front of the eyes. In this case a greater number of ingoing, sensory nerve fibres have been stimulated, and each carries more impulses than before; hence larger regions of the brain have been activated, and so the output goes to many more muscles – not only to the muscle of the pupil.

But by far the greatest complexity arises when we consider what would be the result of *repeatedly* applying this stimulus of a very bright light. We know what would happen: either the person concerned would avoid the situation altogether; or he would come with his eyes already screwed up, in anticipation of the light; or possibly he would wear dark glasses. We can at least be certain that his behaviour would be modified as a result of experience. This process of learning implies that the connexions in the central nervous system are not all fixed: they must be highly labile, and continually changing throughout life, at least in detail. It is as if the telephone system grew new wires according to circumstances.

We are just beginning to learn something about this ability of the nervous system to grow new connexions. It is probably a property of the whole of the central nervous system: that is, of both the brain and the spinal cord. This is of interest, since the spinal cord consists only of groups of fibres passing up and down, together with nerve cells forming 'reflex centres'; such centres are concerned with reflexes like the knee-jerk, which are quite automatic and unlearnt. Nevertheless, ingenious experiments have recently shown that, in an animal such as the cat, repeated stimulation of the sensory nerves involved in such reflexes causes an increase in the response – that is, in the magnitude of the muscular movement. This increased response is evidently due to improved connexions between sensory and motor nerve cells in the spinal cord; it seems likely, from microscopic studies, that the fine processes of nerve cells, through which impulses are transmitted from one cell to another, in some way expand with use, and so become more effective. It has also been shown that disuse leads to a loss of function.

In this example there is no change in the kind of response, such as occurs in learned behaviour generally, but only an increase in the existing response. But it is now generally

Nerve Cells. A diagram showing the fine endings of two nerve cells, on the body of a third. This arrangement is called a *synapse*. Most nerve cells in the central nervous system are in synaptic relationship with hundreds of others

supposed that similar changes take place in the nerve cells of the brain, including those parts of the brain especially concerned with learning; and that here the growth of new connexions can produce complex changes of behaviour. In other words, these microscopic changes are held likely to be a part of the physical basis of memory.

The Brain and Complex Behaviour

We began this account of the nervous system with the simple example of a reflex which could be fully described in terms of stimulus, nerve action, response: nerve action here consists of a straightforward linking of sense organ with muscle or gland. Animals with very simple nervous systems show behaviour consisting of little more than reflexes and other immediate responses to external stimuli. Their whole activity is determined, from moment to moment, by the surrounding conditions: they display little change of behaviour with experience, and they are very dependent on immediate stimuli. Independence of transitory sensory impulses increases with the size of the central nervous system, and of course reaches its maximum in ourselves. It is reflected in the 'absentmindedness' which notoriously accompanies intense concentration on a particular problem. A man has, in his cerebral cortex alone, around 15,000m. nerve cells. Each of these cells is connected to many others, and the connexions are continually liable to change. It is not

Connexions in the Central Nervous System. A highly simplified diagram of what happens when a man sees something, and speaks as a result. Impulses travel from the eye, along the eye nerve, to a relay centre (in the thalamus, 4), thence to the optic part of the cerebral cortex (3); other parts of the cortex are activated, including the motor area (5); impulses from the latter travel to the brain stem (1), and from there to the muscles of the tongue and larynx (2). There is a sensory 'feed-back' from the muscles as well. Some parts of the cortex, including the frontal lobes (6), have neither a primary sensory nor a motor function, but are certainly of the greatest importance in learning: it is these 'silent' areas which are most enlarged in man surprising that human behaviour, dependent on this intricate mechanism, is often unpredictable and baffling.

Nevertheless, it is possible to say something coherent about the kinds of behaviour which this vast mass of nerve cells enables us to perform. We may take, as an example, any skilled activity: let us say, a person sight-reading at the piano. At first it might be thought that the playing of a particular chord could be regarded as a relatively complex, but straightforward, response to a specific stimulus, namely, the sight of a particular pattern of marks on paper. Further reflexion shows that this is incorrect, for two reasons. First, the stimulus (the sight of the pattern) is not specific, or invariable: the chord will be played whether the music is printed, or has been roughly written by the composer; whether the type is large or small, or near or distant. These and other factors provide a considerable variation in the pattern, impinging on the retina of the eye, which induces the pianist to play the chord. The second reason, for saying that here is no simple stimulus-response relationship, is that the details of the actual response may vary: the chord may be played by either hand, or by both, and by various combinations of fingers, yet the sound resulting may be the same in each case.

We have here, then, examples of what may be called 'stimulus equivalence' and 'response equivalence'. There are many other obvious examples from everyday life. A tune will be recognized as 'the same' tune, whether played in the key of C major, or G major; more striking, perhaps, although so familiar, is the fact that we can understand words spoken in a great variety of accents, at a high or low pitch, loudly or quietly, quickly or slowly. On the side of response, a footballer can score a goal with his foot or his head, and a man who has lost both arms can write with a pencil held in his toes. Nor do these facts exhaust the complexities of our behaviour. Much of our most elaborate behaviour is 'spontaneous': that is, it arises from internal activity of the nervous system and other organs, and not from any specific, immediate external situation.

For our present purpose, the most important feature of all these diverse activities is that they are *learnt*: they are the product of individual experience, a result of the life-long process of adapting our behaviour to satisfy our needs and desires in the variety of circumstances which we encounter. The familiar fact that nearly everything we do is a product of learning is very important, in ways which are often over-looked. We must therefore consider the subject in more detail.

The Innate Element in Behaviour

To do this we are obliged, as in so many other regions of human biology, to face the question of the parts played by nature and nurture in the development of behaviour. The problem is this: to what extent is human behaviour deter-mined in advance, by a constitution fixed at conception, and to what extent is it dependent, for its development, on the experience of the particular individual? To give even an approximate answer, we must begin with data from the lives of other animals.

Let us consider a single example from an insect species with an elaborate social organization – the hive bee. If the queen bee is removed from a colony, after an interval a curious disturbance is observed: the bees run 'agitatedly' over the combs, meeting other bees with which they lightly cross their antennae, and disorder spreads soon through the whole colony. In some instances the bees have been des-cribed as vibrating their wings in such a way as to produce 'a low, mournful lament'. Here, in fact, is a notable oppor-tunity to interpret the behaviour of very different animals, in terms of our own thoughts and feelings. Bees are among the most highly organized of social insects, and the very use of the word 'queen' illustrates the long-standing habit of describing insect communities as if they were human.

Nevertheless, it is obvious that this is not justified in the case of the 'queen'. There is no human community in which there is only one fertile female, and of which all other members are her daughters or sons. Yet this is the situation in the hive. What, then, should we make of the consequences of removing the queen? Experiment has helped to provide a partial answer. If the queen is removed from the colony, but placed in a small cage within the hive, where she can still be smelt by the other bees, no disturbance is observed. The situation is as if, in a human community, the most important personage has been imprisoned, in full view of the populace, but in conditions in which the personage can no longer take any part in communal activities.

In such circumstances, human beings would react strongly. Bees do not do so, because their behaviour is, to a much greater extent, dependent on particular, isolated stimuli. They respond, not to change in the situation as a whole (as men do), but to the presence or absence of a smell, a sight or a sound. Bees in the hive behave normally while a particular odour continues to emanate from the queen; in the absence of that particular odour, their behaviour changes.

This is quite characteristic of the complex behaviour of most animals. We know that many animals perform what seem to be very skilled tasks, such as nest building, or finding concealed food, or hiding themselves; we also know that many have elaborate social activities, especially in courtship and the care of the young. In normal conditions their apparent skill is so marked, that it is inevitable that we should think of their behaviour as 'intelligent', or, in their social life, as displaying the emotions which we ourselves experience. Yet further enquiry shows how false this interpretation is. A familiar example is the behaviour of a bird, such as a meadow pipit, with a young cuckoo in its nest. The nestling pipits have been cast out by the cuckoo, and perhaps are squeaking just outside the nest, in full view and hearing of the parent bird; but the latter wholly ignores its own young, and feeds the cuckoo. In doing so, it is responding to the stimulus represented by the open beak of the cuckoo: when this stimulus is presented, in the nest, no other feature of the situation is significant for the parent bird. Like the bees, the bird fails to respond to the situation as a whole, or to adapt itself to a novel state of affairs. Such behaviour is certainly not what one would call intelligent: it is automatic or mechanical.

These responses to limited stimuli, though very much more complicated than reflexes, resemble reflexes in one important respect: they are largely independent of the experience of the individual.

Behaviour of this kind is sometimes called innate. It is, except in detail, comparatively rigid, and there is little variation between individuals. Just as every adult robin has a red breast, so each robin will produce almost exactly the same song in given conditions. Innate behaviour is, as we have seen, often not modified to deal with a new situation: it is, as a whole, not modifiable, but fixed. The only modifiable aspects are in details: a spider of a given species constructs always the same type of web, but its precise shape is determined on each occasion by the structures to which it is attached. More complex learning is involved in the ability of some animals to find their way about a particular area: bees learn the topography around the hive, birds in the region of their nest, and so on. These are examples of behaviour adapted to the experience of the individual, and in a few instances they have been studied in detail in the laboratory. Ants, for example, have been trained to find their way through a miniature maze. Despite this modest degree of adaptability, it remains true that most animal behaviour is fixed within narrow limits by the innate constitution of the individual.

Behaviour of the kind described in this section is sometimes called 'instinctive'. Unfortunately, this word, and still more the term 'instinct', has been used in a great variety of ways, some of them very confusing. We shall return to this difficulty later.

The Learned Element in Behaviour

The next step, however, is to contrast behaviour of the kind just described, with behaviour which is learned, or dependent on individual experience. By 'experience' here we do not necessarily imply *conscious* experience, but only the particular conditions, encountered by each individual, of which those of early life are especially important. Of all the various groups of animals, the mammals are those which show the most plastic behaviour (and have the largest brains relative to body size). Mammals undoubtedly show behaviour patterns which have a large innate component: a probable example is the grooming of the fur, which is easily observed in the domestic cat; but close investigation sometimes shows that behaviour, which seems at first to be obviously innate (or 'instinctive'), is in fact dependent to a surprising extent on learning.

This was shown by Kuo, in his famous experiments on the catching of mice by cats. Kuo studied the behaviour of kittens which had been subjected to different conditions in early life. Some were brought up together with a mouse or rat; some were brought up alone after weaning; and a third group were brought up with their mothers, and allowed to see their mothers kill a mouse or rat every few days. Of those which had been brought up with a mouse or rat, three out of eighteen killed an animal, and none killed an animal of the kind with which it had been brought up. Of twenty which were brought up alone, nine killed animals; and of twenty-one which had seen their mothers killing, eighteen were killers.

This example is particularly instructive, because most people would undoubtedly take it for granted that mouse-catching by cats is 'an instinct'. Certainly, some cats have a very strong tendency to catch mice: the three killers in Kuo's first group are examples. J. B. S. Haldane has suggested that it would be possible to breed for killing behaviour, and so to get a strain of cats which would kill without parental example; and conversely, to breed for 'pacifism', and so to get cats which would never be induced to kill. This suggestion underlines the fact that, in Kuo's experiments, we have yet another example of the inter-action of nature and nurture which we discussed in earlier chapters.

These experiments with cats have not been repeated, and we need to know much more, before we can say just how kittens learn from their parents. But we can at least say that this work shows, not only the importance of learning in mammals, but also the intricate fashion in which the innate and learned elements in behaviour are combined. There are many other examples. Female rats which have been brought up in cages without materials for nesting or other objects which can be carried about, fail to care normally for their young. Hence what would sometimes be called the 'maternal in-stinct' is, even in rats, partly dependent on early learning. Or, to take a very different sort of example, birds of certain species which have been incubated, and reared by a human, may behave towards the man as normal young birds do to-wards their parents: in particular, they may follow him about, whilst ignoring completely adults of their own species. This phenomenon, called imprinting, is evidently due to the fact that, during a short, early stage in development, the nervous system is in a particularly plastic state, and what is seen during this period has a lasting, perhaps permanent, effect on behaviour. Again, there is evidently no fixed 'in-stinctive' recognition of members of the same species.

The Development of Behaviour

We must now consider the bearing these studies have on man. The first thing we may notice is that in human be-haviour there are no complex *innate* behaviour patterns at all. Whether we are building a house, making love, or com-municating with our fellows, we are acting in ways which – consciously or not – have been learnt. Our repertoire of unlearnt performances is confined to the reflex level, as in sneezing, salivation, blinking, and so on. One might add the 'social smiling' of the infant of around three to six months: this response can be evoked by a simple cardboard model of a human face! This is, admittedly, a rather more complex instance than a typical reflex. The same applies to crying. But all our elaborate activities, including courtship, child-rearing, even our food habits, are dependent to a major extent on individual experience. Instead of being rather uniform throughout the species, as are the rituals of mating, nest-building, and so on in, for instance, birds and fishes, they vary a great deal from one community to another: they are the results of social or cultural conditioning.

This predominance of the learned element in human behaviour is, as we have seen, related to the enormous bulk of brain tissue which is not directly under the influence of impulses from the sense organs. This mass of nerve cells does not, on the whole, contain innately determined structural arrangements determining fixed patterns of behaviour. Every human being (except a few of grossly abnormal development) possesses neural equipment which enables him to develop complex behaviour such as speech; but the behaviour patterns arise during development, as a result of a process, in the child very slow and gradual, of adaptive change. This growth of behaviour depends on what the child sees, hears, and feels, and also on what he is able to *do* with his environment. Continuous and varied activity during waking hours is necessary for the full learning process.

It follows that the stages in the development of behaviour in the child are both important and unusually difficult to study. It is of course not a new idea that early training and experience are particularly influential in determining character and ability. We know that certain types of learning are usually better achieved by the young: most people, for instance, find it easier to learn to speak a foreign language during childhood than as an adult. But recent researches have revealed previously unsuspected ways in which the conditions of childhood influence later behaviour.

One example concerns the way in which we learn to

recognize the things we see. An important discussion of this problem, published in Germany, in 1932, was based on studies of what happened when persons, blind from birth, had their sight restored by operation. Later, research was done on laboratory animals.

It had been assumed in the past that human beings (and other animals) have an innate ability to distinguish at least simple shapes, for instance squares from circles. In an adult, or even in quite a young child, this distinction is made 'instantaneously' and without effort. This assumption has been shown to be false.

An adult blind from birth owing to cataract, and successfully treated so as to restore vision, reports at first only a confusing mass of lights and colours. No object, however familiar from past experience of touching, smelling, and so on, can be identified by sight. Shapes are not identified at all: to distinguish a square or triangle from a circle, the subject has to learn laboriously to count the corners; and what is learnt on one day is forgotten by the next. If the names of colours have been learnt, and the subject is shown an orange, he may at once name the colour; but he will not identify the object as an orange until he has touched it.

It was pointed out earlier that we recognize the things we see (or hear) even though the exact appearance they present varies according to the distance, the angle at which we see them, and so on. This *perceptual generalization* is quite absent in those learning to see. In one instance a man who had learnt to name a square, made of white cardboard, failed to identify it when the other side, painted yellow, was shown. Objects, of which the names have been learnt in one set of conditions, are not identified when seen against a different background or in light of a different colour. Such confusions, though never made by a normal adult, have nevertheless a counterpart in adult behaviour: for instance, 'all Chinese look alike' – until we have had some experience of meeting different Chinese; or, all small brown birds look like sparrows – until we have had some experience of bird watching.

Eventually, with great persistence and after months or

years, the congenitally blind person who has acquired vision may learn to make fairly full use of his eyes and even to read, but it is a painful experience.

The general implication of these facts is that in man even the most elementary responses are a product of learning: during the long period of helplessness, and still longer period of dependence during childhood, all the essential behaviour patterns are being laid down, as a result of adaptive changes in the plastic central nervous system.

This applies, not only to intellectual development, but also to the growth of emotional and social attitudes. The work of Freud and his followers has made us familiar with the idea that disorders of behaviour (mental illness) can sometimes be traced, at least in part, to the conditions of early childhood. This motion has a wider application. There is much evidence that family relationships in childhood have an important influence on all the personal relationships of the adult: the child's attitude towards his or her father may influence later attitudes towards those in authority; a boy's feelings towards his mother may be reflected in his later behaviour to his wife; a girl's early impressions of an elder brother may induce a later competitive attitude towards men.

The most notable study of such effects is one published by the World Health Organization under the title *Maternal Care and Mental Health*.* The main theme is the effects of deprivation of maternal care in young children. 'Deprivation' means here that the child is deprived of the care, both of his mother and of any substitute or foster-mother, for three months or more. The important period was found to be the first five years. Many of the studies, on which these conclusions are based, are from excellently run orphanages.

Small children separated from their mothers for any great length of time soon show loss of appetite and reduced activity; they are less vocal, and sometimes appear

* An abridged and simplified version of this report, by Dr John Bowlby, has been published in Pelican Books, under the title *Child Care and the Growth of Love*.

misleadingly 'good'. There is retardation both of physical
and intellectual development, and follow-up studies have
shown that these effects are permanent. (These changes
may be prevented if there is somebody available to become
a complete substitute mother.) Studies of older, delinquent
children have shown that certain criminal types, notably
persistent thieves, show a remarkably high proportion of
histories of grossly disturbed relationships with their
mothers in early years. Youths of this type, with this sort of
history, are lacking in all normal emotional responses: they
are indifferent to punishment, inaccessible to true friendship
– and, of course, they make very bad parents.

It might be thought that perhaps such youths have a 'bad
heredity', and that they would have been abnormal in their
behaviour regardless of their upbringing. A number of carefully controlled studies have failed to show any evidence of
such inherited traits. Moreover, studies of animals have
shown that similar effects can be induced experimentally,
in conditions which entirely exclude genetic influences. In
one set of experiments goats were used: uniovular twin kids
were selected, and, of each pair, one was brought up
normally and one subjected to some maternal deprivation.
The deprived kids showed a profound disturbance of behaviour, including failure to eat normally and agitation
when put in darkness.

Thus the effect observed in human children can also be
studied in other species; and animal studies have in this case
been employed to supplement human studies, and to help to
validate them.

All these examples point in the same direction: they illustrate the diverse and complex ways in which individual
behaviour is shaped by individual experience. Each child is
born with a nervous system so organized that it is continually changing in response to the varied stimuli which influence it through the sense organs; and the particular patterns of stimuli provided by the child's environment have
a lasting effect on his patterns of behaviour throughout his
life.

If this is true we might expect to find confirmation from yet another source. This is the comparative study of different kinds of social organization. We should expect to find that the social behaviour of individual men and women is determined by the particular society in which they are brought up, regardless of parentage. This has repeatedly been found to be the case. There are well-known examples, such as that of an American adopted in his first year by a Chinese family living in China; on returning to his 'native' land as a young man, he found his behaviour (unlike his appearance) so wholly Chinese, that he was obliged to attend 'Americanization' classes designed for foreign immigrants.

We shall return to the connexion between 'race' and behaviour in chapter 8 – or, rather, the lack of connexion. Other evidence from social anthropology is derived from very detailed studies of childhood in certain primitive societies. An example may be taken from the work of Gregory Bateson and Margaret Mead, on the Balinese. They show that many characteristic features of adult Balinese behaviour can be related to the customary modes of child-rearing in that society. As an example, it is observed that in Bali the incidence of muscular fatigue is less than in other societies. This can be related to the fact that learning in early life takes place very largely by direct manipulation of the child's body, or by encouraging imitation, with a minimum of verbal instruction. Such words as are used are mostly 'effectively toned exclamations'.

In Balinese adults it is found, consequently, that the craftsmen use only the particular muscles essential to the particular task: these men evidently have in high degree the valuable gift of 'relaxation'. The Balinese also attach much importance to the position or orientation of the body in space, and have an exceptional dislike of drunkenness, though not on moral grounds.

In general, in each society, every child is systematically moulded in every aspect of his behaviour, his postures and movements, his ways of thinking and modes of feeling, as a result of the impressions he unconsciously receives during every waking moment from the time of his birth.

Heredity and 'Instinct'

If environmental effects are so overwhelming, it may be asked, what becomes of the genetic influence on behaviour? The preceding section, taken in isolation, might seem to imply that genetic differences can be ignored. Yet, as we have seen in earlier chapters, this is not the case. The difficulty of sorting out genetic from environmental effects is particularly acute for human behaviour, because the most conspicuous feature of the human nervous system is its plasticity. An example of this difficulty was given in chapter 3, in discussing the genetics of psychotic behaviour. Nevertheless, there is, as we have seen, undoubtedly genetic variation, in every human population, which influences behavioural traits. It is likely, for instance, that in no imaginable environment could the writer have become a really good mathematician. In general it seems that genetic factors set a limit to what each individual can do, though we rarely, if ever, can state the limit precisely.

This great genetic variability, combined with the plasticity of the nervous system, is essential for the development of complex societies. Such societies require many specialists, in diverse skills. An incomplete list of occupations, compiled by the United States government, includes seventeen thousand titles; many of these no doubt are relatively unskilled types of work, but the truly skilled jobs, needing long training, can be numbered in hundreds. There is undoubtedly much genetical variation in the ability to perform these different types of skilled work, even though each skill is also a product of training.

This dependence of innate qualities on environmental influences, for their expression, can be illustrated from children brought up in grossly abnormal conditions. Among such children there are a few, possibly authentic, instances of rearing by wolves, in complete isolation from human beings from a very early age. Such children are of course without language, and effectively imbecilic: they show no capacity at all for entering relationships with other human beings; they have no 'instinctive' feeling of kinship with other human beings.

Better examples come from children who have been brought up by their mothers in extreme social isolation, but who have subsequently been rescued. One child was confined to a single room, from the age of less than a year until she was about six; she was fed on milk and thin oatmeal, but no solids. When brought to a children's hospital the child seemed to be deaf and blind; she lay limply where she was put, indifferent to everything that went on around her. She neither smiled nor cried. After nine months she was put into the care of one woman, who had no other task but to look after her. Six months later she could walk, was quite fat and could understand verbal instructions, though she still could not speak.

In another instance a six-year-old girl was found to have been brought up in isolation by a deaf and dumb mother. This child inevitably had no understanding of speech, and could not talk. In twenty-two months, however, it proved possible to teach her to talk intelligently and to sing, as well as the other activities characteristic of her age. It is important that none of these activities developed until they were specifically taught.

In view of these facts, and of the others given in preceding sections, what becomes of the so-called human 'instincts'? We have already seen that man has no complex innate behaviour patterns: he has no instincts in that sense. Nevertheless, writers in the past have made lists of human instincts, and most people are liable to take it for granted that they exist.

When the lists of instincts are examined, we find that what they describe are not particular acts of behaviour: they are goals, which most human beings tend to achieve. The expression 'parental instinct' is in practice a name for the fact that most people have children and look after them

– but, alas, there are plenty of exceptions. The term 'instinct of self-preservation' is a name for the fact that, in common with all other animals, most people tend to behave so as to keep themselves alive; but again there are plenty of exceptions, as when someone sacrifices his or her life for another or for a cause.

It may be said that, when one talks of human instincts, one means internal agents which cause people to behave in certain ways. In scientific studies today, if one seeks such internal agents, one looks in the first place in the central nervous system, and secondly in other organs, especially the endocrine or ductless glands. We have, however, already seen that studies of human behaviour show that the brain is a system of which plasticity, rather than rigidity of organization, is the most notable feature. It provides no basis for fixed instinctive patterns of behaviour.

When human beings do display a rigidity of behaviour, this is still a product of early learning. A cynic, reading the passages which emphasize the human capacity for adapting behaviour to new conditions, might comment on the many exceptions to be found among adults. The inflexible habits, attitudes, and beliefs, held to by many even when there are good reasons for discarding them, are, however, products of early training: they vary from one society or class to another, and from generation to generation.

This is not to deny that there are important internal influences on behaviour, *apart from* the learned patterns of the nervous system. When the amount of sugar in the blood falls below a certain level we say we are hungry, and we seek food. Nevertheless, this behaviour is still partly a product of learning: the time at which we feel hungry is that at which we are accustomed to eat; if we pass this time without eating, we may cease to feel hungry, though our physiological need for food is even greater. Thus to some extent we learn to be hungry. Still more are our food habits – what we eat, how it is cooked and served – a product of cultural conditioning.

With sexual behaviour, similarly, we find important

internal influences apart from training. These are clearly
revealed in abnormal cases. A man with a tumour of the
adrenal gland may lose interest in women, but regain it
when the tumour is removed. A woman with a tumour of a
particular part of the brain may be sexually over-active, but
behave normally when it has been excised. Nevertheless,
as we saw in chapter 4, sexual behaviour too depends on the
upbringing and experience of the individual – on learning –
and is not a matter of fixed behavioural patterns.

Thus while it is true that nearly everyone eats, mates,
preserves his own life and protects his children, *partly* under
the influence of unlearned internal processes, *the ways* in
which all these things are done are infinitely variable, and
depend on the customs of the community in which the
individual is reared.

Social Awareness

The unique character of human behaviour does not, however, lie merely in the predominance of the effects of learning. There is also awareness of others. We have seen that
other animals, not only birds and fishes but even bees,
respond to stimuli, or 'signals', given by members of their
own species. This by itself does not constitute what we call
here 'awareness'. A bird may display before its mate, or a
rival, but this does not imply any appreciation that the other
individual is also perceiving, and responding to, the display.

How do we distinguish awareness? In ourselves, we are
subjectively conscious of it, but there are also objective tests.
The important test is: does each individual modify the
signals he gives – sounds, movements, and so on – so as to
ensure that they are audible, visible, or, in general, intelli-
gible, to the other individuals concerned? It is doubtful
whether any animals other than man, and perhaps his
nearest relatives, correct their signals in this way. In man,
such correction is usual; but it is far from universal, as the
study of, for instance, the behaviour of lecturers quickly
shows.

Subjectively, we are aware of something which we call consciousness: and we project this consciousness also into other people: we assume that others have thoughts and feelings similar to those we know in ourselves. This sort of awareness is an essential basis of human social behaviour. Man is not merely a highly social animal, like the hive bee; he is also a communicating animal, at a level of complexity without any parallel in the rest of the animal kingdom. There is nothing, in the social signals given by other species, to be compared with human languages, even the simplest ones. By means of language, we communicate both facts and feelings, and we do so on the basis of our knowledge, not only of our own feelings, but of those of our fellow humans.

This may seem an arid way of saying that men love, and depend on the love of, their fellows. It would however be absurd to attempt an account of human behaviour, and then to omit this, its most distinctive feature. A difficulty is that the language in which we are accustomed to speak of these facts is that of poetry, rather than of science.

In this book it is for the most part the language of science which is used, since, for matters of fact, it is the most effective means of communication. This chapter might have been called 'the human mind'; it was not so called, and the word 'mind' has not been used, because in practice scientists do not find it convenient to discuss their observations in terms of mind. It is true that many scientists do speak of 'mind' as opposed to 'body', and that – for instance – 'psychological' medicine is often sharply distinguished from physical medicine, and mental disorders from others. Nevertheless, the scientific study of human behaviour, as it is actually carried out today, is usually described in terms of the actual behaviour observed (including of course speech, where that is involved), and of the changes in the nervous system, endocrine glands and other organs. We are only at the beginning of this scientific psychology. In everyday language it is normally still implied that each person has a 'mind' which in some way influences his behaviour.

In primitive communities the pre-scientific way of speaking is usual, not only for other humans, but for animals, plants, and even inanimate objects like rivers or mountains. Each of these is said to have a resident spirit which is in some way an active agent working from within, just as we say a person has a mind. This mode of expression arises from that awareness of ourselves and of others which has already been referred to. We are aware of thoughts and feelings in ourselves; we call them our mind, our consciousness, our spirit or perhaps our soul; and we attribute them also to others. It follows that these others too have minds, spirits, or whatever they may be called.

It is a short step from this way of speaking of people, to saying that these internal agents exist independently of the body, and may even become separated from the body.

In science none of these assumptions is found to be necessary, and indeed the facts which can be actually observed contradict them. Intelligence, moral behaviour, every aspect of personality, and life itself, depend on the functioning of the physical organs of the body – the organs studied in the science of physiology. We have our feelings and our thoughts, but, as we saw at the beginning of this chapter, they are not independent of our brains: they are an aspect of our bodily function. This, at least, is the point of view from which the present chapter is written. This, in fact, is the mode of communication adopted by the present writer, for his immediate purpose of conveying the results, so far, of the scientific study of behaviour. It does not alter the fact that men live, work, and play together, and depend for their lives on doing so: it is merely one way of describing the behaviour involved.

Conclusions

The social implications of these facts are clear. Although man is a product of the slow process of organic evolution described in the last chapter, his evolution now largely takes a different form. The most important changes which man undergoes now are those of social evolution – a far more rapid process than the biological variety. Human social behaviour, being so overwhelmingly a product of learning rather than genetic transmission, is determined by tradition, handed down by example or verbally from generation to generation. Tradition is commonly thought of, rightly, as a source of social stability; but it is also an essential basis for social change. Today, when society is altering very rapidly, we can easily see that each new social development is built from material accumulated in earlier periods.

These changes in social organization involve drastic changes in human behaviour; and they in turn depend on the fact that human behaviour is plastic and not genetically fixed. We see, once again, the absurdity of the notion that 'human nature cannot change'. This commonly made assertion always implies that human *behaviour* is essentially fixed: it is therefore the exact opposite of the truth.

In this chapter, then, man is seen as a product of organic evolution, but with a unique form of social organization. The type of social behaviour which man has developed has no parallel elsewhere in nature: it enables man to alter his environment, to suit his own ends, on a vast scale; and it imposes on human societies a tempo of change which, in the twentieth century, is putting a heavy strain on human adaptability.

This account of man is very different from that of even a century ago. It can be traced, in part, to the Darwinian theory of evolution by natural selection, according to which the order we observe in the living world is a product, not of a divine plan, but of a process which can be studied rationally and even investigated experimentally. This attitude to the organic world led biologists to look at animal behaviour as a product of natural selection: the complex and elegant adaptations, shown by each species, to a particular way of life, came to be seen as existing by virtue of their 'survival value'.

This matter-of-fact approach was reinforced from another source. During the same period the science of physiology developed rapidly, largely through the application of the concepts of physical science to the body. Thus, in the age of machinery, the body was studied in part as a machine working in accordance with the laws of mechanics, in part as a chemical system. One of the greatest of the nineteenth-century physiologists was Pavlov; and in the first years of this century Pavlov turned his formidable skill and insight, from the study of digestion, to that of the working of the most complex part of the mammalian brain – the cerebral cortex. His approach remained strictly physiological: Pavlov did not use the contemporary terms or interpretations of the philosophers or psychologists: he did not speak of instincts or even emotions. He was content to try to give an account of certain aspects of the learning process in terms of observable cause and effect. His study of conditioned reflexes greatly stimulated the scientific investigation of behaviour, on objective lines.

Some people find this way of speaking of human behaviour distasteful. Sometimes it is called 'inhuman'. It would certainly be ridiculous to claim that the present scientific account of human behaviour is final or complete: it omits much that is of importance to any ordinary loving and hating human being, and any scientific worker in this field knows how vast is the unknown compared with the known.

Our present knowledge, sketched in this chapter, does, however, give us some insight into our nature as social beings; and it can already contribute something to human relationships. It is still common to find that a schoolteacher or employer – even a parent – will label persistent unsatisfactory behaviour in the young as naughtiness, wickedness, or laziness or some such thing, rather than inquire into the actual causes of the behaviour. These causes may include illness, malnutrition, emotional disturbances, and many other factors outside the child's control. It is quite unpractical to dismiss this rational approach as 'theoretical', or as 'softness': it is as unpractical as if a motor mechanic, faced with an automobile which refused to go, gave the bonnet a kick and called the machine a lazy so-and-so. Indeed, it is worse than this: after all, an automobile has no feelings of its own.

Thus the attitude presented here is not only scientific: it is also humane. Science is the knowledge which can help to guide men of good will in improving the lot of man. The emphasis on the importance of the environment, for the development of human behaviour, does not imply that human beings are mere puppets, pulled this way and that by outside influences. We are not only influenced by our environment: we can also change it.

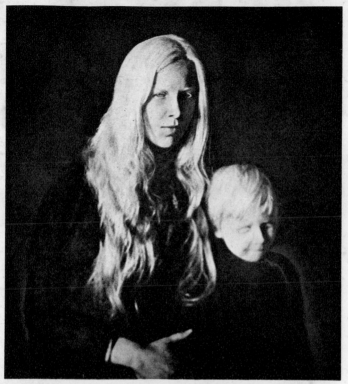

ALBINO CHILDREN – Albinos have no skin or hair pigment; the condition is due to a recessive gene, like red hair.

NEGRO-WHITE CROSSING – The family of a Scottish-Griqua woman who married a European: her sons show various combinations of characters (described in the text).

NEGRO-WHITE CROSSING – An unusual result of crossing between Europeans and Africans. Here the mother is an English-Basuto half-breed who married a European.

CHIMPANZEE – One of man's nearest living relatives.

NEGRIFORM – A Zulu of South Africa,
photographed half a century ago.

CAUCASIFORM – An Arab of North Africa.

MONGOLIFORM – A woman of Inner Mongolia.

MONGOLIFORM – Chinese coolie. (The tooth formation is not a 'racial' character, but suggests malnutrition.)

MONGOLIFORM – Dakota of North America in traditional garb.

MONGOLIFORM – Girl of Tierra del Fuego. This child is pure Fuegan, yet resembles a Chinese. This, with the three preceding photographs, illustrates some of the variety of types within one of the major groups in which men are classified.

AUSTRALIFORMS – Arunta girls of pure Australian aborigine stock.

HAIR TYPES – Photomicrographs of human scalp, showing mode of growth of hair: *left*, in a Chinese, with straight hair of Mongoliform type; *right*, in a Bushman, with spiral hair of Negriform type.

SKIN PIGMENT – Photomicrograph through a thin slice or section of Negro skin: the dead, cornified surface layer (st. c.) overlies a layer of living cells containing black pigment (st. g.). Variation in the amount of this pigment is mainly responsible for variation in human 'colour'.

A PRODUCT OF RACE CROSSING – Offspring of a European and an Australian aborigine. There is no evidence of physical disharmony, such as has sometimes been suggested must result from inter-marriage of diverse human groups.

13

CLIMATIC ADAPTATION: ESKIMO – This man (belonging to the
Mongoliform division) weighed 77 kg. (170 lb.); his height was
1.64 m. (5ft. 5in.). He has the typical thickset figure, flat features
and short limbs of men adapted for primitive life in cold climates.
Heat loss is minimized by this type of physique.
Contrast the next photograph.

CLIMATIC ADAPTATION: DINKA NEGRO – This man weighed 58 8 kg. (130 lb.), but his height was 1.885 m. (6 ft. 2 in.). He was thus much taller yet much lighter than the Eskimo of the preceding photograph. His 'linear' body-build and relatively long limbs are probably an advantage in tropical climates where rapid heat loss from the body is important.

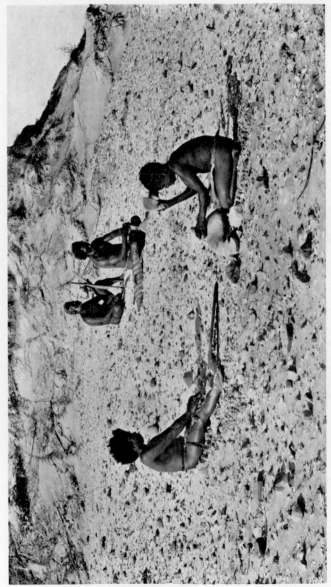

PRIMITIVE TOOL MAKING – Aborigines striking flakes from cores in New South Wales.

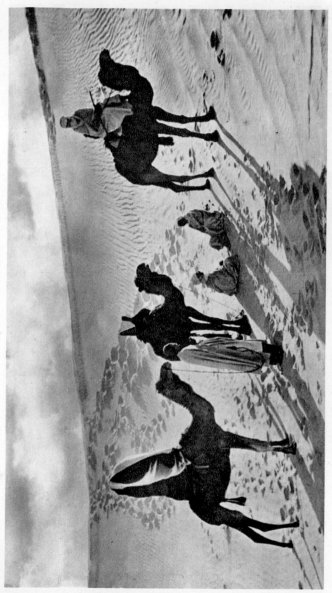

NORTH AFRICAN DESERT – Arabs of Algeria with their camels in one of the biggest of man-made deserts.

REPLANTING THE SAHARA – Reafforestation in Algeria.

GULLY EROSION – *Above*, an eroded hillside in Jackson, Mississippi. *Below*, erosion in the Tennessee Valley area before conservation began.

DUSTBOWL – On the level, almost treeless prairies of North America excessive wheat growing has led to severe wind erosion.

CONTOUR PLOUGHING – A method of preventing loss of water down slopes. This field, in Oklahoma, U.S.A., is to be planted with cotton.

SOIL CONSERVATION – *Above*, the result of uncontrolled erosion in Texas, U.S.A. *Below*, the eroded area has been planted with a cover crop which binds the drifting sands.

'TRANSFORMING NATURE' – A lock on the new Volga-Don canal: part of the vast schemes of irrigation and replanting in the centre of the U.S.S.R.

22

PHYSICAL SCIENCE IN THE SERVICE OF AGRICULTURE — Electric excavators being assembled at the site of the Tahia Tash hydrotechnical system – part of the reclamation and development schemes now in progress in the U.S.S.R.

STARVATION – This baby girl of Thailand has the typical pot belly, spindly limbs, and apparently enormous head of the child severely short of food. She is not merely malnourished, but starved. She is typical of millions. Yet the technical resources exist for the solution of this problem.

MALARIA – This Indian woman, lying in the open with an attack of fever, was brought to a WHO malaria team in the Terai Region, for treatment. Malaria is estimated to infect 300 m. persons in India every year, and to kill 3 m.

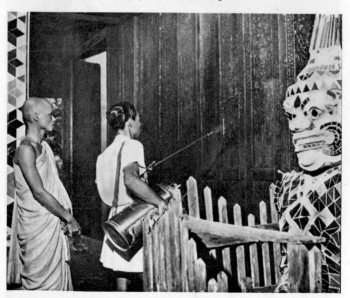

MALARIA CONTROL – Spraying with DDT in a temple in Thailand, to kill malaria-carrying mosquitoes.

MALARIA CONTROL – Spraying with dieldrin, a more toxic substance than DDT, to kill malaria-carrying mosquitoes in the Philippines.

MALARIA TREATMENT – A doctor treating a Punan woman in Sarawak.

27

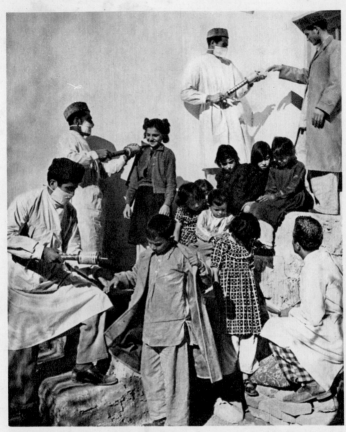

TYPHUS – Members of an Afghan government team in Kabul, dusting children to kill lice which carry the germs of typhus.

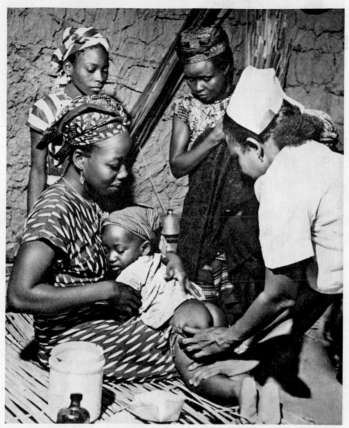

PUBLIC HEALTH – In Liberia a nurse treats a baby for yaws. This infection, common in large parts of Africa, is rapidly cured with penicillin.

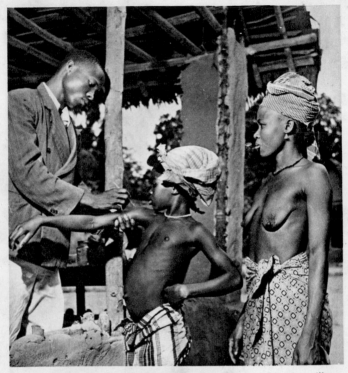

PUBLIC HEALTH – Vaccination against smallpox in a Liberian village.

TUBERCULOSIS : TREATMENT – In India, as in countries further west, tubercle is one of the most serious of health problems, and sanatoria are few. Here a doctor from Ceylon examines a patient in his home, while a WHO nurse advises the family about the patient's needs.

TUBERCULOSIS : DIAGNOSIS – At Patna, in Bihar, the Indian government have set up a tuberculosis control demonstration and training centre, with help from WHO and UNICEF. Here modern techniques of examination are used for the early diagnosis of tuberculosis, which greatly increases the chances of recovery.

TUBERCULOSIS : PREVENTION – BCG vaccination for a baby, at a tuberculosis centre, Dacca, Pakistan.

7

HUMAN TYPES

The world in all doth but two nations bear,
The good, the bad, and these mixed everywhere.

ANDREW MARVELL

IN this chapter we turn from fundamentals, to trivialities to which an unjustified importance has been attached. It deals with the relatively minor physical differences found in the human species today, and particularly with those, such as skin colour, which have a well-marked geographical distribution. Technically, man is said to be *polytypic*: that is, different physical types comprise the populations of different regions. We shall see that the differences are, to a considerable extent, related to the physiological demands of the various climates.

The 'Races' of Man

It is usual to divide the human species into three main groups distinguished primarily by the structure of their hair.

The *Negriforms* have spiral hair and broad noses; they include Bantu-speaking Africans, the South African Bushmen and Hottentots, the Negroes of West Africa, the pygmy Negritos and Negrillos of Malaysia and Africa, the Andamanese and the Melanesians. The Negriforms are very variable in other physical characteristics; they may be black, brown, or yellow; their jaws may be prognathous (projecting) or not; and their skulls may be broad or narrow, although most of them have narrow skulls (plate 5).

The second group, the *Europiforms*, have wavy hair and narrow noses. They inhabit Europe, the Mediterranean countries, Asia Minor, and India; they are also, as a result of recent emigration, the main inhabitants of North America. The Ainus of Japan are Europiform, but in respects other than hair and nose shape resemble their Asian neighbours. The Europiforms may have white or brown skins, and broad or narrow skulls (plate 6).

The third group, the *Mongoliforms*, have lank, straight hair; their noses are intermediate in width. They include most of the inhabitants of Asia, apart from India, and the indigenous peoples of the Americas from the narrow-nosed Eskimo of the north to the Fuegians in the south. Apart from the Eskimo and certain Asian and American groups, their skulls are for the most part broad (plates 7–10).

There is a fourth, very much smaller group, which does not fit into the three main ones. The *Australiforms* (that is to say, the original inhabitants of Australia) have wavy, Europiform hair, but broad noses like those of Negriforms. Their skin is as dark as that of Negroes, but this may well be the product of a separate evolutionary development. It seems quite likely that the aboriginal Australians have been almost or quite isolated from other human groups for a very large part of the time during which modern man has existed, and some anthropologists believe them to be the most primitive of human types; that is, they are considered to resemble most closely the common ancestors of all present-day men. Their average male cranial capacity is 1300 cubic centimetres, which is below the average for man as a whole; the head bones are thicker, and the teeth rather large. However, some authorities believe the Australiforms to be derived from a mixture of two or more human types which had come together as a result of emigration. Nothing conclusive can be said on their precise status or significance (plate 11).

The question is sometimes asked, which of the three main groups is the most primitive? and the answer is sometimes supposed to be that the Negriforms are primitive, because, on the whole, they have not developed such advanced societies as have the others. But if we consider anatomical features (and the three groups are defined anatomically) we find that things are not so simple. We first have to decide what we mean by 'primitive', since it is easy, but unprofitable, to use the word as an undefined term of derogation. In biology one type is said to be more primitive than another when it is regarded as the more similar to a common ancestor of both types. Since the ancestors of man were apes it seems to follow that primitive men are those that are most ape-like. But we know very little of the structure of the apes from which both men and present-day apes are sprung, apart from their skeletons, and so comparison is often made between man and his nearest contemporary relatives, the chimpanzee and gorilla. These of course have undergone evolutionary change, just as man has, during the last few million years, and so are not a reliable guide to what is primitive. And if we make the comparison we find no clear picture. The Caucasiforms are ape-like in having a good deal of hair on their bodies, in having wavy hair, and in their thin lips; on the other hand in the formation of the face they are least ape-like. The Negriforms are ape-like in their broad noses, but less ape-like than Caucasoids in their thick lips and the structure and distribution of the hair. It is evident that no definite statement can be made on which of the main human groups is anatomically primitive. Men and women of the four types described can and do intermarry and produce offspring of mixed characteristics without any difficulty apart from social barriers. Consequently, wherever there are mixed populations intermediates are found (plates 2, 3, 13).

This applies even more obviously when we come to study the sub-divisions of the three principal groups. It is customary among anthropologists to classify the whole of the human species in about thirty divisions or 'races'. They will not be described here. However, owing to the political implications that have been given to the term 'Nordic' the European types are worth a mention.

It is usual to describe three main European types. The *Mediterranean* type is described by Huxley and Haddon as having:

. . . an average stature of about 5 feet 3 inches, slender build, long head and narrow oval face, straight nose rather inclining to be broad; the eyes are very dark.

This type is represented in various parts of Europe, especially in the west, and also in North Africa. The Semites, that is, the peoples such as the Arabs and the original, Palestinian Jews, who speak Semitic languages, include a large proportion of individuals of the Mediterranean type.

A second type, the *Alpine*, the same authors describe as:

. . . very broad-headed, [with] chestnut brown or black hair, hazel-grey or brown eyes. The nose is inclined to be broad and is frequently concave. The stature is medium, about 5 feet 4½ inches, and the body is thick-set. The range of this type is from Russia to central France. The Eastern members are termed Slavs.

For the third European main type, the *Nordic*, the description given by Huxley and Haddon is:

. . . florid or reddish-white skin, straight, wavy or curly hair of a yellow, light brown or tawny colour; typically the eyes are blue or grey. The head is mesocephalic with a tendency to dolichocephaly [of medium width with a tendency to narrowness]; . . . the face is long with a prominent, narrow, usually straight nose and a well-developed chin. This is the characteristic type of Scandinavia; it is also common in the north central European plain and frequent in the British Isles.

It will be noticed that the descriptions are rather vague. Moreover use is made not only of differences which are largely or entirely independent of environment (such as those of eye colour), but also of some known to be influenced by environment, such as stature. This is characteristic of definitions in physical anthropology, whether what is defined is called a race, a regional group, or simply a type. The reason for the use of the word type in this book is that it is unambiguous: it is quite legitimate, even if rather pointless, to speak of a Nordic type, for instance, provided that 'Nordic' is fully defined. There is then no difficulty in deciding whether any particular individual belongs to the Nordic type or not.

Almost any European can, by looking at the people he meets every day, see that intermediates exist between the three types just described. Nevertheless it might be true that in any given part of the continent a majority of the people belong to one type. It is, indeed, easy to get this impression from some anthropological writings. However, investigation shows that the impression is misleading. In one instance 250 Swiss soldiers, from German-speaking cantons, were studied. None was found to have the combination of height, narrow-headedness, light eyes and blond hair of the Nordic type; 9·2 per cent had the Alpine combination of characters; 0·8 per cent had the Dinaric combination (which is similar to the Alpine); and 0·4 per cent that of the Mediterranean. Thus only 26 of them, or 10·4 per cent, belonged to one of the anthropological types, and the remaining 224 showed a mixture of characters. Even in Sweden, which has the highest proportion of Nordics, army recruits in 1897–8 were found to include only 11 per cent of the Nordic type.

Not only are there no populations in Europe today of which most of the members are of one type; there is no reason to think that there ever were such populations. The existence of a good deal of variation within the various species of fossil man was mentioned in chapter 4. When a group of human fossils is found in one place, and belonging to the same period, whether of our own or another species, the degree of variation in the skeletons is similar to that found in the mixed populations of today. It will be noticed that, in comparing populations, one has to speak in terms of the distribution of characters, as described in chapter 3 (page 44): populations do not, as a rule, differ sharply, but only in degree, or quantitatively.

The existence of a great deal of variation in human populations is clearly very important. Some aspects of it were discussed in chapters 2 and 3, and others will appear in the next two chapters. We have seen that this variation is due partly to differences in genetic constitution, and that each individual has a unique combination of genes. If we consider characteristics that are largely independent of environment we find that every possible combination of them exists. Thus blue eyes can appear with both dark and fair hair, Negriform hair with a fair skin, and so on. Different combinations are, indeed, found in members of the same family: when both parents are European one child may approximate to the Nordic type and another to the Alpine. It is because of this occurrence of many different combinations of characters that man was classified above primarily on the basis of hair structure, since this is a single character of which the development is not significantly influenced by change of environment. In defining the Negriform, Caucasiform, and Mongoliform types it was also possible to use the shape of the nose, since the distribution of the different nasal types coincides, on the whole, with that of the hair types. The exceptions to this rule are found where there has been intermarriage between members of these groups; and in the Australiforms, with their combination of Caucasiform hair and Negriform nostrils.

Skin and Hair

Many of the general points which have arisen in the preceding paragraphs can be illustrated by considering in more detail some of the physical features in which men differ. The anatomical features commonly used to differentiate human groups are nearly all superficial in the most literal sense: that is, they are external features. A distinguished anatomist has pointed out that if the bodies of, say, a Negro and a European were both flayed, so that skin and hair were removed and the face obliterated, it would be impossible to tell for certain which was which. 'Racial' differences, it has been said, are only skin deep.

The most obvious of these differences is in skin colour. The colour of a man's skin is mainly determined by three things: first, the amount and distribution of a black pigment (melanin); second, the outer layer of dead cells, which varies in thickness; and third, the blood in the vessels below the surface. Melanins are the only substances responsible for the major differences of colour between the natives of different parts of the world: there are no different black, brown, and yellow pigments, and the many different shades are due to the combined effects of the three factors just mentioned. People of northern countries would have very nearly white skins, instead of pink, but for the effect of the blood; this whiteness can be seen in an anaemic person, or in one who has lost much blood. It is not due to a white substance in the skin, any more than is the whiteness of a cloud or a mist, but to the scattering of light by the surface cells. Some black pigment is present in the skins even of the palest people. The only exceptions are albinos, who typically have no pigment in the skin, hair, or iris of the eye. (They consequently have pink eyes, since the blood shows through.) Albinism is a rare condition which may occur in any human group, including those with the darkest skins; it is usually due to a recessive gene like that responsible for red hair (plate 1).

In general, the greater the amount of strong sunlight in a country the darker the native inhabitants are found to be. The main exception is in the American Indians, who are all rather similar in colour from Alaska in the north to Tierra del Fuego in the south; but these men are in America as a result of a relatively recent immigration, of less than ten thousand years ago, and so presumably retain the hue of their nomadic ancestors.

The dark skin of a Negro is not due to the *direct* effects of the sun: Negroes have the capacity to form melanin in their skin without exposure to the sun. This capacity varies in a fairly regular way in different groups of men between the poles and equator, and the differences between individuals in this respect are clearly genetical in origin. (The capacity to respond to sunlight by melanin formation, as when we go brown in summer, also varies, but that is a separate point.)

It is possible that the dark skin of tropical peoples is a product of natural selection, since it gives protection against sunburn. It is believed to be important in protecting the

sweat glands from damage. In view of this probable biological usefulness (or *survival value*) of very dark pigmentation it is quite likely that it has been evolved separately in
different human groups inhabiting different tropical areas.
Certainly the genes which are especially concerned with
melanin formation are different in different groups: in
West African Negroes they are numerous, but in the dark
Bantu-speaking Africans only two or three genes may be
involved. Hence the results of crossing with whites are
different in the two cases.

Colour variation is of course familiar in other species, and
particularly in domestic animals. Haldane has pointed out
that race horses vary a great deal in colour, and that there is
no connexion between their colour and desirable qualities
such as the ability to win races. As we shall see in the next
chapter, there is a parallel here with man.

The next obvious external feature is *hair*. Human hair
varies in structure, colour, and distribution on the body.
The essential difference between Negriform, Caucasiform,
and Mongoliform hair is the shape of each individual hair.
Within the first two types there is a good deal of variation:
the Papuans and Melanesians have long hair, Negroes
have short, spiral hair, and Bushmen very short, tightly-
coiled hair. Similarly, Caucasiform hair may be almost
straight or quite curly. Whatever the structure of hair its
usual colour is black, and only among some European
peoples are there many exceptions to this rule. The pigment
responsible is the same melanin as that found in the skin.
Red hair, however, has a special pigment; it turns up here
and there throughout Europe and western Asia, but is
especially common among the Irish and Welsh, the Scottish
highlanders, and among Jews and Finns. As for the distribution of hair on the body, Caucasiforms tend to have
most body hair, and Negriforms least. Apart from the temporary effects of permanent waving (or straightening in
Negro women), environmental influences have little or no
effect.

Face and Head

Other facial characteristics can be dealt with shortly. *Eye colour*, that is the colour of the iris, is generally brown or black, but where the skin and hair are lightly pigmented blue, grey, and green eyes are quite common. It is however possible for dark people to have grey or blue eyes, and for blonds to have dark eyes. The function of the iris pigment is probably to protect the interior of the eye from the harmful effects of sunlight; consequently light-eyed people are at a disadvantage in sunny countries, and are commonly obliged to wear dark glasses.

Eye form varies owing to differences in the arrangement of the skin around the eyes. Mongoliforms tend to have 'slit eyes', and some, particularly in Asia, have the 'epicanthic fold', a fold of skin that covers a part or the whole of the edge of the upper eyelid. This fold can occur in Negriforms and Caucasiforms, but in them it is rare.

As for *nasal form*, the flat, broad type of nose (platyrrhine)

Epicanthic Fold. Centre, no fold, as in e.g. European; other drawings show different types of fold, as seen principally in certain Mongoliform types

Cranial Index. Outlines of skulls seem from above: left, brachycephalic; right, dolichocephalic

is probably primitive. It seems likely that the leptorrhine, or narrow-nosed condition, is a result of natural selection: in general, the hotter and moister the air, the broader the noses of the native inhabitants; in colder climates it may be an advantage to have a high, narrow nose in which the air is warmed before it reaches the lungs.

We come now to a feature to which anthropologists have attached much importance in distinguishing the smaller anthropological groupings: this is *head form*. There are many ways in which the human head varies, including the flatness of the face and the degree of projection of the jaws (prognathism); but the character most studied is the ratio between the maximum breadth and the maximum length. This can be measured in a living person, and is then called the cephalic index; in a skull it is called the cranial index. If the maximum breadth is x and the maximum length y, the index is

$$\frac{x \cdot 100}{y}$$

On this basis heads are classified in three groups:

Index of or over 82: brachycephalic (head relatively
   short or broad);
Index from 77 to 82: mesocephalic (intermediate);
Index under 77: dolichocephalic (head relatively
   long or narrow).

On the skull these limits are conventionally two units lower.
The classification is quite arbitrary, and the selection of
figures a matter of convenience.

The broadest heads are found among Mongoliforms, the
narrowest among Negriforms. Some Asiatic groups average
86·8, and one West African people 71·8. European averages
vary a great deal. It is a curious fact that central Europeans,
including Germans, are decidedly brachycephalic (a non-
Nordic characteristic); in the north, in Britain and in Spain
averages are mostly between 76 and 79. However, in every
European population, and indeed in most populations
throughout the world, there is great variation, and some
people are decidedly narrow, others broadheaded.

Cranial Indices. In the fifth to eighth centuries skulls in Switzerland were
narrower (more dolichocephalic) than those of the nineteenth century.
The polygons show the two distributions, nineteenth century to the right.
It is impossible to tell to what extent genetical change or environmental
differences have influenced this variation with time

Cephalic Indices. The distributions of cephalic indices in three European groups. This sort of variation, with different averages but greatly overlapping distributions, is typical of differences between human groups, or 'races'. Cranial or cephalic index is of no social or biological importance, as far as is known, nor is it correlated with characters of social significance

Body Form

The tallest men are the Negroes of the Sudan and the Lake Chad region in Central Africa, the shortest the pygmies, also of Central Africa, with an average height of only 4 feet 6 inches (150 cm.). The Negro neighbours of the pygmies, who eat similar food, are 10–15 cm. taller. Why there should be this great difference is quite unknown. Nearly every group shows great variation among its members. In chapter 9 we shall see that this variation is partly due to differences of environment, as well as genetical differences within each nation. For the present we are concerned with the characteristics of whole communities. For instance, the Japanese are commonly regarded as a 'short race'. Certainly the average height of Japanese adults in Japan is less than that of Europeans or Americans, but to speak of them as a short *race* suggests that their stature is

Stature in Human Groups. Histograms showing the distribution of stature in three groups, illustrating overlap

determined genetically and is consequently unalterable, except possibly by selection during many centuries. This is not the case. The children of Japanese emigrants to the United States or Hawaii are a good deal taller, on the average, than children in Japan itself: in one large-scale inquiry it was found that for boys of fifteen years the difference is about 10 cm. Chinese show similar differences. Probably they are due largely to improved diet.

The importance of food is illustrated by experiments in which the diets of various Indian groups were fed to rats. The rats, which were all genetically similar, reflected in a remarkable way certain of the characteristics of the group whose diet they received. Thus the Pathans are physically impressive, and the rats fed on their national diet were large, developed very little disease, had large litters, and had a low infant and maternal mortality. Madrassis, at the other extreme, are physically much inferior; rats fed with their diet (largely rice) were small, had poor coats, much disease, small litters, and high death rates. Thus some of the so-called racial differences between Indian nationalities are probably due to dietary differences.

We shall refer to similar experiments in chapter 13.

Meanwhile, if we turn from stature to *body-build* (or somato-type) we find that there is less information on what determines it, but what there is reinforces the impression gained from the study of cephalic index and stature. Every kind of body-build is found in almost every human community, though the proportion that each type makes of the total may vary. There is also evidence that, as would be expected, environment may influence body-build. Both in the United States and Japan it has been found that there are more tall, slender individuals among the rich. It has also been claimed that peasants and farm labourers tend to the opposite type. These facts – if they are facts – have been attributed to environmental influences, including differences in nutrition and in occupation. But very much more work is required before we can reach any definite conclusion.

There is little satisfactory evidence that particular temperaments are regularly associated with particular physiques.

'Let me have men about me that are fat', said Caesar,

> Yond Cassius has a lean and hungry look:
> He thinks too much; such men are dangerous.

But it is doubtful if he was justified. There seems, from careful study of large numbers of people, to be little or no connexion between physique and temperament. Body-build is however probably influenced by diet.

The attempt has been made to relate physical differences between human groups to glandular function. A change in the functioning of the system of endocrine or ductless glands can produce drastic physical and behavioural changes: for instance, thyroid deficiency causes cretinism, abnormality of the pituitary gland may cause giantism, and, as we have seen, several endocrine glands influence sexual development and behaviour. There is however no evidence that, for example, pygmies are of small stature owing to thyroid deficiency, or that the tall, slender Negroes of the Nile region owe their physique to a subnormal production of the sex hormones.

Climate and Man

Physique can however be related to climate. Indeed, much of the external variation between large human groups may, as we have already suggested, be an *indirect* effect of the different climates in which they live. The effect is indirect, because (it is assumed) it is a result of the natural selection process. It is not like the darkening effect of sunlight on a pale skin (which is a case of individual adaptation), but is evidently due to the fact that, in a given area, some types survived longer and so tended to produce more offspring.

It is obviously highly probable, as we have seen, that this applies to dark skin colour in hot countries, and to narrow nose form in cold ones. It is further thought, however, that some groups, long isolated in particular areas, have evolved special characters, through the natural selection effect, which adapt them in still more detail to their particular climate.

Desert peoples, for instance the Tuareg of North Africa, the Somali of East Africa, and the aborigines of North and Central Australia, tend to be lean and skinny, with long limbs and shallow bodies, giving the greatest possible surface area to body weight and so promoting heat loss. It has even been tentatively suggested that hair form comes into this picture: the spiral arrangement of the hairs is concentrated near the heat equator, and it is suggested that the 'peppercorn' type of head hair allows a relatively rapid evaporation of sweat from the head. On the other hand the mat of closely-packed coiled hairs found in the Negroes of the Sudan and in the Melanesians has been supposed to create an insulating air chamber on top of the head, analogous to that produced by a pith helmet and protecting the head from the heat of the sun. This is, to say the least, a speculative notion.

Contrasted with dwellers in the deserts, are the peoples of the lands which surround the Arctic sea. They are thickset, with plenty of fat throughout the body, and even round the ankles and wrists. People of this build tend to lose body heat at a relatively low rate, and so may be supposed to be better able to cope with a very cold climate. The typical appearance of the Mongoliforms of eastern Siberia is also supposed to reflect the climate of the area. They have flat faces, reducing the chances of frost-bite; slitty fat-lidded eyes, which may be protection against sun glare as well as frost; and scanty beards, so that there is little likeli-hood of condensation of moisture from the breath around the mouth. It is believed that this type is the product of a stringent selective action during the rigours of the ice ages. Since then, they have multiplied and spread into some of the warmer parts of Asia, and into the Americas.

The idea of selection for certain bodily characters in the extremes of hot deserts and the northern steppes is, then, at least plausible. We cannot however apply, with any con-fidence, the same sort of explanation to the occurrence of pale skin in northern Europe. The blond, with his lack of skin pigment, light coloured irises and hair, may appear occasionally in any group; it seems that in the fog-wreathed lands of Britain and Scandinavia he is, at least, at no dis-advantage, as he might be, in primitive conditions, in hotter lands; it is also possible that the absence of skin pig-ment may promote the formation of vitamin D in the skin, under the influence of sunlight.

Whatever the validity of these notions about the selective action of different climates in the past, there is one major fact which is, for the present, far more important. This is, that all healthy men, of whatever type, are highly adapt-able. Recently there has been much careful study of the bodily changes which take place in men who have to acclimatize themselves in unaccustomed conditions of heat or cold. It is found that, after a period of a few weeks, Europeans can work as well as indigenous peoples in the tropics; the comparison has to be made, of course, between healthy men of each group. It has further been shown that Asians and Europeans undergo the same changes of ac-climatization, when transferred from one climate to another.

It is also true that men of a particular physical type may be found living in widely different climatic conditions. This does not apply only to the populations of European origin, now to be found in many parts of the world. There are, for instance, the American Indians who live all the way from Antarctic Tierra del Fuego to the tropical Amazon; there are the Negroes of the West African tropics who resemble the highland Basuto; and the Australiforms who live both in deserts and in high mountains.

The hazards, encountered in the past, by Europeans living in hot countries, were not for the most part strictly climatic. In part they were psychological; in part they were diseases such as malaria which can now be overcome. To-day, in any case, we are coming more and more to create our own climate in our houses: not only can large buildings continuously maintain a sub-tropical climate even during, say, a northern European winter; they can also, in tropical lands, maintain a temperate climate: the refrigeration, as well as the heating, of houses is perfectly practicable, and is increasingly used.

What is Race?

The facts of variation in physical characters are certainly confusing, especially since it is usual to speak of human groups as if they were sharply marked off and distinct from each other. We now find that for the most part they are not sharply marked off, and that different physical features can occur in any combination. A recently observed example of the latter is the occurrence of spiral hair, of 'Negriform' type, among Norwegians; this type of hair is evidently due to a single gene change, and so is transmitted in a simple way from parent to offspring. Another example is provided by the Polynesians, who have a combination of Caucasiform, Negriform, and Mongoliform characters.

At the same time, there are marked differences between large groups; many of these differences are genetically determined, and some at least seem to be products of natural selection. On the other hand, some important features such as stature are influenced by environment, and may be conspicuously altered in one or two generations.

When this point is reached the question may be asked: what then is race? This question presupposes that, because there is a word *race*, there must be something corresponding to it – something of which it is the name. This is very far from being the case. If you look in a dictionary you find a large number of different meanings for the term race, and if you look in the writings, not only of laymen but also of experts, you may find it difficult or impossible to make out which meaning the term is supposed to have.

However, most people have something fairly definite in mind when they speak of races. They may think of human groups relatively well marked off from each other, such as Negroes and Europeans (ignoring, for convenience, the existence of intermediates due to intermarriage). Or they may think of differences such as those between Scots and Greeks, although in this case there is a great deal of overlap and the distinction is one of averages: for instance, the average degree of skin pigmentation, or the proportion of blue-eyed individuals. And sometimes they may even think of national, or cultural characters. Always, however, or nearly always, the characters are thought of as innate – as genetically determined and unalterable by environmental changes. We have already seen to what extent both physical and behavioural differences are dependent on environment, and in the next chapter further information on psychological differences will be considered.

The division of mankind into 'races' by genetically determined characters, or, better, by actual genes, is usually based on the assumption that, if an individual possesses genes determining, say, black skin, then that individual must be more closely related, by descent, to all others with these genes, than to persons who do not have the genes. But this does not follow. We have already had the example of the appearance of spiral hair among Norwegians. Apart from this sort of effect, it is quite possible that natural selection has independently produced similar effects on large populations in different regions: perhaps the Australiforms and the African Negroes have independently developed heavy skin pigmentation, as a result of natural selection in hot climates. We shall see, in chapter 9, that there is clear evidence that this sort of thing has occurred. For this reason, no attempt is made here to outline the attempts at classification of mankind by means of blood groups. The genetics of blood grouping is well established, but the biological significance of variation among men in blood characteristics is not clear. In particular, we cannot be certain that similarity of one population to another, in the proportion of blood groups, necessarily indicates close relationship.

Meanwhile it is possible to give a reasonable definition for the word race, so that if the term must be used at all it can be used precisely. A race may be defined as a group which shares in common a certain set of genes, and which became distinct from other groups as a result of geographical isolation. The possession of genes in common is not alone sufficient to qualify a particular group as a race: no biologist would speak of the race of albinos, for example, or the race of red-haired people. Races in our sense arise as a result of isolation from other groups, and this fact is included in the definition. A definition of this sort, though fairly precise, is not much help in the study of human differences. It is useful mainly in avoiding the errors that come from the use of a term that is undefined, or has a number of different and incompatible meanings. These errors are the more likely to arise when, as with race, the term is often used to arouse emotion rather than to give information. In fact, the question 'What is race?' is not a very profitable one to ask. The question that we are concerned to answer in this book is: What are the *facts* about human diversity? In this chapter we have outlined the facts of physical diversity; in the next we turn to differences of behaviour.

8

RACE THEORY

> Of all the vulgar modes of escaping from the consideration
> of the effect of social and moral influences upon the human
> mind, the most vulgar is that of attributing the diversities of
> conduct and character to inherent natural differences.
>
> JOHN STUART MILL

It is quite obvious that most of the physical qualities discussed in the last chapter have little or no direct social importance. A man's physique may qualify him for some types
of work, and disqualify him for others, but the shape of his
head or the amount of melanin in his skin are not likely
to be considered by a foreman recruiting stevedores, or by
the examiners for a medical degree. Most people, if they had
to make a list of the socially desirable qualities, would no
doubt suggest some of the following: emotional stability;
health and energy; intelligence and initiative; moral behaviour. They would not include any particular eye-colour
or nose shape. Some, however, if the point were raised,
might assert that there is a connexion between, say, skin
pigment and moral behaviour: for example Lombroso
describes the Negro as follows:

> The principal thing is always . . . the stifling of the primitive.
> Even if he is dressed in the European way and has accepted the
> customs of modern culture, all too often there remains in him the
> lack of respect for the life of his fellow men, the disregard for life
> which all wild people have in common. To them, a murder appears
> as an ordinary occurrence . . .

This rather elaborate statement has its cruder counterpart
in the sort of thing some South African whites will say if they
are asked to discuss the status of the Negroes in the Union:
'The blacks would murder every white man in the country

if you gave them half a chance'. Later in the chapter we shall return to attitudes of this kind. In the next sections our task will be to examine dispassionately the evidence bearing on behavioural (psychological) differences between human groups. A serious difficulty is that it is much less easy to measure intellectual and moral qualities than it is to measure stature or muscular strength. We cannot go systematically through a list of behavioural characteristics, and compare them for different human groups. All we can do is select from the miscellaneous information available the most significant facts, and show how they illustrate certain principles.

Intellectual Ability

The behavioural quality that has been most measured is often called *intelligence*. The measuring is done by various systems of intelligence tests. The tests do not measure mechanical or mathematical ability, or emotional stability, or initiative, or moral outlook; but a high score can confidently be taken to imply a high degree of verbal ability even when the test itself is not verbal. In general, university teachers make high scores in intelligence tests, and so do members of the other learned professions. It has been remarked that this must be expected, since the tests were designed by professors. However, the fact that intelligence tests can give information about only one facet of the personality does not signify that they are useless. The research of which they are a result represents a valuable attempt to get an objective, quantitative expression for an important human quality. More than that, intelligence tests have been of undoubted value on a vast scale in, for example, the British and United States armies, in both of which they have been successfully used (together with other tests) in the selection of men and women for different tasks.

Intelligence tests, however, were originally designed for testing the educability of children. (We shall see later that they have many defects.) For this purpose it was desirable to have a system which would enable teachers and psychologists to compare children of different ages. This is what the *intelligence quotient* (IQ) does. The method is this. For a given community, such as London, a representative sample of schoolchildren of all ages from five to fourteen are given tests, and the average achievement for each age is worked out. Afterwards, any child can be tested and compared with the norm. If a child of ten scores the average mark for ten-year-olds his mental age is ten; if he scores the average for eleven-year-olds his mental age is eleven (and some people might call him 'precocious'). To calculate IQ:

$$IQ = \frac{\text{mental age} \times 100}{\text{age in years}}$$

Thus the IQ of the ten-year child with a mental age of eleven is 110. Up to fourteen years mental age increases at a regular rate, but after that the rate of increase slows down. In England it is considered that an IQ of 120 or more is required if a child is to profit from a higher education; and children with IQ of less than 70 are classed as dull and backward, and may be given special schooling.

Since IQ is calculated by comparing mental age with age in time, it cannot be applied to adults. A man of forty will score no higher, as a rule, than he did at twenty, although his age in time is doubled: his mental age remains unchanged, or nearly so. In this and the next two chapters, therefore, in discussing the results of these tests on different human groups, the letter I will be used to refer to scores obtained in intelligence tests by adults, irrespective of the particular set of tests used. 'Intelligence', like 'race', is popularly used in a variety of ways, and this is not the place for a discussion of its various meanings; the word is therefore best avoided.

If we are to compare average I's, say, of American Negroes and whites, we cannot interpret the figures correctly unless we know something about the extent to which

I is influenced by heredity and environment. It has been claimed, and still is sometimes claimed, that the results of intelligence tests are unaffected by environmental changes: that differences in health and education, for instance, are not reflected in the intelligence quotient. Chapter 2 gave the general, biological grounds which justify us in doubting claims of this sort, and there is now much direct evidence that I is considerably influenced, not only by genetic variation between individuals, but also by environmental differences.

Illness, accident, and malnutrition may affect IQ, but their influence is demonstrable only in extreme cases. Changes that have permanent effects on IQ are those which last for some years, and this applies particularly to changes that occur before the child is seven years old. Attendance at nursery school, for instance, has been shown to influence IQ, and, in general, schooling is found to have more effect than the economic or cultural background of the home. This effect of schooling is reflected in the rise in IQ that takes place in Negro children in the United States when they are brought by their parents from country districts to cities. The earlier they come to town, the more nearly, on the average, do they approximate in IQ to the white children in the same schools.

It is in the United States, with its very mixed population, that the greatest volume of work has been done on racial and national differences of I. The first fact fully established was that, in the United States, literate Negroes had, on the average, lower I's than literate whites. This was clear from the results of testing army recruits in 1917. It was noticeable that recruits from the different states gave widely different averages, although within each state the Negro average was always lower than the white. The differences were so great that Negroes from some northern states scored *higher* than whites from the south. Since the southern states were, and are, backward in educational matters, this suggested that there was an environmental effect arising from variation in schooling. The lower average of Negroes in each state might, it follows, be due to the fact that nearly everywhere in the United States Negroes are economically and socially inferior to whites, and have correspondingly inferior facilities for their children. Other investigations have brought evidence that Negroes can sometimes reach white average levels, or even surpass them. Thus in 1923 it was reported that 500 Negro children tested in Los Angeles had a mean IQ of 104·7, which was a little above that of the whites.

It has been suggested that results of this sort can be accounted for by selective emigration of the more able Negroes to places such as Los Angeles. The migration theory is however pure surmise, and there is no evidence for it. Comparison of the IQ's of children of parents who have emigrated has shown that, on the whole, they do not differ from those of the non-migrant children shortly after migration has taken place.

The results of testing American whites and Negroes can be summarized in Klineberg's words: 'The most probable interpretation', he says,

is that when American Negroes live under relatively favorable environmental conditions their test scores are correspondingly high, and when whites live under relatively poor conditions their test scores are correspondingly low. It is apparently not 'race' but environment which is the crucial variable. As for the factors in the environment which are mainly responsible . . ., it is likely that the nature of the available schooling plays a major role. A glance at the figures for per capita expenditure for Negro and white children in the segregated school system of the South brings into sharp focus the handicaps of the Negro children; the figures also reveal that Southern white children suffer similar, though not such extreme, handicaps.

The results of comparing Negroes with whites have been given at length, partly because there is a widespread belief in the inferiority of dark-skinned persons and partly because of the abundance of evidence. These results are, moreover, quite characteristic of those obtained from any study of the correlation between physical features (such as skin colour, nose shape and so forth) with I. Investigation has, for instance, shown no correlation at all between head shape and I, or between hair colour and I. Comparison of individuals of Nordic, Alpine, and Mediterranean types in Germany, France, and Italy has revealed no significant differences between them, although, in each country, city dwellers (as in the United States) were found to score higher, on the average, than country folk. Once again, it seems, we have an example of the importance of environmental differences.

Even if further investigation shows that some correlation does exist between some physical character and I, we can be fairly confident that every large human group will be found to overlap every other in the distribution of I among its members: every group will be found to include people of both high and low I. It follows that the results of intelligence tests are not likely to justify social discrimination against any particular group. The knowledge we have suggests that we can look forward to the appearance of many men and women of intellectual ability from 'races' and nations which at present produce none, or very few; what is needed is the improvement of educational and other facilities.

Crime

We cannot yet measure many other aspects of human behaviour as we measure I. Some types of behaviour of social importance are, however, reflected in the figures of conviction for various crimes. Since it has often been held that some 'races' are particularly prone to certain types of crime it will be useful to examine the evidence on this point.

Statistics of crime are very difficult to interpret. This is clearly shown by the difficulties met with in the United States, with its mixed population. Suppose, for example, that the Irish and the Italians in America are to be compared, we can hardly hope to learn about the criminal propensities of the Irish and the Italians in general: the immigrants from the two countries may constitute two quite unrepresentative samples: it might be that, on the whole, the best types of Italian were reaching America, and the worst

types of Irish, or vice versa. If, on the other hand, the figures
for the Irish in Ireland are compared with those for the
Italians in Italy the comparison is likely to be vitiated by
differences in laws and in enforcement in the two countries.
Even in a single country different groups may be treated
differently: it is a commonplace, admitted by American
sociologists, that Negroes in the United States (and especially in the south) are more likely to be arrested for criminal
offences, and, once arrested, more likely to be convicted,
than whites.

Another type of difficulty is met if the attempt is made to
compare the criminality of Jews and non-Jews. Professor
Bonger, a Dutch criminologist, has published figures for the
criminality of Jews in Germany and other countries for
various years from 1882 to 1916. They show that Jews were
less likely than others to commit crimes of violence, sexual
crimes, theft, or embezzlement. Murder and theft, in particular, were about three times as common among non-Jews.
But Jews had a worse record for fraud and forgery. This
might be held to support the view that Jews are 'naturally'
dishonest. In fact, it gives us no evidence on this question at
all. A very high proportion of Jews in most countries are
shopkeepers or are employed in business, and a correspondingly low proportion in manual work. Manual workers,
whether in town or country, have little opportunity for
fraud or forgery, and even those with criminal tendencies
are therefore unlikely to commit these crimes. To get
significant figures we should therefore have to compare, not
Jews in general with non-Jews in general, but, say, Jewish
shopkeepers with non-Jewish, and so on. If such a comparison showed marked differences it would then be necessary
to see whether the differences could be ascribed to features
in the family life and upbringing of the two groups, or
whether there was evidence for 'natural', or genetical,
differences.

There is, in fact, no evidence whatever for 'racial' or
genetic differences in criminal tendency between large
groups. On the other hand it is obvious that upbringing has

a very marked effect on behaviour. What in most communities would be called murder is in some regarded as a virtuous and even necessary act: in such diverse areas as Sicily and parts of India vendetta and family feuds are, or have been, a normal element in the life of the people. What is more, the effect of upbringing in such matters can be shown very clearly not to be transmitted from generation to generation; this is done by studying families which have migrated to a new environment. Here, for instance, are the figures for persons committed for homicide or assault in Massachusetts in 1915:

Group	Commitments per 100,000
Born in Italy	192
American born, one or both parents born in Italy	24
American born of American parents	24
American born, one or both parents foreign but not Italian	22

These figures suggest that in large groups of people, the amount of crime is very strongly influenced by the environment, in particular, the 'culture', in which they are brought up. Another example illustrates a further point. Here are the figures of convictions of first and second generation Irish immigrants in Massachusetts in 1908–9:

Offence	Irish Immigrants	Second Generation	Native Whites
Homicide . .	2·3	1·0	0·5
Rape . .	0·0	0·3	0·7
Gaming . .	1·2	2·7	3·6

Thus a change of environment may influence not only the amount of crime, but also the nature of the crimes committed.

Some work has been done on the social factors that influence crime. Both in New York City and in London it has been found that there is a high correlation between over-crowding and child delinquency. Of course, overcrowding and poverty go together, and poverty, or certain conse-quences of it, may be specifically responsible for increased delinquency. Klineberg, however, quotes a social experi-ment in which an area in Chicago with a high delinquency rate was provided with a large number of recreational facilities, such as gymnasiums, playgrounds, and clubs. These measures alone brought about a rapid decrease in delinquency.

It must not be thought that this argument is intended to prove that we are all alike in our inherited capacities for crime or for virtuous behaviour. We need not doubt that there is great genetic variation in the ability, in any particu-lar environment, to become law-abiding or the opposite. What the argument does suggest is that the differences be-tween large human groups, in the amount of anti-social behaviour that they display, reflect primarily differences in custom; and that these differences can be rapidly altered. As far as we know at present any group can, given the appropriate conditions, produce large numbers of crooks; equally, given other conditions, we may suppose that any group can reach a state in which the behaviour of its members is almost uniformly lawful.

The Origin of Race Theories

Since no rational case can be made for theories of the in-herited and unalterable superiority of one human group over another, it is reasonable to ask how 'racism' has become so widespread. The defeat of the German fascists, the most notorious of the propagandists of race theory, has indeed put views on the superiority of a German or 'Aryan' race in the background. But there remain plenty of Englishmen who think that men with dark skins are their natural inferiors, and Americans who think the same of Negroes and Asians.

This is a point where it is not possible to separate human biology from sociology and politics. Colour bars, for instance, are found where men of one physical type are ruled by aliens of another type. This is the case in the colonial empires of Britain, France, and Holland. This political structure is often supported by biological assertions. A slightly different situation is found in the United States, where the blacks are in a numerical minority, and are the descendants of slaves brought from Africa.

Certainly the ruling group have sometimes an obviously more advanced type of society than the ruled. The important question is whether this relationship can be regarded as permanent. In the most advanced societies of the 20th century it is taken for granted that every individual should enjoy certain rights, including a free education up to a definite age and the vote in elections for central and local governments. But it is a fact that these rights are denied to a great part of the world's population. The study of history, without any help from biology, suggests that we are not justified in thinking this situation permanent or inevitable. Countries such as China, India, and Egypt, which until recently were going through a period of colonial or semi-colonial status, have in the past had civilizations that were far in advance of those of Western Europe at the time. Chinese emperors have been in a position to treat white ambassadors with open contempt, and dark-skinned North Africans have written of the immature barbarians of northern Europe. The facts given earlier in this chapter confirm the plasticity of human behaviour from generation to generation (also discussed in chapter 6), and suggest that it is possible for changes to take place very rapidly. Thus theories of racial superiority may be regarded as reflecting the political situation in any particular historical period, but as having no biological foundation.

This is not the whole story: it does not account for race *hatred*. It is sometimes thought that dislike of one human type for another is inevitable. This is certainly untrue, since children of different types brought up together show no special antagonism. There is no doubt that race hatred exists only where it has been taught. The ease with which

it can be taught is perhaps one of the most remarkable
things about it. A full explanation would require a complex,
psychological discussion, but one important factor is the
common desire for a scapegoat. When the Germans were
going through a bad time the anti-semitic doctrines of the
Nazis encouraged them to put the blame for their difficulties on the Jews. Most people have aggressive tendencies
more or less kept in check; some give them an outlet by
playing strenuous games or by watching films about gang-
sters. However, it is convenient to have some class of people,
marked off fairly sharply from one's own group, towards
whom one can direct this aggressiveness without offending
the neighbours. This fact was exploited by the fascists in
Britain: in the East End of London they tried to generate
anti-Semitism; in Cardiff they attacked the Negro community; in Liverpool the immigrant Irish were the target.

These psychological tendencies are in fact encouraged by
all who profit from racial and national divisions. In many
parts of the world today dark-skinned people form an important source of cheap labour for farmers and industrialists. If their wages and conditions of work were improved
profits might fall, or disappear. Thus in one gold-mining
district of South Africa in 1937 the 36,000 European workers
had an average annual income of £390, while the 280,000
non-Europeans received £47. If all types of workers combined in trade unions, as has happened in some parts of the
United States, the inferior position of the non-Europeans
would no doubt rapidly improve, to the disadvantage of
their employers. Thus in South Africa, as in many other
countries, it is to the advantage of the ruling and employing
group to maintain 'racial' divisions, and to support them
with lies about human biology.

The Jews

The so-called 'Jewish problem' resembles the problems
touched on in the last section in having political, economic,
psychological, and religious aspects; some of them have

already been mentioned. Anti-semitism is so profoundly irrational that it can hardly be made the subject of a straightforward, biological discussion; or at least if it were, the argument would have no effect on anti-semites, and would be superfluous for anyone else. However, the biological facts about Jews are not well known, and are worth summarizing. Huxley and Haddon say:

The Jews can rank neither as nation nor even as ethnic unit, but rather as a socio-religious group carrying large Mediterranean, Armenoid and many other elements, and varying greatly in physical characters. Like many other groups its members are held together partly by external pressure of various kinds, partly by a long historic memory, partly by a sense of common suffering, partly by a religion.

During the Roman Empire there was a great increase in the number of Jews, as a result of the conversion of people of many different types in many countries to Judaism. Physically the Jews today are very variable, and in each country they tend to resemble the non-Jewish natives. This is due to mixed marriages with non-Jews, and is most apparent in Jewish communities which have been established for many centuries. Chinese Jews are Chinese in appearance, Abyssinian Jews resemble other Abyssinians. The so-called Jewish nose resembles that often found in persons of the Armenoid type, and is not by any means universal among Jews nor confined to them. In parts of Poland, and in Alsace, a high proportion of Jews are blonds, although typically Jews (like most people) are dark. There is no uniformity in head shape or in stature. Many people claim to be able to identify Jews by their appearance, but when their claims are tested on large numbers of people they make many mistakes: they often fail to identify Jews as such, and they may identify as Jews people, for instance Armenians, who are not Jewish at all.

As for statements about the Jewish character, they have been sufficiently dealt with already. We can summarize by saying that, not only are the Jews not a race in any sense of the word, but their behaviour, social or anti-social, is just as

much a product of the conditions in which they live as is
that of any other group.

Mixed Breeding

Another question which arouses much emotion is that of the
desirability of marriage between persons of widely different
physical type. Where racism and colour bars exist, such
inter-marriage is certain to be regarded as a grave social
crime, and in some countries it is illegal. There have been
instances in British colonies of white women receiving terms
of imprisonment for cohabiting with natives. Even where the
law does not intervene convention will often make intermarriage difficult and dangerous.

The question for us is whether there are biological objections to intermarriage. It is sometimes believed that there
are, because the children of such marriages are in some
countries often very unsatisfactory. This, however, is a *non
sequitur*. Where there is a colour bar it is often the poorest
people of the two colours who intermarry, and poverty
alone (as we shall see in the next and later chapters) is a
severe handicap. Moreover half-breeds may be despised by
both elements, and so suffer psychological disadvantages as
well.

Intermarriage does not necessarily produce either biological or social difficulties. In New Zealand there has been
successful intermarriage between Maoris and whites: there
is little colour feeling, and a Maori has been acting Prime
Minister. In such diverse regions as Hawaii and South
America 'race crossing' has been and is practised without
ill effects. A traveller in South America describes 'a blond
Negro talking Spanish to a red-headed Chinese'.

Attempts have been made to show that marriage between
certain types, such as Negroes and English in Liverpool,
produces children in whom the different parts of the skeleton
do not conform: in whom, for instance, the teeth of the
upper and lower jaws fail to fit together in a normal manner.
The results so far used to support this view have however

not taken account of the effects of malnutrition, and are therefore unconvincing.

If the whole of history is examined, it is found that 'race mixture' has been frequent, and it is impossible to show that it has had undesirable results. In general, it can be confidently said that 'race crossing' is a social, not a biological problem. Biologically, the marriage of very diverse types presumably produces a larger number of genetic combinations than had previously existed. From this point of view it is desirable, since it increases the possibility of genetic combinations of especial value to society.

THE INEQUALITY OF MAN

We hold these truths to be self-evident: that all men are created equal; that they are endowed by their Creator with certain unalienable rights; that among these are life, liberty, and the pursuit of happiness.

AMERICAN DECLARATION OF INDEPENDENCE

MAN, like most animal and plant species, reproduces sexually; his genes are consequently, as we have seen, recombined in new groups at each fertilization, and, apart from uniovular twins, each individual is genetically unique. We know that there is no good evidence for innate psychological differences between races. Despite this, there is certainly much genetical variation *within* each human group.

The subject of innate inequality has become peculiarly confused with the political question of equality of opportunity. Despite the magnificent prose and admirable intentions of the American Declaration of Independence, it is not true that all men are created equal. The Declaration was primarily concerned to assert the right of every person to life, liberty, and the pursuit of happiness; but this holds irrespective of innate differences between individuals. The main source of the confusion has been the attempt by some to claim especial virtues for particular classes: just as some 'races' have been said to be superior to the rest, so genetic superiority has been claimed for the middle or upper classes within a single nation.

Eugenics

This sort of claim has been especially associated with eugenic propaganda. The founder of the eugenic movement was an Englishman, Francis Galton. Galton was a brilliant mathematician; he was a pioneer of the use of statistical methods in biology; he invented the finger-print method of identification; and he interested himself in a wide variety of research problems, including some unconventional ones, such as the statistical investigation of the efficacy of prayer. He was the first President of the Eugenics Education Society (now the Eugenics Society), which was founded in London in 1908.

Some of the early pronouncements of leading members of this society, including scientists, were of such a character as to bring the ideas of eugenics into disrepute. A distinguished mathematician remarked, for example, that the upper classes contained all the finest examples of beauty, goodness, and taste. It was asserted that the poor were genetically less fit than the wealthy, and on these grounds old age pensions (five shillings a week at the age of seventy), and free meals in schools, were opposed, since such measures were held to encourage the improvident poor to breed more and so to produce an excess of inferior types. Attention was drawn to the fact that, at that time, the more wealthy families produced fewer children than poorer ones. It has been said that the eugenics movement was a passionate protest against the fact that the meek do inherit the earth.

These views have been, and still are, supported by transparently false arguments. The legends of the 'Jukes' and the 'Kallikaks' are still repeated in supposedly serious publications. These concern two families, of which the second has been given an invented name. In both stories it is implied that an initial pairing of two persons has given rise, solely because of bad heredity, to numerous degenerate, defective, or criminal descendants. In the second story, that of the Kallikaks, it is alleged not only that the union of a soldier with a defective girl produced many inferior descendants; but that the marriage of the same soldier to a respectable young woman founded a family of upright, hard-working, worthy citizens. These tales originated when knowledge both of genetics, and of the social effects of bad conditions, was slight, and it must be admitted that the most responsible eugenists no longer make use of them. The importance of environmental agencies, such as nutrition and housing, has (as we shall see in chapters 13 and 14) become so clear that poor physical development is no longer attributed to 'bad inheritance'; and mass unemployment has made it difficult to regard poverty as an inherited character. It is therefore easier to consider the question of eugenics in a matter-of-fact way, and to enquire to what extent our knowledge of human genetics could be used for eugenic purposes.

There is, in principle, nothing absurd in the idea of the planned breeding of human beings. The selective breeding of domestic animals is such a well-established practice that it was inevitable that men should think of applying similar methods to themselves. Such speculation did not await the development of human genetics: the subject was discussed in the ancien world. In the fifth book of Plato's *Republic* we find the following passage:

And those of the youth who have distinguished themselves, whether in war or anywhere else, ought to have awards and prizes given them, and the most ample liberty of embracing women, so that under this pretext likewise the greatest number of children may be generated of such persons.

However, neither the Greeks nor any other large human group have yet tried to put the principle of selective mating into practice. (The Germans under the Nazis were perhaps an exception.) There are primitive peoples among whom children thought to be defective or superfluous are killed; but, although this practice may have a favourable effect on the populations concerned, it is not advocated by modern eugenists.

Most eugenic programmes aim at preventing the breeding of the 'unfit'. This is *negative eugenics*, by contrast with positive eugenics aimed at promoting the breeding of the especially gifted. The means of preventing reproduction include propaganda and contraceptives; the segregation of persons in institutions; and sterilization, either optional or compulsory. Among other countries Denmark, Norway, and Sweden have sterilization laws, and some States of the U.S.A. In Nazi Germany a sterilization law giving very wide powers was passed in 1934. Legislation has been proposed for the United Kingdom, but has not been before Parliament.

What can sterilization do? This depends on the precise way in which defects are influenced by the genes. Some diseases can be said without qualification to be inherited, because environment plays no significant part in their advent. Of these, a few are due to dominant genes. Thus the condition of brachydactyly, or short fingers, due to a failure of normal growth in the middle bone, is passed on by an affected person to half his or her children, on the average. The condition is transmitted only by affected persons, and never skips a generation. Brachydactyly is itself a not very severe defect, and does not prevent a useful and normal life. On the other hand, lobster claw, or split hand, which is sometimes transmitted in this fashion too, is a severe handicap. There are at least sixteen other defects known to be transmitted in the same way, but some of them are relatively slight. Moreover, they may vary in severity: for instance, lamellar cataract may consist of a large opaque body involving most of the lens and causing nearly complete blindness, or only a very small defect compatible with excellent sight.

It is clear that sterilization of all persons with lobster claw could be expected to bring about a rapid reduction in the number of people with that defect. Since the gene responsible takes effect in every individual who carries it, all these individuals can be identified. However, the total amount of serious defect due to genes of this type is very small in any large population, and the eugenic effect of sterilizing affected persons, or of otherwise preventing their breeding,

Transmission of a Dominant Character. Part of a pedigree of 'congenital' stationary night-blindness, a defect due to a dominant gene. Note that it appears regularly in each generation; it is transmitted only by affected persons (of either sex), but not to all their offspring

would be trivial. Not all defects due to dominant genes can be eliminated by controlling breeding. Huntington's chorea, a severe disease of the nervous system, has a late age of on-set: affected persons may have already had several children when it appears.

Some other diseases are due to recessive genes. With these it is unusual for affected individuals to have affected par-ents. Just as a red-haired person may have parents both with non-red hair, so a child with, for example, 'congenital' deaf-mutism may have normal parents: each parent has passed on one gene responsible for the complaint. Sterilization of all persons suffering from congenital deaf-mutism would do little to reduce the incidence of the condition: according to Haldane 'there would be no noticeable effect in less than thirty or forty generations'. Normal persons carrying the gene would continue to produce deaf mutes as before.

There are some genetically determined diseases of such severity that affected persons hardly ever survive to produce offspring. In other words, with these diseases the aspiring eugenist is forestalled by natural causes. But if all affected persons are prevented from leaving offspring, how is it that the genes concerned persist in the population, and continue to produce deficient individuals?

An example is haemophilia. As we saw in chapter 3, haemophilia is due to a recessive sex-linked gene: it is known only in males, who derive the gene from their mothers, and who rarely survive to have children. The repeated appearance of haemophilics in a population is due to mutation: the gene responsible for haemophilia may be regarded as an inexact copy of a normal gene; and it has been calculated that this normal gene mutates at the rate of one in fifty thousand. This is probably an unusually high mutation rate. Another example is retinoblastoma, a rare and fatal form of cancer determined by a dominant gene. This gene, too, evidently has a high mutation rate.

It is clear that deficiencies maintained in a population by recurrent mutation cannot be seriously affected by eugenic measures.

So far we have considered only diseases determined in a relatively simple way. But advocates of negative eugenics have commonly been more concerned with conditions, such as mental deficiency, which are far from simple. Intellectual attainment, like stature and some other qualities discussed in chapter 3, is influenced by many genes. It is sometimes claimed that the level of intelligence of whole populations is threatened by the excessive breeding of mental defectives.

If 'mental deficiency' were a simply defined condition, like albinism, and transmitted in a straightforward way from parent to offspring, it might be possible to make a rational plan to reduce its incidence. But the opposite is true. The children who attend special schools for mental deficiency include a great variety of types, each owing the deficiency to a different set of causes, not all of them genetic. Some types are curable, for instance by psychotherapy. At least five, and perhaps as many as twenty per cent can, by the application of existing knowledge, be so improved as to become useful and normal citizens. As for the genetics of mental deficiency, out of every hundred children with one or both parents defective, about seven or eight are themselves found to be mentally deficient. A larger proportion are found to be backward, but the majority are normal. Just as mentally defective parents can have normal children, so can normal parents have mentally defective children. Indeed, most defective children have normal parents.

It follows that eugenic measures can do little to prevent the appearance of mental defectives; and that, if all defectives were sterilized or otherwise prevented from breeding, this would prevent the production of many more normal children than of defectives.

Genes and Environment

It does not, however, follow that we must resign ourselves to the appearance, in every population, of people handicapped by the effects of disadvantageous genes. Sometimes straightforward treatment, that is, environmental action, can reduce the ill effects of such genes. Severe short sight, for instance, is a grave handicap, making a person almost blind for distances of more than two or three feet; but spectacles, or, if necessary, contact lenses, can provide a complete correction. A very different example is diabetes, in which, too, there is a genetic element: many diabetics, some of great distinction and giving valuable service to the community, have been kept alive and vigorous for many years, by means of insulin. Preventive measures are also possible.

But there is a more fundamental point to make here. It is probable that improving the environment can, and does, reduce the number of disadvantageous genes in a population. This is so surprising, and so important, that it deserves a rather full treatment.

One of the most notable biological features of human populations is their *polymorphism*. We have already seen that man is highly polytypic: that is, geographical groups show marked differences which are in large part genetically determined. But within each group, or population, there is also great variation between individuals; and this variation, too, depends largely on genetic differences. Obvious superficial examples are in facial structure, general physique, and hair colour. (This statement does not contradict the assertion that such characteristics may also be influenced by environment.) It is this variation within the group which leads us to say that man is highly polymorphic. How is this polymorphism maintained?

This question most clearly arises when we consider the continued appearance of disadvantageous genes. We have already seen that this is sometimes, as with haemophilia and retinoblastoma, a consequence of repeated mutation of normal genes. This mutation counteracts the effects of 'selection' against the abnormal genes, and ensures that a few people with these abnormalities will appear in every generation. But for some conditions the numbers in the population are too large for this explanation to be valid: there must be some other effect which is maintaining the unwanted genes despite the disadvantages which they confer. It is, of course, just these genes which eugenists wish to eliminate by restricting breeding.

An explanation of the presence of these genes has been put forward on theoretical grounds, and has very recently been confirmed for one particular instance. Sickle-cell anaemia, a disease of the blood, is a condition found in people who inherit a particular gene from both parents;

such people are said to be homozygous for the gene, and
to have the genetic constitution SS (see chapter 3). The
disease is often fatal early in life, and only a small proportion
of homozygotes survive to have children. Persons with only
one of this type of abnormal gene (heterozygotes, of the
constitution Ss) are normal, except that their red blood
corpuscles, in certain conditions, become sickle-shaped;
there is no evidence that heterozygotes are at any disadvantage compared with people with two normal genes
(ss). Most people in the world have this last constitution,
but among certain groups, notably some African Negroes,
there is a high frequency of the abnormal gene which we
denote by S, and therefore a considerable incidence of
sickle-cell anaemia.

How is it, then, that the abnormal gene is not eliminated
as a result of selection against the homozygotes? If there
were no opposing effect, a gene which conferred such a disadvantage in the homozygous state would soon disappear.
The answer cannot be mutation, because mutation rates
are far too low to account for this case. The suggestion is
that the heterozygote (Ss) has an advantage over both
homozygotes (SS and ss); and that the advantage is more
than enough to balance the selection against SS.

It has now been shown that this is what actually happens
in certain regions. Heterozygotes for the sickle-cell gene are
almost completely immune to a dangerous form of malaria
(sub-tertian). This disease is prevalent in parts of Africa,
and it is in these parts that the incidence of the gene is high.
Sub-tertian malaria occurs also in the south of India, and
here too the population is found to include many with the
sickle-cell gene.

As we saw in chapter 7, the possession by Africans and
Indians of this gene in common is *not* evidence for 'racial'
affinity: it reflects the fact that the two groups have been
subjected to a similar environmental influence, and so
to a similar selection pressure. When the environment is
changed, the selection effect changes. Africans in North
America, where there is no sub-tertian malaria, have a

greatly reduced incidence of the gene. The gene is being eliminated, as a result of the disadvantage which it confers on the homozygote, since, in the absence of this type of malaria, the heterozygote is evidently at no advantage.

It is probable that many genes are maintained in populations, by a selection effect of the kind which operates for the sickle-cell gene. If this is so, there is a clear eugenic conclusion to be drawn. It is that, to eliminate such genes, the most effective action is to alter the environment in such a way as to remove the selection pressure which enables the genes to persist. Probably, this has already happened on a large scale in communities in which (as will be discussed in chapter 14) many formerly prevalent diseases have been prevented. Had the genes been eliminated, by some eugenic measure, before the diseases had been disposed of, the result would have been to weaken the resistance of the population to infection.

The most general lesson, to be learnt here, is the complexity of the problems which face the eugenist. If we wish to improve the genetic constitution of a human population, we cannot safely proceed on any simple assumption: we cannot say merely that 'like produces like' (for it often does not), and therefore encourage the breeding of the people we approve of, and discourage breeding in those whom we deplore. If this were done, the results might be very different from those we desire or expect. We can be certain that, when it becomes possible to construct a detailed eugenic programme, based on knowledge, it will be much more complex and subtle than anything so far proposed.

Measuring 'Intelligence'

Even if negative eugenics, in the usual sense of the term, can be of little use, it might still be true that there are important genetic differences between classes. We have seen in the previous chapter that no such differences can be demonstrated between races or nations, but it does not follow from this that they are not to be found between, say, the professional and managerial group on the one hand, and the unskilled labourers on the other. This is a difficult question to investigate, because in most countries the conditions in which the children of these two classes grow up are exceedingly different. The influence of environment both on physique and on intellectual abilities has been repeatedly mentioned already. In chapters 13 and 14 more detailed accounts will be found of differences in nutrition and in exposure to infection. There is no doubt that these influences have an important effect on height, weight, strength, and length of life, but on genetical differences we have no precise knowledge.

If we wish to consider psychological differences we are compelled, as in the previous chapter, to fall back on measurements of intelligence quotients. Before doing this, however, some further indication of their limitations must be given. This is especially necessary now that so much importance is given them in schools in Britain: the result of a test may determine whether a child gains entry into a grammar school, preparing for the professions, or to a technical or modern school which offer inferior opportunities.

It is well established that ordinary examinations, as applied to large numbers of children in, for instance, the General Certificate of Education, are most unreliable tests. In experiments, not only have different examiners given widely different marks to the same paper, but the same examiner has given equally different marks when faced with the same paper on different occasions. Sometimes, in subjects such as English, the difference may be that between failure and distinction. It has been thought that intelligence tests could overcome these difficulties, by providing an objective and reliable means of assessing general educability.

A major question, then, is whether the tests have 'predictive value'. To be useful in the prediction of future performance, the result of one test on a given child must be very similar to the result of testing the same child after an interval of years. It is well established that if a whole group of people is tested, and the average is taken, then that average will be found to be much the same years later. This is the justification for the discussion of group averages in the previous chapter. A steady group average could, however, conceal much variation among individuals, if some improved and some declined in the ability to answer the tests.

To find out whether intelligence tests are reliable, it is first necessary to establish test-retest correlations. Ideally, the retest, made shortly after the first test, should give exactly the same score as the first test: the correlation would then be 1·0. In fact, such correlations are usually about 0·9. In a typical test, this means that, of ten children scoring 100 on the first test, one will score above 112 or below 88 on the second. This is hardly satisfactory, when it is realized that some decisions regarding a child's future are determined by a much smaller margin of marks. But, worse than this, the correlations are far lower, if retests are made after an interval of years.

It is found that intelligence tests given to children of, say, five or six years, have virtually no predictive value at all: the correlation with the results of tests given later is so low as to make the tests useless. The rate of intellectual development is evidently different for different children: one may do well early in life, and slow down later; another may do the opposite. In fact, the IQ of normal children may vary by as much as 50 points over a period of years. These facts are of great practical importance. Many English primary schools divide the children, at eight years, into three streams, on the basis of tests, and the A stream, consisting of the highest scorers, are prepared for entry to the grammar schools while the remainder, taught at a lower intensity, are expected to go to a technical or modern school. In Scotland, too, there is a similar segregation, for some children, at five years.

It is quite clear that this system must cause much injustice and waste of ability. The remedy is being applied by some local authorities: it is the development of 'comprehensive' secondary schools, that is, schools which take all the children of over eleven or twelve years in a given locality, regardless of their supposed attainments. Every child then has access to every type of secondary education. Only such schools can allow for the known facts regarding the development of ability in children.

At later ages intelligence tests have some predictive value, but they are never more than, at least, a very rough guide to the ability of any particular individual. There are, moreover, other ways than those mentioned above, in which intelligence tests are misleading, or give inaccurate results. One depends on the fact that they consist of questions which are designed by psychologists who themselves may have preconceptions about what a child may be expected to know. As a result, one set of tests may favour town children more than those brought up in the country; another may be biassed in favour of children of middle-class parents.

Wasted Abilities

Despite these serious defects, it is sometimes possible to draw at least tentative conclusions from studies of the IQ's of large groups, such as the different classes making up a nation. There are two questions to ask here. First, is there any connexion between IQ differences and genetical differences? In other words, do we have IQ's similar to those of our parents, *irrespective of environmental influences*? The second question is: What is the distribution of IQ in the different social classes?

As for the genetical effect on IQ, there is ample evidence for a high correlation between children and parents, and between sibs. This could be attributed to similarity of environments. A check has been made by a study of children in orphanages, who are found to show a slight positive correlation in their IQ with that of their parents. In particular, orphanage children of professional class parents show a slightly higher average IQ than the rest. Since members of the professional classes have higher IQ's than other sections of a population the orphanage results presumably reflect a genetical difference. A clearer illustration of the genetical effect is given by tests on twins. Uniovular twins on the average show much closer resemblance in intelligence tests than fraternal twins. On the other hand, as we have seen, tests of uniovular twins show also that the environment *can* have a marked influence on IQ. This is what we should expect from the importance of learning, in the development of human behaviour, which we discussed in chapter 6. An example of the same thing is given by the children of bargees. Up to the age of six these children do not differ significantly in IQ from other children, but after that age their IQ's fall below normal. This is evidently a result of lack of schooling.

The second question, that of the distribution of IQ in the social classes, is partly answered in the figure below. It will be seen at once that in England the highest income

'Intelligence' Quotient. Distributions of ability to answer 'intelligence' tests among children of different economic classes in England. Group 1: parents unskilled; 2 semi-skilled; 3 skilled handworkers; 4 'brain-workers'. The wealthier children score better, on the average, than the poor, but there is a big overlap. The lower average of the poor is probably due largely to environmental effects

group has the highest average IQ, and the highest proportion of very gifted individuals. On the other hand there is a big overlap: even the lowest group has a considerable proportion of individuals with high IQ's. In fact, since the lower income groups form the great majority of the population, they include more individuals of exceptionally high IQ than the higher groups.

We cannot say to what extent the difference between the classes is genetically determined. We have already seen that some, at least, is probably due to the inferior amenities of the poor. The immediate conclusion to be drawn, for practical purposes, is that there is no sharp distinction in IQ scores between the different classes: all classes have individuals with both high and low scores, and intelligence tests provide no grounds for educational discrimination between classes.

These facts and figures can be supplemented by the results of taking the IQ's of pupils in different types of school. Let us consider the distribution of intelligence in children aged between nine years and twelve-and-a-half. In England and Wales, out of every hundred children with quotients of 120 and over, about 84 are found in the free schools (used by the poor) and 16 in those in which fees are paid. These figures apply to the period of the 1930s, but, despite changes in educational administration, there still remains a privileged class with better opportunities than the rest. These facts would be of no immediate practical importance if the opportunity for higher education, and for advancement in the professions, were evenly distributed throughout the population. But it is not so distributed. Of every hundred able pupils in free schools only 36 have the opportunity for a higher education; on the other hand, in the schools in which fees are paid, out of every hundred pupils *without* high ability just over 50 have the opportunity of a university education. In the words of Gray and Moshinsky:

. . . while nearly all the children of the larger business and the professional classes who possess ability have the opportunity of higher education, the corresponding figure for clerical and commercial employees is approximately fifty per cent, for skilled wage-earners thirty per cent, and the unskilled wage-earners twenty per cent.

There are two points of view from which this situation can be considered. Many will regard it as a glaring instance of social injustice. It indicates no disagreement with that view to say that it is also an instance of gross social inefficiency. This aspect is being widely emphasized as this book is written. The problems of a post-war period have found most countries with far fewer trained scientists and technicians than they need. In Britain a government White Paper has urged a rapid doubling of the number of students in the universities. The same report points out that there is a large untapped reserve of ability among the children of the poor. This view has been reinforced by investigations in which the I of university students has been compared with that of the general population. In England rather less than two per cent of the population reach the universities. If we take the half of these with the higher I's we find that their I is 124 or more. This group, being only half the university population, amounts to about one per cent of the total population. The next question is: What proportion of the total population have I's similar to those of the best half of the university students? The answer is that, at student ages, 5·3 per cent have I's of 124 or more. It follows that only about one in five of those whose I is within the range of that of the best half of the students ever reaches a university. Of course, I does not test all the qualities needed in a university student. No doubt some of those with high I's would be quite unsuited to a university education. This indeed applies to those who are already students as well as to the less fortunate. But, when all allowances are made, it is still clear that university education is open to by no means all those who could profit from it.

It is not possible to give figures for other countries comparable with those which have been worked out for England, but the variety of conditions elsewhere can be illustrated by considering three other great powers. First we may take

China in 1947, where a majority of the population was illiterate: only a very few had any formal education at all. Despite this, a few small, ill-equipped universities showed that there was no lack of talent. Today, in the 1950s, this talent is being developed on a large scale.

The second country is the U.S.A. In the United States as many as 15 per cent of the population receive some kind of university education. Most of this 15 per cent are drawn from the upper income group, referred to above as 'professional and managerial', and about 90 per cent of the children of this group go to college. The middle income group send only fifteen per cent of their children to college, and the third group, of the lower paid workers, send only five per cent. Yet the great majority of American children (about 60 per cent) belong to this last group. A Harvard University committee considers that about 125,000 American children each year could profit from going to college, and would go if they could, but are prevented by poverty. More recently the President's Committee on Higher Education has reported that, on the basis of ability alone, there are two or three times as many potential university students as actually reach a university. The Harvard committee assert further that

if . . . the social environment of these young people should improve materially, more of them would almost certainly show higher promise. There is experimental evidence that ability can be improved as a child's early surroundings are improved – evidence which, as was said, the growth and spread of talent which have accompanied the decline of privilege in the modern era tends to confirm.

Finally, in the U.S.S.R. there is a system of free, compulsory education for all children; all schools have the same status, and there is no section of the population whose children attend university by virtue of their parents' wealth. The Soviet educational system is still undergoing rapid change and development, and it is not yet complete; when this phase is over it may give valuable information on ways of avoiding the waste of talent that undoubtedly occurs elsewhere.

Declining Intelligence?

The emphasis on the reserve of ability to be found among the poor and unprivileged may seem to conflict with a widely propagated theory that the 'national intelligence' of Britain is declining. The theory is based on the following argument: the rich (that is, the professional and managerial class) have children whose average IQ is higher than that of the children of the poor; but the poor on the average have larger families than the rich; the difference in IQ between rich and poor is, at least in part, genetically determined; therefore the proportion of those with high intellectual ability is steadily being reduced.

This view has been criticized on various grounds. For instance, as we shall see further in chapter 15, the differential fertility between rich and poor may be only a temporary phenomenon. More important, it has been suggested that the difference in IQ between rich and poor children may be a product of the inferior conditions, both physical and intellectual, of the poor. The theory has now however been directly tested. In 1932 87,000 Scottish children aged eleven years did intelligence tests; in 1947 nearly 71,000 eleven-year-olds did similar tests. Out of a maximum score of 76 points the average in 1932 was 34·5; in 1947 it was 36·7. This difference can be shown not to be due to chance, and it follows that the IQ of Scottish children has risen during the period of fifteen years covered by the investigation. We do not know what has caused the rise: it may be improved environment, especially nutrition; it may be 'test sophistication', which is a name for the fact that children and their teachers can undoubtedly get wise to the tests, and prepare for them. Whatever the explanation, two further large-scale studies, in England, have also brought evidence for a general, though slight, rise in intelligence quotient.

The 'declining intelligence' theory has also been criticized on theoretical grounds. It is quite true that persons
of exceptionally high 'intelligence', as measured by tests,
tend to have fewer children than the average. The same,
as it happens, is true also of imbeciles and idiots. But both
classes of persons continue to appear in the population, often
as the offspring of near-average parents. It seems that ordinary people are in general more fertile than individuals at
either extreme. This principle applies generally. It could be
predicted, for instance, that the 'national stature' of many
countries must be declining, on grounds exactly comparable
to those on which the declining intelligence hypothesis is
based. But it can be shown that stature is, if anything, increasing.

In general, we know little of the selective and other
influences acting on human populations, or of the genetic
changes taking place in them. It is however permissible to
conclude that alarm about declining intelligence is premature.

Ability and Social Usefulness

The general conclusion, from the study of psychological
differences between classes, is the same as that on race
differences: that there is no sound evidence for average
genetical differences between groups. This is true, even
though the individuals within any one group differ very
greatly from each other. It may be expected that any large
human group, whether it is defined geographically, or by
physical features, or by economic status, will produce a proportion of persons of high ability, and also some of low
ability. It is perfectly possible that some groups differ in
average innate ability from others, but there is no reason to
think that, if they do exist, the differences are great enough
to justify reserving educational privileges, or entry into
certain professions, for members of a particular class.

We have so far ignored the fact that human society
requires many widely different types for its smooth running.

It is safe to say that most individuals could find something useful and pleasant to do among the available occupations. Even mentally deficient persons are found to be employable on simple tasks. To put the point in a more general form: if we wish to assess the worth of an individual we must specify very precisely the mode of life the individual is to adopt.

To sum up, it seems that every 'race', and each economic class within a nation, can produce its quota of the good and bad, intelligent and stupid, strong and weak. This is just as well. The view is becoming more and more widely held that every human being is entitled to certain essentials of civilized life, including food, clothes, and shelter, together with a certain amount of leisure in which to enjoy them in his own way. If this principle had to be applied to large populations incapable of making an adequate contribution to world prosperity, the outlook would be depressing: the more advanced peoples would have to accept for many decades a much lowered standard of life, while a large fraction of the products of their labour went to the less fortunate and the less capable. The actual outlook is quite different. There is every reason to think that, once depressed races and classes are set on the road of social development, they will soon make a contribution to the material and intellectual wealth of mankind commensurate with their numbers.

SEX DIFFERENCES

> Social progress can be measured with precision by the social
> position of the female sex.
>
> KARL MARX

THE most obvious aspect of human variety, the division
into two sexes, remains to be discussed. Unfortunately
the amount of precise knowledge of sex differences, apart
from the obvious anatomical and physiological ones, is sur-
prisingly small, while misunderstanding and prejudice are
correspondingly great. Dogmatic but quite unsupported
views are widely held on what is typical and unalterable in
the characters, temperaments, and abilities of the two sexes.

In most societies the different social positions of men and
women are based directly on their different rôles in reproduction: women bear children and suckle them, and so are
tied to the home and to household duties; men are not so
tied, and must undertake the outside tasks: hunting in
a primitive community, tilling the fields in a peasant community, and carrying on the various trades and professions
in a modern society. It is natural to take this situation for
granted, and to believe that women are not fitted for the
tasks normally carried out by men. Thus a century ago there
were no women doctors, and many took it for granted that
women had not the capacity to become doctors. Many such
assumptions are based on nothing more than local custom:
in the third century A.D. a Greek, Athenaeus, exclaimed,
'Who ever heard of a woman cook!'

In this chapter we shall not be concerned with the main
physical differences between the sexes: these can be studied
in textbooks of anatomy and physiology. We shall deal with

the secondary differences – those arising only indirectly from the different reproductive functions of men and women. Once again we shall have to try to sort out the effects of heredity and environment. Owing to its social implications this question has become, like that of race and of eugenics, partly a political one. It has been asserted that conventional views on the abilities of women are determined, not by the true facts, but by prejudice associated with their depressed position in a society run by men. It has been claimed that there is no evidence that women are less well endowed, either physically or mentally, than men, and that given the opportunity the two sexes could compete on equal terms in every field of human endeavour.

In the rest of this chapter we shall try to summarize what accurate information exists on this subject.

Physical Differences

From before birth there are sex differences in growth rates and in the development of various organs. Boys, on the average, are slightly heavier than girls at birth; on the other hand, girls show a more advanced development of the skeleton. There is no possibility of these differences being determined environmentally. As for the adult skeleton, it is usually possible for an anatomist to determine the sex even of a quite small part, such as a fragment of the skull. About one skeleton in forty may prove difficult to place. These differences may be influenced by the different conditions in which the sexes are brought up, but it is reasonably certain that they are mainly due to genetic differences.

Boys are not only slightly heavier, on the average, at birth, but also (among Europeans) about one-third of an inch taller. This superiority of height does not persist: by eleven years the average heights of the sexes are about equal, and at thirteen girls are about three-quarters of an inch taller. But girls slow down and stop growth earlier than boys. By eighteen most have stopped, whereas boys are on the average nearly three inches ahead and still growing.

(There are many individual exceptions to these generalities.) We can be certain that all this reflects genetic differences in growth capacity, even though environmental agencies may play some part. In some societies the growth of most women is checked prematurely by early childbearing, and the difference of stature between the sexes is therefore increased. It is possible that there are less obvious environmental effects operating even among the children of the western world today. Some may act in the opposite direction. In Italy, for instance, boys are more prized than girls, and better looked after, and as infants they are therefore kept more carefully in the shade; but the action of sunlight on the skin produces vitamin D, and in times of food shortage, as in the period after the second world war, this may be important. Doctors doing relief work certainly found a higher relative incidence of rickets (which is caused partly by vitamin D deficiency) among boys. Whatever moral one draws from this, it is an example of an environmental effect influencing the two sexes differently.

Males are not only bigger than females; they also have a higher metabolic rate on the average: that is, chemical changes in their bodies go on more rapidly, and so males on the whole require more food.

Muscular strength parallels growth changes. In one study of 87 girls and 89 boys, in California, grip, pulling, and thrusting strength were measured regularly throughout school and college life. Sex differences were found to be small up to the age of thirteen; after this the rate of change became much less in girls, but greater in boys. As a result, after sixteen almost no girls reached even the average performance of boys, and nearly all the boys were above the girls' average. It is hardly possible to attribute this difference to environment, especially since all the children studied had plenty of opportunity for developing muscular strength through games, and nutritionally they were all in much the same state.

Muscular *skills*, on the other hand, seem to be distributed between the sexes in a more complicated way. It is a commonplace that as a rule boys throw better than girls. This might often be because they are encouraged to play more ball games. It seems, however, that there is a more fundamental difference involved. The form of the limbs, and in particular of the bones of the arm, is different in the two sexes: so girls, for anatomical reasons, may be obliged to throw in a less effective way than boys. And it is reasonably certain that the anatomical differences are determined genetically. But throwing is, perhaps, not of much importance. In some other types of skilled activity girls do better than boys from a very early age. Anything requiring the performance of delicate movements is found to be done better by girls: for instance, they learn to dress earlier, on the whole. It has been claimed that differences in the capacity to carry out fine movements can be observed as early as nine months.

So far, then, there is some objective basis for referring to women as 'the weaker sex': they are measurably less strong than men, on the average (though not less skilled), and the difference is probably mainly a genetical one. But in another respect it is men who are the weaker sex. They die more easily. This is largely due to a lower resistance to infection which holds throughout life. This does not, however, apply in all countries: in India and China, where women suffer conditions especially bad for health, the death-rate of women is higher than that of men at most ages.

Intellectual Differences

It might be expected that, on coming to psychological differences, the first step would be to compare the average IQ's of the two sexes. This, however, can be done in a sentence: the IQ's are identical. Unfortunately this tells us nothing about the relative intellectual abilities of the sexes: the fact is, the best modern intelligence tests are *designed* in such a way that boys and girls of equal age show the same average performance. However, if individual tests are studied, among the various sorts from which IQ may be calculated, it is found that boys and girls by no means do equally well in each. If we summarize the main points of difference shown in all kinds of tests, we find that the boys show better mechanical ability and are more likely to excel in mathematics; on the other hand girls from a very early age are more articulate; they talk more, and more intelligibly. They are also superior in 'aesthetic sense': for instance, they discriminate colours better than boys. Their memory too is said to be better, at least in early childhood. Later, they are better at languages. A general difference is that boys are more variable than girls: there are more extreme types among males, for instance more with a very high IQ and more imbeciles.

An important question is whether intellectual development shows any parallel with the growth changes and physiological modifications during adolescence. It has been said that, just as girls stop growing earlier, so their 'intelligence' reaches its maximum before that of boys. (To show this it is of course necessary to use tests other than those that have been standardized to show no difference between the sexes.) Whether there is any basis for this view or not, it is certain that there is a great overlap of intellectual ability between men and women. There are no grounds for denying women a higher education in any subject.

Although the psychological differences just described are quite likely to be due mainly to genetical differences, we are entirely justified in remaining sceptical on that point. It is extraordinarily difficult to discern the more subtle environmental influences, and to distinguish their effects from genetical ones. We saw something of the complexities of early learning in chapter 6. In most societies girls and boys are treated differently almost from birth: they are dressed differently, talked to differently, and *expected* to show different interests. We cannot say to what extent this attitude has prevented the appearance of eminent women in the arts and professions. The difficulty in allowing for the effects of social convention is probably greatest if we try to deal with differences of 'character' or 'temperament'. Child psychologists and others commonly assert that, for instance, boys are more aggressive than girls, and girls shyer. We need not doubt that this is true, but unfortunately it is not easy to measure aggression or shyness, and so it is difficult to make statements of this kind quantitative and precise. It would be very rash to claim that a difference of this sort is quite independent of the social environment of the child. In any case all these statements concern the averages shown by groups: they tell us nothing about particular persons. When Samuel Johnson was asked, 'Which have the most brains, men or women?' he replied, 'Which man, which woman?' His reply could not have been more to the point.

Women in the Community

A possible way of assessing the environmental effects on behaviour differences between the sexes is to study different types of society. In chapter 8 we saw that racial or national groups show great plasticity of behaviour in response to different environments. Do the two sexes show a similar plasticity?

It is immediately obvious that in some respects they do. The behaviour of a well-to-do business man in Western Europe or the United States during the late nineteenth century might be contrasted with that of the dandy of less than a century before. Similarly we may make the obvious comparison of the Victorian lady dressed, perhaps, in ankle-length skirt and bustle, and the mid-twentieth century young woman in slacks and sweater.

This type of comparison, however, though interesting, is superficial, and does not take us very far. Much greater claims have been made for the alterability of the behaviour of men and women – and particularly women – than are justified by the changes that have taken place in the past few centuries in the western world. In 1869, for instance, John Stuart Mill wrote:

What is now called the nature of women is an eminently artificial thing, the result of forced repression in some directions, unnatural stimulation in others. It may be asserted, without scruple, that no other class of dependents have had their character so entirely distorted from its natural proportions.

It is, of course, quite reasonable to suggest that the character of men, too, in 1869, as today, was in some sense 'distorted from its natural proportions'. Mill's emphasis on women was a protest against their position as dependents. The buying and selling of wives had not long been given up in England when Mill wrote.

The protest against the subjection of women, and the demand for their emancipation from all the social and economic disadvantages imposed on them, has been supported by pointing to societies in which the rôles of the sexes have been apparently the inverse of those familiar to us. Thus in our society women are expected (on the whole) to play a passive part in love-making; to be dependent rather than self-reliant; to be modest, chaste, home-loving, and motherly; and to be particularly interested in self-adornment. It is claimed, however, that in some civilizations, notably those of Sparta and ancient Egypt, these characteristics have belonged on the whole to men, and not to women; and that this inversion was related to the economic subjection of men which was characteristic of these societies.

The extent to which this account of these ancient societies is accurate has been questioned, and we cannot confidently assert from the evidence they provide that a complete inversion of behaviour is possible. On the other hand, in some primitive societies today, such inversion has been reported from direct observation. The best-known work of this kind was done by Margaret Mead in New Guinea. Of three tribal groups in that country, Dr Mead claims that one, the Tchambuli, shows a relationship between the sexes the exact opposite of what we accept as usual. In both the others, however, there is 'no idea that men and women are different in temperament'. Of these two, in the Arapesh the behaviour of both men and women is uniformly gentle and unaggressive, and what we should describe as maternal and passive; this group practises agriculture. On the other hand the Mundugumor, who are head-hunters, are, men and women alike, aggressive and 'masculine'.

Apart from primitive societies we have, in the Soviet Union, a country in which the social and legal attitude towards women differs greatly from those of most other nations. The Soviet constitution states:

Women in the U.S.S.R. are accorded equal rights with men, in all spheres of economic, state, cultural, social, and political life.

One result of this was that, even by 1939, women doctors in the Soviet Union slightly outnumbered men, and today the proportion is far higher; another consequence has been the much commented on women engine-drivers and ships' captains. On the other hand the following statement appeared in a report on 'Soviet Women and Defence':

Not all jobs were open to Soviet women, however. The Soviets saw nothing incompatible between the doctrine of equality of the sexes and the doctrine of protection of women from influences that would impair their ability to bear healthy children.

In particular, women in the Soviet Union are not considered fitted for the heaviest types of physical labour.

Conclusion of this kind have been reached, in the U.S.S.R., not on the basis of preconceptions about the abilities of the two sexes, nor on political grounds, but empirically: the experiences of the rapidly changing Soviet state have been responsible for sudden modifications of outlook and policy. In the early stages, immediately after the revolution, the emphasis was on equality, as a revolt against the degrading rôle allotted to women in Tsarist Russia. Since the second world war, and now that the equal rights of women and men have come to be taken for granted, emphasis has been laid on the importance, both to the individual and to society, of motherhood, and special measures have been taken to make the task of bringing up children attractive and free from financial difficulties.

The distinctive feature of Soviet policy is not that it is based on special knowledge or on one consistent and unvarying plan, but that it is conscious and deliberate. If one thing (such as co-education) is considered, on the basis of experience, not to work, something else is tried. At present it is not possible to draw final conclusions from Soviet experience, any more than it is from the studies, mentioned above, carried out by physiologists or anthropologists in other countries. Just as we have yet to determine the innate abilities of different races, so we are very far from knowing what members of either sex could do, in more satisfactory environments than those so far achieved.

Part Three

Life and Death

The first human societies were small family groups, and only when agriculture was invented, perhaps eight thousand years ago, did populous human communities come into being. Gradual improvement in the techniques of cultivation made it possible to produce a food surplus, which could support those who grew no food but worked in industry or trade, or administered the state; this was the foundation of civilization. But food supplies have never been entirely reliable for any large human population. Today we can not only see the world's food problem as a whole, but also discern the biological and economic changes required to solve it.

The other major biological problem of the twentieth century is the conquest of infectious disease. Much of the world still suffers from the same epidemic and endemic scourges as our ancestors of centuries ago, although it is known how to prevent them. In the advanced countries, where they have been prevented, there remain formidable problems such as high infant mortality, tuberculosis and 'mental' illness, but these too can be solved.

If full use is to be made of biological knowledge for human benefit, human populations, most of which are increasing, must attain an equilibrium with their environmental resources. This can be achieved if schemes of development, especially of undeveloped areas, are given adequate priority. Given a suitable distribution of effort, an increasing population can be an economic asset.

MAN AND SOCIETY

Thou shalt eat the herb of the field; in the sweat of thy face
shalt thou eat bread ...

GENESIS

THIS chapter is a connecting link between the fifth and sixth
on human evolution and behaviour, and the four which follow on food, disease, and population respectively. It deals
with the evolution of human society. In chapter 5 man was
described biologically, and his relationship with other mammals, especially the apes, was emphasized. But, as we saw
in chapter 6, man is distinguished by a unique form of social
organization. It is unique because other highly social
animals, such as ants and bees, have the patterns of their
behaviour fixed independently of experience, whereas one
of the most notable things about man, compared with other
animals, is his capacity for learning, especially in his early
years, and the consequent plasticity of his behaviour. The
single species, *Homo sapiens*, has therefore been able to produce many different types of society; and in some areas (such
as Western Europe, or Central Asia) society has changed
from one type to another very rapidly.

There is a notion that some types of human existence are
more natural than others, though what *natural* means in
this context is rarely explained. The 'state of nature' in
which primitive man exists is sometimes contrasted with
the 'artificiality' of modern times. The implication is that
primitive men live like most other animals, without social
organization, tools, or speech. But this is not true. Even
before *Homo sapiens* appeared there were all these things,
together with fire: wherever and whenever he has lived

man has assembled in groups and has altered his surroundings so as to satisfy his needs. This is what is meant when it is said that man 'creates his own environment'.

Social organization developed from family groups. Among apes today the group consists typically of a single dominant male with a number of females and their young. There is no division of labour between the sexes and all have to forage for food. In primitive man monogamy is typical. The women contribute to food-getting by gathering food plants and the men hunt. The division of labour between the sexes also makes possible greater protection for the young by the mother; as we know, this is essential, since in man social behaviour depends on the young gradually learning appropriate habits and customs.

Savagery

This early type of society is technically called savagery, though not in any pejorative sense. It refers to the state of all pre-*sapiens* man; and *Homo sapiens* himself has lived for 90 per cent or more of kis time in the same state.

Savage man is usually nomadic. The present tense can be used here, not merely as a literary device but because there are several groups which have never progressed from savagery (at least, until very recently indeed): for example, the Australian aborigines, the Eskimo, and some of the inhabitants of Malaya and of Central and South Africa. He lives by collecting food, plant or animal, over a wide region, and a great area of land is needed to support each individual, compared with that required in an agricultural community. The sparse population is divided into family units which may include twenty persons. Occasionally there may be larger gatherings, since at a season of plenty, when much food can be gathered in a small space, members of different groups may meet. Only on such occasions is there opportunity for the exchange of knowledge and views. However, both knowledge and ideas are likely to be very limited. In small groups there is less opportunity for division of labour apart from that between the sexes, especially when nearly all waking time is needed for food collecting; and without it, technical advance cannot go far.

The tools of savages, to judge by the behaviour of apes today, may first have been sticks; but by the time of Peking man stone choppers had long been manufactured. As containers there are gourds and shells and perhaps baskets, but no pottery. For coverings skins, grasses, and bark may be used, but there are no textiles. There are no domestic animals, either for food or for draught. There is private property in weapons, digging sticks, collecting bags, and trinkets, but not in food.

Neanderthal man – our immediate predecessor in Europe – probably had all these resources. Stone tools were more skilfully made, by flaking, than were those of earlier man; in particular there were well designed scrapers and points. There were a few bone tools. Traps were made. Burial of the dead suggests some kind of religion or magic, and cannibalism, which was also practised, may have had a similar foundation, since, as in the Christian ritual, the eating of a person's body is sometimes supposed to confer the strength or virtue of the eaten on the eater.

This summary takes us to the end of the whole of the lower palaeolithic period, including the Mousterian culture for which Neanderthal man was responsible. ('Palaeolithic' means 'old stone age'.) More information is given in the chart on page 201. In the upper palaeolithic we come to the stage, called the higher savagery, at which our own type, *Homo sapiens*, first appears. As we have seen, a few men remain today in this stage of social development, but in the Mediterranean area certainly, and no doubt in other parts of the world, men lived in this way during a period beginning at least 70,000 years ago and ending less than 10,000 years ago. The variety of cultures that existed during this long period is only imperfectly known: large parts of the world are almost unexplored for possible remains, and most of our present knowledge comes from France and the

North of Spain; North Africa and parts of Asia have however yielded valuable material. Even in these limited areas it
is possible to distinguish a series of distinct phases, in each of
which the design of tools and clay vessels, artistic styles and
mode of life all have characteristic features. The different
cultures do not correspond to the different physical types
shown by skeletal remains. Thus one culture, called the
Gravettian, has left widespread traces in Western Europe;
and it is found that Gravettian equipment was used both
by 'Cro-Magnon' man – a type regarded as typically
'European' – and by the Grimaldi type which in skull
character has been held to resemble a typical Negro. Both
types are found together in the Guttes de Grimaldi at
Mentone. This fact gives further support to the conclusions
on race differences reached in chapters 7 and 8.

H. sapiens, from the first we know of him, had much more
elaborate flint tools than his predecessors. After a large
fragment had been struck from the main mass much skilled
secondary flaking was done to get the desired shape. Bones,
antlers, and teeth also were used as instruments. Stone
lamps, pestles and mortars were made. There was still no
pottery, but clay modelling was done. Remarkable works
of art, including figurines, are found in the caves used as

OLD STONE   NEW STONE   BRONZE   IRON
AGE   AGE   AGE   AGE

Axes over Half a Million Years

dwellings, but we do not know what the significance of these works was to palaeolithic man. Skins were probably used for clothing, and sinews for bows and harpoon lines. Spears and arrows had flint or bone points.

Thus from the first *H. sapiens* has shown a high level of manual skill, together, perhaps, with an aesthetic sensibility. Nevertheless, for tens of thousands of years man remained in the pre-agricultural phase, and lived by hunting, shooting, and fishing, and by the collection of wild plant food and honey. It is likely that, as a rule, there was a seasonal nomadism, in which the movement of the small family groups was determined by the travels of game in search of food and water. In winter, caves, or simple structures with the floor below ground level, were occupied. A typical group would perhaps occupy four or five huts, each housing several people.

The use of well-constructed huts was developed in Europe in the latest pre-agricultural period. This new phase, the mesolithic, or middle stone age, lasted a relatively short time before it blossomed out into the agricultural revolution. The characteristics which distinguish it from the old stone age are the domestication of the dog for hunting; the use of nets, hooks, and lines for fishing (but perhaps it is that these have been preserved only from this more recent phase); and the construction of canoes, paddles, skis, and sledges for transport. There was thus a greater variety of technical skills, but no fundamental difference from the palaeolithic. In general, savagery, whether 'higher savagery' or not, whether carried on with mesolithic equipment or that of the old stone age, is a precarious existence. It has been calculated that the human population of the world before agriculture was practised may have been no more than 10 m. – about the number now living within 20 miles of the City of London. England is believed to have had a population of about 200 at that time, and, when agriculture first began, of 2000. These figures, though little more than guesses based on the known population densities of present-day primitive peoples, at least give some idea of the poverty of human existence before agriculture was invented.

Primitive Barbarism

The great change came about 8000 years ago. At that time cultivation of domestic plants began in the sub-tropical zone which includes North Africa, Syria, Iran, and Turkestan; the whole area today is dry and largely desert, but during the Pleistocene it had had a good rainfall. At first, cultivation was no doubt confined to the most favourable regions, such as the Nile valley, where there was plenty of water. The type of cultivation was that called 'extensive': that is, there was frequent breaking of new ground as the old lost its productivity. There was thus a less permanent type of settlement than is found among people practising intensive cultivation – the continued use of the same plots of land for an indefinite period. (Extensive cultivation was still being used in Western Europe after the collapse of Rome.)

No doubt men had already used the seeds of wild grasses as food. Flint sickles found at Mount Carmel suggest that cereals were eaten by the mesolithic cave-dwellers, probably before 6000 B.C. The first step in agriculture was to induce suitable grasses to grow annually on selected plots within a settlement. In the Mediterranean area two wheats, wild Einkorn and wild Emmer, were domesticated, together with wild barley. Rye and oats came much later, at first as weeds of wheat and barley fields. Their advantage was their capacity to give good yields in more northern climates than wheat would stand. The earliest known civilizations, those of Syria, Mesopotamia, and the valley of the Indus, occupy an area roughly coinciding with the distribution of the wild ancestors of wheat and barley, and the civilizations of Europe and Western Asia may be said to be founded on the productivity of these two plant species.

The domestication of animals for food began at about the same time as cereal cultivation. The dog had preceded

DATE	ECONOMIC SYSTEMS (Mode of Production)	TECHNICAL PERIOD (Tools and Materials)	INVENTIONS AND INNOVATIONS
2000–	**CAPITALISM Wage Labour** [Europe and N. America] WESTERN EUROPEAN CIVILIZATION **FEUDALISM, Serfdom** [Europe]	MODERN	INVENTIONS OF MODERN ERA Steam Engine [1781] Printing [1381]
1000–		IRON	
0–	GRECIAN & ROMAN CIVILIZATION		Crop Rotation
			Watermill
1000–	**ANCIENT CIVILIZATION** Slavery [S. Europe, N. Africa, Middle East especially; also India, China, Central and South America]	BRONZE	Iron used
2000–			
	INDUS CIVILIZATION		
3000–	FIRST EGYPTIAN AND MESOPOTAMIAN CIVILIZATIONS	NEOLITHIC	Wheeled Vehicles Plough
4000–			Sail
5000–	**PRIMITIVE BARBARISM** i.e. Agriculture and Stockbreeding without cities		Copper Smelting
			STOCK-BREEDING AGRICULTURE
6000–		MESOLITHIC	
7000–	**SAVAGERY**		

THE DEVELOPMENT OF HUMAN SOCIETY IN THE WEST

The approximate relations in time of the stages in the development of civilization, and of some major technical advances. The sequence shown applies mainly to the Mediterranean area and Europe. A chart of this sort necessarily gives only a much simplified picture of what happened; for sources of more information reference should be made to the bibliography agriculture, as an adjunct to hunting. Cattle, sheep, goats, and pigs were brought in early. The use of the horse, ass, ox, and camel for transport and traction came later. The early stages of settled agriculture, with both cultivated cereals and domestic herds, have been most studied at the ancient settlements of the Faiyum and Merimde in Egypt, and Sumer in Mesopotamia. It is at the latter that the use of sheep's wool for clothing is first recorded, probably 4000 years before the present era. Dairy farming also seems to have begun in Mesopotamia, perhaps 1000 years later.

The type of culture associated with the most primitive agriculture is called neolithic – the culture of the new stone age. The Maoris of New Zealand were still at this stage in 1800. Our knowledge of the neolithic phase throughout the world is exceedingly fragmentary, but it is probable that agriculture arose independently in several regions. Certainly it seems that the maize and potato agriculture of Central and South America owes nothing to the ancient Egyptians, and in China that based on millet and the pig may have been a separate development.

Wherever it was adopted agriculture had the most profound effects on human life. Its primary function was to ensure a greater and more reliable supply of food, but in doing so it made possible a vast number of new techniques and activities which, in their combined effects, transformed man from a rare creature into the dominant species that he is today. The earliest agricultural communities were probably ten to twenty times as large as the nomadic groups of savagery. Among the two or three hundred persons specialization of labour became possible, and this in turn gave rise to more complex and more skilled operations. Among the earliest trades so established were those of the weaver, the potter, and the flint polisher. There was at this stage, however, no major technical advance from savagery, apart from the development of agriculture and stock-breeding themselves. The possibility of great technical developments depended, in the first place, on the acquisition of sufficient agricultural skill to produce a *surplus of food* from the soil. This made possible the existence of people, such as skilled flint workers and other specialists, who produced no food for themselves. An important contribution to farming technique was made by the traction plough – the plough drawn by oxen (or, later, by the horse): this greatly increased the arable area that one man could cultivate. The use of domestic animals as a source of power was in fact of fundamental importance. Another technique of the greatest value was that of irrigation, which was developed on a large scale in Egypt and Mesopotamia. The immediate consequence of these advances is illustrated in the Faiyum: in this prosperous peasant community of between 6000 and 5000 B.C. there were two groups of silos, numbering 67 and 98 respectively; each held, on the average, about 8 cwt. of grain, which was probably the yield of two or three acres.

Civilization

Civilization has been called the culture of cities. Cities are themselves large gatherings of men not engaged on food production. They appear first in the valleys of the Nile in Egypt, the Tigris and Euphrates in Mesopotamia, the Indus in northern India, and perhaps simultaneously the Yangtse-kiang in China. A further, separate civilization arose in Central and South America. We have seen that an important function of a food surplus is to support workers in crafts and industries other than agriculture and stock-breeding. The surplus however does more than that. From very early it was also a basis for trade. Certain important commodities are found only in a few places: raw materials such as flint, and later copper, tin, and iron were mined and transported long distances, either in the crude state or in the form of finished products such as axes, vessels, shields or ornaments; and other consumer goods such as pottery and trinkets entered largely into the trade of early civilization. Thus human communities became more complex, and came to need a central administration, a legal system, and machinery for keeping order and enforcing the law. Cities were the centres, therefore, not only of craftsmanship and trade, but also of administration; and the food surplus had to support a ruling class of priests and kings who took taxes or tribute in the form of food. This was the origin of the *state*, the apparatus of government and control by a relatively small ruling class.

A series of new discoveries and inventions followed. In the fourth millennium B.C., that is, between five and six thousand years ago, the wheel was invented, and used both for transport and in the making of pottery. Oversea trade led to the development of the sailing ship, and this in turn to the establishment of navigational methods. Navigation requires a knowledge of the stars, and so is one of the sources of the science of astronomy. The other early source is the needs of agriculture itself, since to plan the sowing of crops according to the seasons a calendar is required. The great pyramid of Egypt is so designed that the dog-star, Sirius, is visible in a central chamber only at the equinoxes. The Egyptians had a year of 365 days and no leap year, and this calendar was probably used first in 4242 B.C. Knowledge of astronomy and of the working of the calendar was no doubt a prerogative of the priest-kings, and since this knowledge was a source of their power, we can guess that they guarded it jealously: they provide an early example of the restriction of learning to a particular class. The association between religion and the calendar is exemplified in England by the famous neolithic temple at Stonehenge, which is so arranged that on midsummer day the sun rises in line with two marked points.

In Egypt the needs of agriculture stimulated the growth also of geometry, owing to the necessity for re-surveying the fields each year after the Nile floods had obliterated all landmarks. The history of ancient civilizations illustrates very clearly the way in which the development of science is related to human needs.

The use of written numbers and alphabetic scripts dates from about 3000 B.C., and is contemporary with the Asiatic discovery of bronze. At this time the civilization of the

Indus valley had reached a very high level of development. Among the technical problems that arise in all cities are the supply of clean water and the disposal of liquid waste. At the city of Mohenjo-daro, on the River Indus, there was a well-organized system of aqueducts and drains, and there is evidence of deliberate town-planning by the city government.

Civilization not only creates material wealth and an elaborate technology, but by making leisure possible it leads also to development of the arts. At the same time the media for artistic expression are augmented. The artists of the higher savagery took advantage of the leisure made possible by a plentiful game supply to paint and draw on cave walls and on bone. The artists of civilization could express themselves also as architects, using inorganic materials for building; and in Egypt a heptatonic musical scale was invented. In this way, on the basis of a successful agriculture, the main features of all civilizations up to 200 years ago were developed nearly 5000 years before the industrial revolution in Europe. Even a money economy was established in Mesopotamia.

Between the ancient civilizations and the present one is a long period of continuing, relatively slow technical and economic change. Stone implements gradually gave place to metal: at first copper was used, and later tin and copper together, to make bronze; later still iron, which is more difficult to extract from its ores but far more plentiful, came into general use, and it is only now, in the twentieth century, that other materials such as aluminium are beginning to replace it for some purposes. There were important improvements in power production. First, water power, which began to be used in the late Roman Empire, for such purposes as grinding wheat and separating ores, became very important in some areas; second, the invention of the horse collar in mediaeval times, in place of a strangling yoke, greatly increased the effective muscular power of horses. This, with the invention of iron horseshoes, enabled the farmers of the middle ages to cultivate lands hitherto inaccessible to the plough.

With the development of wood pumps men were able to mine more deeply and more widely, and the mineral and technical wealth of human communities increased correspondingly. New techniques and new ideas came from many lands. The Chinese provided sailors with the magnetic compass; and with the introduction of the rudder, and the invention of methods for sailing into the wind, sail conquered the high seas. China also provided gunpowder – a decisive instrument of war until the other side acquired it; and, again from China, came paper and printing – both essential for the foundation of an educated community.

Economically, the great iron age civilizations of the Mediterranean – of Italy, Greece, Palestine, and North Africa – were based largely on slavery, at least for industrial production. Productive and other manual work was done by classes sharply marked off as of inferior status, and a relatively small ruling group had the prerogative of administration and access to a good education. The consequent separation of those with clerical knowledge from the people with practical skills had an ill effect on technical and scientific development which is still reflected in administration and education today. In Europe, after the fall of Rome, this system gave place to feudalism, under which the cultivator was typically a serf, limited to working on one particular patch of soil. This led to an increase in the productivity of the soil in the temperate forest area, where regular rotation of crops became customary. It was accompanied by the development of guilds of craftsmen and merchants which led to an improved status for their members.

The conventional account of the middle ages is that given by historians interested primarily in political and perhaps economic history, and in the arts. Here we are concerned rather with techniques, and especially those which played an important part in agricultural and industrial production. Some historians indeed consider that this aspect is a key to the understanding of the period. Farrington quotes an American, Lynn White:

The cumulative effect of the newly available animal, water and wind power upon the culture of Europe has not been carefully studied. But from the twelfth and even from the eleventh century there was rapid replacement of human by non-human energy wherever great quantities of power were needed or where the required motion was so simple and monotonous that a man could be replaced by a mechanism. The chief glory of the later Middle Ages was not its cathedrals or its epics or its scholasticism: it was the building for the first time in history of a complex civilization which rested not on the backs of sweating slaves or coolies but primarily on non-human power.

The Scientific Age

Today civilization has begun a change greater than any of those of the past. It is taking place with remarkable rapidity on the historical time-scale, though with painful slowness for those who live through it. In 1850, in Western Europe, the efforts of three-quarters of the population were needed to provide a food surplus adequate for the remaining quarter not engaged in food production. Today, in advanced areas, the figures are reversed: one quarter produce enough surplus for three-quarters of the population. Thus in such countries as France, the United States, and New Zealand (all of which normally export food) 50 per cent of the population live in towns. In Great Britain, which imports food in exchange for manufactured goods, the figure is 80 per cent. On the other hand, in the whole of Asia, where, except in the U.S.S.R., modern agricultural techniques have, until recently, hardly been practised, only about 15 per cent of the population are reckoned to be town dwellers. The change in agricultural productivity per man is partly a reflexion of the technical advance of industry. The invention of machines which enable us to make use of the energy in coal and oil has made it possible, in the advanced countries, to replace the muscle power, not only of man but now also of domestic animals, by more effective installations. Large numbers of workers have been released from food production, with a great potential increase in material wealth and leisure. This state of affairs is at once based on and has led to the development of our knowledge of the physical sciences. The other basis of modern agriculture is applied biology, of which some features are discussed in the next chapter.

The economic counterpart of these technical developments is capitalism, which had replaced feudalism in most of Europe by the end of the nineteenth century. Under capitalism not only land, but also capital goods such as mines, factories, and transport services, are privately owned; or if they are not, they are operated by a state which is itself controlled by the owners of large capital installations. It was indeed the single control of big productive units that made the large scale application of modern techniques possible: previously the individual craftsman had often owned his own tools and equipment, but a blast furnace, the machinery for a mine, or a steam loom, could not be worked by single individuals, or even by a family; in practice they were worked by a number of wage-earners and owned by the employer. Today capitalism in its turn has in some countries already been replaced by yet a further economic system, socialism, under which private ownership is restricted to personal property, and the means of production are communally owned and controlled.

None of these phases of human society is the prerogative of any particular biological type. We have seen that this applies to palaeolithic cultures. The great invention of agriculture itself seems to have been made separately by widely different groups. Again, the early civilization of the Indus has been described as the product of 'peoples of mixed origin and diverse racial types'. The various prehistoric cultures of Europe are often attributed to groups of contrasted physical types, such as 'tall long-heads' and 'lightly built round-heads'. Certainly the various migrant or conquering groups differed on the average in such physical characters as stature or cephalic index, but there was continual intermingling of peoples and exchange of ideas and techniques. In the same way, today, the modern culture originating in western Europe has been absorbed, in many of its features, by such diverse groups as the New Zealand Maoris, the Japanese, and formerly primitive peoples in northern Siberia.

In the first ten chapters of this book the topic has been human diversity in time and space: what determines human differences, and the social consequences of the differences. But when we study civilizations and cultures we can look at mankind as an entity – not indeed, because there is any uniformity of cultures, but because wherever he is, and of whatever type, man has certain fundamental problems to solve; the different kinds of society, with their various types of economy and techniques, are his attempts to solve those problems in the varied circumstances in which he lives. Among these problems are the three great biological ones: the supply of food, which has already been partly discussed in this chapter; the prevention of infectious disease; and the maintenance of the population by the bearing of children. These are the subjects of the next four chapters.

12

FOOD AND SOIL

> One of the most ruinous limiting factors is the capitalistic system – and this is one of the gravest criticisms that can be leveled against it. The methods of free competition and the application of the profit motive have been disastrous to the land. . . .
>
> Throughout virtually the entire world, land is not used to produce the crop best adapted to it on a permanent basis but to produce as much cash as possible, as cheaply as possible, and as quickly as possible – the same system exalted by the manufacturer.
>
> WILLIAM VOGT
> Chief of Conservation Section, Pan-American Union) in 1948

NONE of the advances in food production has yet prevented food shortages. Increased food supplies led also to great increases in the density of human populations, and when their food supply fails the disaster is correspondingly great. This sort of thing is familiar enough to the biologist: animal populations are prevented from indefinite increase by *limiting factors*, and food supply is sometimes the factor which determines the maximum size of a population. Other possible factors are the amount of space for breeding, and the number and efficiency of predators or parasites: for instance, the cats of a village may reduce the maximum population of mice. Man himself is a limiting factor, or creates such factors, for many animal and plant populations: in the attempt to grow or to capture food for himself he is obliged to reduce the food available for other species, to destroy their living-space and sometimes to kill them directly, either because they themselves provide food or because they interfere with his activities.

There is thus a complex interaction between human populations and the populations of other species, both plant and animal, in all the regions of the land and sea where man lives or works. The study of this interaction, which is a part of the science of ecology, is important for many reasons, including the fact that it is a necessity for a scientific agriculture. The need for science in farming has become especially obvious during the twentieth century. One reason for this is the increasing consciousness of what scientific method can do, when it is applied to such problems as the improvement of soil or the breeding of better strains of crop plants or domestic animals. A second reason has been the enormous scale of human food production during this century, accompanying the increase of human populations in every continent; these changes have led to disruption of balanced communities of animals and plants in many parts of the world, and consequent loss of soil fertility and other natural resources. Yet a third reason is that, for the first time, the problem of feeding the world is being considered as a single problem: as we shall see in the next chapter, it is now possible to say with some precision what constitutes an optimum diet, and to show that the great majority of people in the world do not get one.

This chapter, then, is devoted to the relations of human populations to their environment, and in particular to the plant and animal communities which are of especial importance to us as farmers. Among these communities of living things is the soil itself, largely inanimate but dependent for its fertility on its living inhabitants. Much of what follows is devoted to problems and difficulties which have arisen from the advances of civilization described in the last chapter.

A Plundered Planet?

The wealthy civilizations, with their dense populations and advanced techniques, are a measure of the success of agriculture in providing a surplus of food beyond the needs of the producers; this success is reflected also in the recent rapid growth of human populations, of which the figures are given in chapter 15. These expanding human communities have displaced previously existing communities of other species. In North America, for instance, when European colonization began, the number of indigenous human beings was of the order of 1m., but there were probably 50m. bison, and vast herds of other large mammals such as elk, deer, caribou, antelope, and moose. All these species now exist in only small numbers, or are on the verge of extinction. It is believed that in Canada alone there were 50m. beavers, and this number was reduced to 1m. before protection was introduced. There has been a similar destruction of large mammals in East and South Africa.

More obviously, increasing human numbers, and the expanding need for more agricultural land, have led to the destruction of forests over vast areas. Britain and Western Europe, for instance, were formerly for the most part forest lands except in the higher mountains, but only relatively small wooded patches now remain.

Changes of this sort are, up to a point, inevitable if large human communities are to exist at all. They can, however, lead to further changes which in the long run make a prosperous agriculture impossible. The most serious of these changes are in the soil. If forests are removed from sloping ground in areas of fairly high rainfall, the soil, deprived of its protective covering, is liable to be washed away down to bare, unproductive rock. This is *water erosion*, and it is going on now in great areas of fertile ground in the Americas, Africa, and Asia. (Soil erosion must be distinguished from the much slower process of rock erosion referred to in the chapter on evolution.) Another form of water erosion takes place in the plains below the despoiled hills: a result of the destruction of forests is to alter the character of the rivers and streams; instead of flowing at a relatively even rate they dry up in the dry season and during the rains become raging torrents which cut deep grooves, or gullies, in the soil of the plains. This is shown in plate 19.

In the dry season, on the other hand, there is drought: the soil dries and becomes powdery, and may be blown

The World's 'Negative' Areas. Deserts – hot or cold, including mountain ranges – are shown black. Some of these areas can, with irrigation, be made fertile, and this is already being done in small regions of North Africa and the Middle East, and a vast region of Central Asia (see plates 22 and 23)

away, as is seen in plate 20. The same result often comes from loss of plant cover due to overgrazing. This is *wind erosion*, and the spectacular effects it sometimes produces have made it famous. Osborn describes 'the shock that came to the people of America in 1934'.

In that year a vast transcontinental dust-laden windstorm, darkening the sun, broadcast the fact that large once-fertile portions of five western states . . . had become a desolate dust bowl. This catastrophe was the result of overgrazing by too large herds of cattle and sheep and of ploughing for crops grasslands that should never have been converted to this use.

H. H. Bennett, another American authority, has said:

In the short life of this country we have essentially destroyed 282m. acres of land, crop, and rangeland. Erosion is destructively active on 775m. additional acres. About 100m. acres of cropland, much of it representing the best cropland we have, is finished in this country. We cannot restore it.

It takes nature from 300 years to 1000 years or more to bring back a single inch of topsoil and we sometimes lose that topsoil as the result of a single rain, if it is an especially heavy torrential type of rain.

The first examples of soil destruction have been taken from North America because that area has been very fully studied, and because there the destruction has been exceptionally rapid. But every other continent has suffered erosion and it is believed that a total of nearly 2000m. acres is affected. Some extinct civilizations seem to have been helped on their way by the disappearance of their agricultural resources. The Maya civilization of Guatemala created deserts by the destruction of forests, just as today the soil of Mexico is being washed into the sea as a result of ill-planned attempts to cultivate land on the steep slopes of the mountains. North Africa was once an area of a dominant civilization, but is now principally desert; this could probably have been prevented with a different system of cultivation. The area between the Tigris and Euphrates was once, in Osborn's words, 'a land suggestive of the Garden of Eden, a rich land whose people lived well, built flourishing cities, established governments and developed the arts'. Its degeneration into desert seems to have been helped by the cutting down of forests, perhaps over-grazing of grassland, finally, the wrecking of the irrigation works which coincided with political collapse.

It is not suggested here that the collapse of these ancient civilizations is to be simply explained by defects in their methods of land management. It might indeed be argued that the errors of the farmers should be attributed to imperfections of economic or political organization, and that these were the significant causes of collapse. Later in this chapter we shall see that the destruction of natural resources today cannot be adequately discussed unless economic, as well as biological, problems are considered. The facts that are fully established are the creation of deserts in once fertile lands by a series of civilized communities, from three thousand years ago up to the present day.

It has been suggested that these calamities have been brought about, not by man's activities, but by climatic influences. It is obvious that climate has played a part, but it is extremely doubtful whether this can anywhere have been a decisive one. Serious soil erosion occurs only where agriculture is practised; it follows that climate can be blamed for it only if there have been climatic changes for the worse since agriculture began. There is little evidence for such changes: olive groves can still be made to flourish in North Africa, in the very places where they were cultivated by the Roman colonists; indeed, a few have survived the past two thousand years. Palestine, extensively eroded, can nevertheless support the same crops as were grown in biblical times, given proper care. In India and China there has been much erosion, but alongside the areas of bare rock are terraced and irrigated lands which have been continuously cultivated for three thousand years. Soil erosion cannot be considered as anything but man-made.

The material destruction of soil is the final result of bad land management, and much damage can be done before erosion itself occurs. In Africa the Sahara is said to be advancing in some areas at the rate of half a mile a year, but this is only one consequence of the mismanagement of the grass-covered savannahs. The great plains of North Africa, potentially fertile and capable of carrying a prosperous agriculture, have a dry season which is sometimes as long as eight months; only a carefully preserved plant cover, either of grasses or larger plants, can prevent severe drying and loss of fertility. Excessive grazing by domestic animals, of which the goat is particularly destructive, is in vast areas eating away the plant cover, and ruining the land. From America Vogt gives another example:

Virgin soils in Ohio, with unimproved seed and no insect control, yielded a hundred bushels of corn per acre, and sixty bushels of wheat. Crops now average forty-two bushels of corn and twenty of wheat. And even this yield per acre in one of the most advanced states in the Union, where there is greatly increased knowledge of disease and pest control, fertilizers and plant breeding, is being maintained with difficulty and at great expense.

The 'Balance of Nature'

Soil erosion and loss of fertility can be regarded as results of the upsetting of a natural balance or equilibrium. Forests or grassy plains can remain stable for very long periods; rivers change their character only through millions of years. If there are grazing animals their numbers may be restricted by predators (such as lions), by the water supply, or by other limiting factors. Soil losses are made good, probably more than made good, by material derived from dead plants and animals.

Agriculture cannot avoid upsetting this balance. The vital necessity is that it should be replaced by another equilibrium, one chosen by man to suit his own ends. This is not only a matter of preserving the soil: it involves also allowing for the activities of many plant and animal species which are indirectly, and often quite unexpectedly, affected by agriculture. The most obvious of these species are the pests, and especially those which attack crops in the fields. By greatly increasing the growth of some plants, particularly cereals, man has created conditions favourable for the rapid multiplication of various fungi, insects, and rodents, many of which had probably been hitherto comparatively rare species.

The most spectacular of the onslaughts on our crops are those due to locusts; there are seven important species, and between them they cover the Americas, Africa, the Near East, central Asia, India, China, Indonesia, and Australia. Unwise cultivation may increase the number of swarming grounds. In the Americas plagues of the related grass-hoppers cause similar damage as well. Other spectacular disasters to field crops are due to field mice: the grain-producing areas of Europe, Asia, and North America are subject to periodic plagues of small rodents which do damage on a scale similar to that of locusts. The third main group of pests are the parasitic fungi: the potato blight swept Europe in the nineteenth century and caused the total loss of the potato crop in Ireland in 1846; in 1870 another fungus, a leaf rust, wiped out the coffee plantations of Ceylon, and the country was saved from ruin only by the establishment of the tea industry. In Central America and the West Indies the Panama disease has come near to causing the complete destruction of banana cultivation.

These dramatic effects of pests and disease organisms are well enough known, and they are of first-rate importance. But a great proportion of the food losses due to pests goes on continuously and unobtrusively: the pests are there all the time, and they take their regular toll which may amount to 10 or 50 per cent of the total. This is especially the case with the losses of stored food. Food may be stored by peasants in a rolled mat, a bamboo cylinder, or a pit in the ground; by farmers in corn rick or barn; by merchants in warehouse or silo: in all these places the concentration of foodstuffs encourages the multiplication of rats and mice, weevils and other insects, mites, and moulds. So universal are these pests that throughout the world farmers and ware-house-keepers often regard their presence as inevitable. World transport has further ensured that, however narrow the original range of a particular species, it has good opportunities of spreading to every country in which suitable conditions exist: the brown spider beetle, as one example, coming probably from Tasmania, has so spread during the past 70 years that it is now found in every grain warehouse in Europe and North America.

These are examples of fairly direct and simple connexions between human activities and changes in animal and plant populations. There are many more complex interactions. In North America agriculture chronically suffers severe losses from small rodents. These pests are preyed on by carnivorous mammals, such as foxes, by birds of prey, and by snakes. All these predators have been systematically persecuted by farmers, and by those who preserve game, who have thus, in all probability, greatly increased the rodent damage.

Sometimes it is not a question of whether to kill or not to kill. Some farming communities favour the careful preservation of hedgerows and small woodlots, others destroy them; a point in favour of their preservation is that they are nesting places for small birds which eat injurious insects.

To continue on these lines would be merely to lengthen the list of examples of natural interactions. The further examples could be taken from the management of fisheries and of whaling; from forestry; from the control of the living population of the soil; and from every other department of land or wildlife management. Man is a part of nature, and to achieve satisfactory control of his environment he has to study the whole nexus of relationships in which he is involved.

Feeding the World

So far in this chapter the emphasis has been on difficulties and problems. But it would be far from true to suggest that the whole history of food production is one of blunders and mismanagement. There are examples even of very primitive groups in which admirable principles of land management have been applied. In New Guinea some of the mountain dwellers, with a neolithic economy, use a system of crop rotation combined with terracing which ensures the preservation of the soil and its fertility; they also use the vegetation for green manure, as they clear ground for planting. In the lowlands the neighbouring peoples use a system of ditching which both drains swamps and provides new, unexhausted soil to spread over the surface. In many parts of Africa the Africans have used crop rotations in which leguminous plants are sown at regular intervals to replenish the nitrogen of the soil. The most important principles of land management, such as irrigation and drainage, terracing, manuring, and plant selection seem to have been developed independently in the Old World and the Americas, some of them before civilization began in either group of continents.

All the great civilizations have depended on a successful and stable agriculture. We have seen that some, such as those of North Africa and the Near East, collapsed and their agriculture with them. But others have continued. Large areas of China have sustained a stable agriculture for thousands of years, by the use of irrigation, terracing to prevent erosion, and extensive manuring (commonly with human excrement) to preserve fertility. There is however considerable erosion both in China and India. In Western Europe on the other hand the plentiful and evenly distributed rainfall, and the relative flatness of much of the ground, have made possible an even more stable system of cultivation; moreover, since Western Europe was the original home of modern science, scientific methods have been extensively applied there, and so the productivity both of arable land and animal stocks is very high.

The problem which now faces the whole of humanity is to develop these existing systems so that every human being is adequately fed. How far short of this they fall today can be only roughly estimated; some of the estimates are given in the next chapter. But there is no doubt that hundreds of millions chronically suffer actual hunger, and even more are malnourished. Moreover the population of the world is increasing at the rate of 20m. a year. The next chapter deals with this problem from the point of view of the needs of human beings as consumers of food. Here we are concerned with production.

The total land surface of the world is 36,000m. acres, but the greater part of this is totally unfit for any form of agriculture at present imagined. The limiting factor is water: the annual rainfall must be at least fifteen inches for cultivation to be possible, and there are difficulties if it is less than eighteen inches; in equatorial lands, with high evaporation, the necessary minimum rises to forty inches. It is estimated that on this basis about one-third of all land could be cultivated. To what extent is this 12,000m. acres actually used by the 1400m. people – two-thirds of humanity – who live on the land?

The answers to this question vary with the method of estimation. It is probable that about ten per cent of all land, or less than one-third of the land that could be used, is in fact cultivated, but that only 4 per cent of all land is used for crops which provide human food:

of total land surface:
    land that could be cultivated = 34 per cent
    land that is cultivated   = 10 per cent
    land used for human food   =   4 per cent

These estimates imply that there remain enormous areas still to be opened up, but they are misleading if they are taken to show that it would be easy, within a few years, greatly to increase the world's cultivated area. Two hundred years ago there were vast fertile plains in the New World, Australia, and elsewhere, waiting to be ploughed and sown with wheat. Today all the easy ground has been occupied (and some of it, as we have seen, plundered). A great deal of what remains is tropical forest.

Characteristics of Earth's Land Area

Despite the difficulties, attempts are already being made to cultivate the tropics. Modern machinery, such as bull-dozers, and the new insecticides, have helped to make such projects feasible. One scheme, which has had a good deal of publicity in Britain, was to clear 3·2m. acres in Tanganyika, Rhodesia, and Kenya and to plant the areas with ground-nuts for the production of edible fat (of which there is a serious world shortage). Under the original plan there was to have been an annual production of 600,000 tons of ground-nuts by 1951, but this estimate proved to be far too optimistic, and the main scheme had eventually to be aban-doned. But the important question is: are schemes of this sort practical, and can they contribute to the world's food within, say, the 1960s? Even if it is true that the authorities initiated the ground-nuts scheme without adequate prepara-tion, we may reflect that governments are more usually attacked for procrastination and lack of initiative than for impetuosity. Some of the difficulties of this East African scheme are however of general significance. It has been proposed, for instance, that as an alternative to ground-nuts in some areas, sunflowers should be grown and oil extracted from their seed. And the question has been raised whether the bees, necessary for the pollination of the sunflowers, will be present in sufficient numbers; this depends on conditions in the surrounding terrain, and these have to be studied by biologists before an answer can be given. Here again we have an example of the necessity for studying the whole living nexus, if an efficient agriculture is to be achieved.

On the general prospect of the use of forest lands a recent report of the Food and Agriculture Organization is optimistic:

Here is virtually a new continent, the unused forest, equal in area to the whole of Asia (excluding the U.S.S.R.), which remains to be explored and used for human benefit. These forests could contribute not only fuel and lumber but also by chemical transformation, pulp, plastics, sugar, ethyl alcohol, yeast, and fodder cellulose. It may be that in time they will provide a large proportion of the world's clothing materials and animal feeding stuffs, thus releasing important areas of cropland for food crops.

When the attempt is made to develop a backward area, or even, perhaps, an advanced one, special problems may arise with the human population. At first sight it might appear that a big productive scheme would be certain to benefit the native inhabitants of the area, but in fact it can do so only if their customs and needs are properly considered. Primitive customs are quite unadapted to modern, large-scale agriculture. It follows that, unless a policy of ruthless exploitation and contempt for native needs and abilities is adopted, all such schemes must include provision for the education and general raising of the living standards of the people.

The need for the planning of an area as a whole, and for ensuring that those taking part do so willingly and with knowledge of its value to themselves, has been recognized in a number of big schemes of land development in advanced countries. Of these the Tennessee Valley Authority is an example of what modern engineering can do to make soil fertile by irrigation, provided that all possible means are used for the development of the area, including education and financial help. Similar schemes have been proposed for the Missouri Valley, for the Jordan River in Palestine, for various Indian rivers, for the Niger River in French West

Africa, and for a number of others. The Amazon Basin is the subject of a United Nations plan.

The biggest scheme of all is the one begun during the 1930s in a vast area of the U.S.S.R. A very large part of the Soviet Union is too cold for ordinary agriculture (which is one reason why so much work has been done there on cold-resistant wheats and other crops); and of the remaining land much is liable to severe drought. The remedy in the dry areas is irrigation, and this is planned on an unprecedented scale. An area the size of Europe, west of the Caspian, until recently desert, is being transformed, not only by irrigation but also by afforestation and the application of every aspect of scientific agriculture, from pest control to the study of the mechanics of soil particles (plates 22, 23).

The Improvement of Agriculture

Although vast schemes of conservation and development are essential, they are not the only means of increasing food production. Throughout the world agricultural methods remain for the most part primitive, and, without increasing the cultivated area or any drastic change of method, production could be greatly raised. The output of food per man in advanced countries is estimated by the Food and Agriculture Organization to be about ten times what it is in the backward lands. The population of the backward areas is nearly three-quarters of the world's total. In Britain the productivity per acre and the output per man are three or four times higher than even the more backward areas of Europe; and on the average about four times as much milk is produced by each cow. Yet even British farming could be improved, since many farms, in which every advantage is taken of technical improvements, have a productivity twice that of the average. Indeed there is good reason to think that improved farming in temperate lands would yield a greater increase of food than could be got from tropical development.

Rising Food Production. Slow but steady rise in wheat yields in U.K. and U.S.A. during recent decades, due to gradual improvement in the standard of husbandry. The increase in maize yields in the U.S. after 1936 was due to the introduction of hybrid maize – a product of applied genetics

The general, all-round raising of the standards of cultivation depends on the systematic improvement of every aspect of farming practice. Improvement is needed, and is practicable, in the plants and animals themselves; in the fertility of the soil; in the control of weeds and of animal and fungal pests; and in the number and design of the machines used.

The milk yields of many herds, even in Western Europe and the U.S.A., can be doubled in two generations by proper breeding; such breeding can be greatly accelerated by the use of artificial insemination, which enables the best bulls to serve at least ten times as many cows as would otherwise be possible. The scope for improvement in the wretched cattle of the backward areas of the East is far greater. Stock can also be bred for cold climates. Recently the cattalo, a hybrid between buffalo and domestic cattle, with some admixture of yak, has been produced to deal with the conditions of parts of Canada in which ordinary cattle fail. The cattalo has a heavy coat; it will eat shrubs or paw through snow to get herbage; and it stores much fat in its body against the winter. It is an excellent source of beef.

Besides the improvement of stock by breeding much can be done by better feeding, for instance by the development of pasture of higher quality. Indeed, breeding and the improvement of stock management must go together, since breeding can be done effectively only if a suitable environment can be provided for the herd. The development of the grasslands themselves also depends partly on genetical methods: in the past it has been usual to regard 'grass' as a natural phenomenon not much amenable to human interference, but today, on the best pastures, it is treated like any other crop: special seed mixtures are used, selected for the particular conditions of soil and climate, with corresponding improvement of the sward and of the livestock that feed on it.

The use of special seed from selected plants is one of the most important means of raising crop production generally. A famous example is hybrid maize. The usual method of preserving a good strain of a plant or animal species is to inbreed among individuals of the strain (as was described in chapter 2) so as to preserve the favourable genetical qualities; but if this is done with maize a loss of yield results. Inbred lines are therefore grown only by seedsmen in breeding stations: to produce the seed for the farmer the inbred lines are crossed, and hybrid seed is distributed for use on the farms, where it gives a high yield. Hybrid maize has made possible yields 25 per cent higher than before, and more than 90 per cent of the maize now sown in the Corn Belt of the United States is hybrid.

Breeding is capable of producing not only improved

varieties, but quite new types with unexpected combinations
of characters. Much has been done on these lines in the
U.S.S.R. (There is a story of some botanists trying to develop
a radish-cabbage hybrid: they succeeded, only to find that
the new plant had the leaves of a radish and the root system
of a cabbage. Fortunately, further effort gave the desired result.) The most remarkable of the new hybrids is perennial
wheat, a result of crossing wheat with wild couch grass.
One variety, known as 34085, is drought-resistant, fungus-
resistant, and has an exceptionally high gluten content. It
is not cold-resistant, but can be grown in the southern areas
of the U.S.S.R. where wind erosion is serious and the protection of a perennial covering for the soil is most needed.
It is reported to give at least two crops a year, and of course
does not require annual sowing.

A better known example of the possibilities of plant breeding, already mentioned in chapter 2, is the production of
highly productive wheats which are also resistant to the
fungus disease called stem rust, which is exceedingly destructive in North America.

Much more of this sort of work remains to be done:
research on rice, which is the staple food of at least one third
of mankind, is far behind that on the wheats and on maize,
though what has been done has given valuable results in
India, where experimental farms have a productivity twice
that of the average. Research on millet, another important
staple of the East, has hardly begun.

If we turn to the improvement of the soil we find a similar
picture of much valuable knowledge imperfectly applied,
combined with the need for yet more knowledge. The importance of fertilizers and manures is very well known:
nearly every gardener uses both inorganic fertilizers and
manure derived from a compost heap (which may have
been chemically treated) or possibly from the leavings of
horses in the street outside. Primitive systems of cultivation,
as we have seen, relied on human and animal manure, and
on plant residues, to replenish essential elements taken from
the soil by their crops. We must still do the same, and on a

larger scale; the sewage from the great cities is a valuable source of manure, and far too little is returned to the fields: it has been referred to as a river of valuable elements awaiting recovery. But we can also supplement the organic manures with synthetic nitrogenous substances: it has been estimated that in Britain the addition of one hundredweight of ammonium sulphate to each acre of average arable land can increase the yield of wheat by nearly two-and-a-half hundredweight. To get the best results potassium and phosphate must be added as well. In advanced countries such practices are commonplace, but over the greater part of the world they remain almost unused. The quality as well as the quantity of plants can be improved by synthetic nitrogenous fertilizers. For instance, the protein content of grass can be doubled, with corresponding benefit to the livestock that feed on it.

Recently, there have been important refinements in our knowledge of soil chemistry. In large areas of Australia a serious condition of livestock, called pining disease, was found to be due to a mineral deficiency of the soil which affected the plants of the pasture and through them the grazing animals. The element that was deficient was not any of those well known to be important, such as nitrogen, phosphorus, or potassium, but a comparatively rare one, cobalt. Since then similar phenomena, involving several elements besides cobalt, have been found in many parts of the world; even in Britain cobalt deficiency has been found in the words of one writer, 'from as far south as Bodmin Moor in Cornwall, to as far north as Ross-shire in Scotland. Few things are more spectacular than the recovery to full health of "pining" animals after a trace of cobalt has been provided'.

We are, however, only at the beginning of a systematic knowledge of the effects of soil chemistry and physics on plant growth. We still do not know why some plants ('lime lovers') can grow only on alkaline soil, while others must have acid soil. Even the significance of humus for plant growth is controversial. Interesting research is now in progress, on the use of soil improvers – substances which increase the water-holding powers of the soil and so enable the soil to support more plant growth. If these materials prove effective, they may both increase yields in fertile lands, and contribute to the reclamation of deserts.

Care of the soil requires more than attention to its chemistry. *Irrigation* may be needed to prevent excessive dryness and consequent loss of fertility and eventual wind erosion. Irrigation is indeed one of the oldest means of preserving soil fertility. The Nile valley is probably the oldest irrigated area in the world, but in the last half-century it has nevertheless been extensively developed, and the system changed from basin irrigation, or one-crop agriculture based on the annual flooding, to perennial irrigation which allows the growing of several crops a year. For some months in each year no Nile water enters the sea direct: the sea receives only water that has been pumped from the main drains after passage through the irrigated soil. India, with 70m. acres, has the largest irrigated area of any country, three times the area in the United States. There is nevertheless need for much more irrigation in India, and still more elsewhere, and the great river valley plans are largely based on schemes of irrigation.

Erosion is controlled also by preventing loss of plant cover due to overgrazing, by the planting of woods and forests to act as wind breaks, and by special techniques such as ploughing along the contours of hills to prevent a too rapid drainage of water down the slopes. Even beavers have been pressed into service in North America: in areas where water erosion was serious small numbers of beavers have been introduced and allowed to build dams. In one area, where water erosion and flooding were causing loss of orchard trees, twelve beavers were released; two years later sixty new dams had been built and the flooding greatly reduced. Beavers have been used also to conserve water for irrigation.

The various methods of soil conservation are capable of bringing dramatic improvement in regions where bad management has not gone too far. It is now reported, for instance, that even in the notorious dust bowl of North America agricultural production is higher than ever before.

The very fertility of cultivated soils, however, gives rise to special problems: having made soil fertile we inevitably encourage the growth of unwanted species as well as crop plants. But weed control has recently made great strides: it has been found that substances, sometimes called plant growth hormones, which in some conditions can be used to stimulate the growth of parts of plants, can also be used as selective weed-killers; by destroying the unwanted species, but leaving the crop plant unharmed, they can double the yield per acre on some agricultural land.

We have already seen that, just as fertile ground attracts weeds, so does the accumulation of food on cultivated land and in stores attract animal and fungal pests. Here again we are not obliged to resign ourselves to extensive losses: much has been done to enable us to prevent them. The detailed study of the way of life of particular pests has in many instances made possible their large scale destruction. Locusts have for thousands of years made their inexplicable and unpredicted descents on cultivated land, leaving starvation behind them. Only since the first world war has it been found that, when they are not swarming, locusts live as harmless grasshoppers of different appearance from that of the swarming phase. Swarms develop only in certain limited outbreak areas, and are induced partly by climatic influences, some of which are known. It is now possible to predict outbreaks of the red and the migratory locusts, in Africa, before they occur, and by the use of new insecticides, such as gammexane, the swarms can be intercepted and destroyed before they do any harm. In the early 1930s swarms from a single outbreak area near the Middle Niger swept over nearly the whole of Africa, and did enormous damage. During the 1940s similar outbreaks threatened; but by that time a control organization existed, and for the first time in history Africa survived a period of locust attack without serious loss. Much remains to be done: the desert locust, whose outbreak areas are in inaccessible desert areas of the Middle

East, is still a grave menace to large areas of Asia and Africa, and is swarming as these lines are being written. But the fundamental knowledge needed for control is now available.

The example of locust control is one of many. Although there are serious pests which we are still quite unable to control, and much more research will have to be done, for many species the deficiency is not so much in knowledge as in application: there is, for instance, no locust control organization in South America comparable to that in Africa.

Agriculture and Society

The facts of this chapter show that man's relationship with his environment, and especially with the food-producing part of it, is continually changing. Some of the changes are for the worse, but we have the knowledge to prevent them; the scope of possible change for the better is incalculably great. It follows that calculations, such as those which pur-

Population and Food in War-time. Estimates of world population showed a continuing slow rise during the second world war, while food production declined. The post-war recovery could be made far steeper if greater effort were diverted to scientific farming

port to deduce the amount of arable land per head necessary for a satisfactory standard of living, can have little
validity. There is one much quoted statement, based on
North American practice, that the area needed is 2·5 acres
to each person; the actual amount of arable land in the
world has been variously estimated at from just over one, to
nearly two, acres per head. But since climate, crops, land,
and farming methods vary enormously from time to time,
from country to country, and even from farm to farm, such
statements have little real significance.

These calculations will have even less point if completely
new methods of food production are introduced on a large
scale. It has long been possible to produce sugar from wood
shavings by a method known as the Bergius process; other
foodstuffs, including protein, could be made from coal; the
cost is very high, though it is likely that it could be reduced
with further research. Another possible source of food is the
microscopic plants – the green algae – of sea or freshwater:
the plants might be grown in shallow coastal basins with
plenty of sun; another method, already successfully tried,
would be to grow them in sewage. This method could yield
far higher quantities of foodstuff per acre than any conventional agriculture. By controlling the conditions in
which they grow it is possible to influence the food substances manufactured by the plants: in some conditions certain species can produce a very high fat content; in others,
large amounts of protein are produced. The final product
might be used for animal feeding stuffs, and so release arable
land for the growing of bread grains; fats might be used
even for human food. The capital outlay required for an
economically worthwhile installation might be very great;
but not greater than that needed for the production of
atomic bombs.

The importance of these novel suggestions is that they
illustrate the unlimited possibilities of technical advance.
Given a practical problem, however vast, we are quite justified in turning confidently to the methods of science to solve
it. As we shall see repeatedly in the next three chapters the

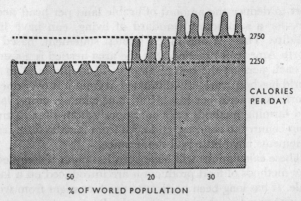

2750

2250

CALORIES
PER DAY

50   20   30

% OF WORLD POPULATION

Starvation. The relative numbers of people in the world at different
levels of calory intake, according to F.A.O. Only the one-third (approximately) above 2750 have enough to eat

most formidable obstacles often arise only when the main
technical difficulties have been overcome, and when the
application of the new knowledge becomes a task for the
whole community.

For scientific knowledge to be applied fully it is not
enough to have a few scientists, however well endowed with
money and ability, working on the problems. Large organizations have to be created, staffed in part by technically trained men and women, who can transmit the results
of research to the public in general, or to particular sections
such as the farming community. Nor is the relationship a
simple one of the scientists telling the technicians, and the
technicians telling the public. The flow of ideas is in both
directions. Laboratory research is essential, but a great part
of scientific agriculture has to be worked out in the fields or
milking sheds themselves. If it is to be done on an adequate
scale the farmer must not only be ready to accept sound
methods when they have been worked out: he must be
prepared to make an actual contribution, by recording the
results of applying new methods or by taking part himself
in large-scale experiments.

Organizations for large-scale research and application are most successful when they operate as part of a general economic advance. A report of the Food and Agriculture Organization has said:

The over-all objective is to raise real incomes, for otherwise the consumption goals cannot be realized. A given level of food consumption is a direct function of a certain level of income. Although studies in this direction are in their infancy it can be roughly estimated that an increase of 40 per cent in per caput food expenditure in a low-income country would normally be associated with an increase of 40 to 50 per cent in real income. . . . There is here a job of economic engineering – to increase real income per person in the low income countries by at least 50 per cent in a short period of time and, in doing so, to maintain a balance between industry and agriculture appropriate to the country in question.

It is however not enough for action to be taken on a national scale. Mankind can be adequately fed only if the problem is faced as a single one for the whole world. The existence of F.A.O. reflects the understanding of this fact. Before the second world war, among the absurdities of world economic disorganization was the fact of mass starvation and malnutrition side by side with the deliberate destruction of food, such as wheat and oranges, in producing countries: the food destroyed could not be sold at a profit, and so it was considered by the producers better to let piles of oranges rot, under the eye of an armed guard, rather than to distribute them to those who needed them. That is what happened in times of glut. In a bad year even those who could afford to pay might be unable to get the food they wanted. In a unified world economy a surplus of wheat would be stored against a bad year; surplus oranges would be canned, probably as juice. Similar treatment would be given to other surpluses. Much new organization and equipment would be required, perhaps on an even larger scale than that created during the war for military purposes. Up to the present however the pressure for a rational economy has failed to prevent complaints in North America of 'over-production' of food. By 1949 plans for restricting the wheat harvest were once again being put forward. In 1950 it was reported that the U.S. Government was destroying potatoes, and feeding millions of dollars' worth of raisins to pigs. There were vast accumulations of dried eggs (of which some was used as fertilizer for arable land), of butter, and other foods. As this book goes to press, in 1954, the United Nations again reports unsaleable surpluses of cereals, dairy produce, and much else.

Malthus Today

In some people the world's food problem has induced a profound pessimism. Since the second world war, apparently authoritative predictions of disaster have been made, based on increases of population and a declining or stationary food production. The history of such predictions is a long one, beginning with the *Essay on the Principle of Population* first published by Malthus in 1798. The core of the Malthusian view, in Malthus' own words, is that 'the power of population is indefinitely greater than the power in the earth to produce subsistence for man'. According to Malthus, where food is abundant men multiply rapidly until their numbers outrun the food supply; where food is already scarce, populations grow little, or not at all. These statements, as we have seen, can sometimes be applied to animal populations in nature; the question is, to what extent do they apply to man? During the nineteenth century, at least in the Western world, they seemed to have no application: the increase in the world's agricultural land and the improvement of agricultural techniques outstripped population growth. Nevertheless in 1898, at a famous meeting of the British Association, the president, Sir William Crookes, pointed to the exhaustion of easily cultivated lands which remained to be opened up, and predicted famine if yields were not increased. Unlike Malthus, however, Crookes suggested a way out: his solution was a vast increase in the use of nitrogenous fertilizers. This increase was in fact achieved, with valuable results for many crops, though it did not make much contribution to raising the yield of wheat.

We have already seen what scope there is for increasing food production, by both conventional and unconventional methods. There are many facts of recent history, overlooked by prophets of doom, which tell a very different story from the neo-Malthusian one. Sugar production in Java is an example. In the period 1910–30 productivity per hectare doubled, as a result of improved strains and methods of cultivation. During this period the human population increased by only 30 per cent. This dramatic success for scientific agriculture so alarmed the producers, that an international agreement was made to restrict sugar production.

It is sometimes said that, whatever effort is put into food production, the 'law of diminishing returns' will eventually operate, and further improvement will become impossible. This argument rests on a misunderstanding: the law of diminishing returns, as applied to agriculture, states that returns per head in a densely populated agricultural country will be less than those in a less densely populated country (other things being equal) *if additional capital or improved farming methods cannot be used*. In practice, however, more capital or improved methods are continually being introduced. In these conditions, the law of *increasing* returns operates. This law, which is rarely, if ever, mentioned by the neo-Malthusians, states that in a modern industrial community the denser the population, and the larger the scale on which production is carried out, the greater the resulting economies. Indeed, modern industry, on which modern agriculture depends for its machines, its fertilizers, and much else, is wholly dependent on a relatively dense population.

To this it may be added that the population, for efficiency as well as happiness, must be healthy. Some pessimists have expressed the remarkable view that the endemic diseases of undeveloped lands – malaria, hookworm, and the rest – should be encouraged, or at least should not be treated since they help to keep human numbers down. But these diseases, most of them chronic infections, also help to lower productivity. Recently, in an area of eastern Bengal, only one season's work on a scheme of malaria control is reported to have increased the rice yield of the area by 15 per cent.

It is sometimes argued that, however true it may be that food supplies can be increased, yet population will nevertheless always outstrip them. This, of course, is what Malthus himself asserted. Yet in the past hundred years the effects of increased production in highly developed countries have been the exact opposite of those predicted by Malthus and his followers. As we shall see in more detail in chapter 15, instead of a rise in fertility and an ascending population growth curve, there has been a dramatic fall in the birth rate and the attainment of almost stationary populations in many countries. In the 1930s it was fashionable to express alarm about the 'sterility' of Western nations and the grim prospect of a declining and ageing population. It seems to be a general rule that improved living standards are accompanied by a decline in births.

This does not signify that there is no problem. It is true that human numbers are increasing; it is true that many people have too little to eat; it is true that both food production and food distribution are inadequate and badly organized. But there is no need for these facts to evoke a surrender to despair. The pessimists generally attribute the actual difficulties of the present, and the assumed difficulties of the future, wholly to uncontrollable 'natural laws' or tendencies. In one respect, however, they underestimate the obstacles. The obstacles they ignore or gloss over are those made by man. If new means of making food are devised, it may be asked whether they will be used: perhaps they will be resisted by farmers anxious to keep up prices; or they may be deemed secrets of military importance, and suppressed. There are plenty of motives for slowing production: it is not the limitations of science which lead to the hoarding of food in an underfed world, or to agreements to restrict output.

It has been suggested, indeed, that the principal motives

for Malthusian propaganda are selfish ones. If it can be 'proved' that it is impossible for the peoples of undeveloped lands to achieve the standards of the West, then it is justifiable to continue to exploit them as before; thus Malthusian ideas become allied to racism. Certainly, the notion of the Chinese or the Indians becoming highly industrialized, and competing for export markets, horrifies some business men, however much such a development would increase the total wealth in the world.

It is obvious however that not all the adherents of Malthusian pessimism are actuated directly by conscious self-interest. Many of those who cling to this attitude seem to be influenced by a profound and irrational will to believe the worst – a feeling no doubt engendered by the depressing features of contemporary affairs. That there is a compulsion to insist on a gloomy future is shown by the frequent linking of Malthusian ideas with predictions of 'declining intelligence' in Britain, the United States and elsewhere. We have seen in chapter 9 how questionable this notion is. But some people continue to propagate it.

Today, faced with formidable difficulties, both biological and economic, we can adopt one of two attitudes. We can conclude that there is nothing to look forward to but widespread famine and tens of millions of deaths from starvation and disease, and that the Malthusian dilemma of limited food and unchecked reproduction is insoluble in the foreseeable future; or we can admit the difficulties, agree that famine threatens in many parts of the world (as it has threatened for the past seven thousand years), yet nevertheless deny that this state of affairs need continue: the technical difficulties can be overcome; the economic system can be changed.

Unmitigated gloom is rarely found among those who are actually trying to produce more food. We have seen something of the biological advances already achieved, or possible. Of equal importance are the advances in social and economic organization. The great schemes of land development and conservation, described earlier, demand unified planning and administration which can be done only by governments. A fully mechanized agriculture, making use of every means to raise production, is impossible in a system of peasant farming, with small farms worked, as a rule, by primitive means under a heavy burden of debt.

It is a commonplace that we are living in a period of drastic and rapid social change. This fact is reflected in the contemporary transformation of world agriculture, from a system largely of small-scale peasant farming with primitive methods, to one of communal farming in which full use is made of scientific knowledge. What Sir John Russell has called 'the shrill sensationalism of some of the pessimistic writers' is a product of emphasizing only one feature of the contemporary scene. We must accept that feeding the world adequately presents great difficulties, which can be overcome, on the most optimistic estimate, only after decades of effort. Nevertheless the effort has already begun; existing biological and economic knowledge can take us a great distance if it is applied, and it can be rapidly increased. To the extent that we fail, the failure will be a social and political one, and not a consequence of something inherent in nature and unalterable.

13

FOOD AND NUTRITION

If every just man that now pines with want
Had but a moderate and beseeming share
Of that which lewdly-pampered Luxury
Now heaps upon some few with vast excess,
Natures full blessings would be well dispenc't
In unsuperfluous eeven proportion,
And she no whit encumber'd with her store.

JOHN MILTON

ONE of the scientific triumphs of the twentieth century has been the growth of our knowledge of nutrition. It is this knowledge which made it possible, in the preceding chapter, to write of 'adequate' and 'inadequate' diets. Although much important detail remains to be learnt, it is already possible for a well-advised government to have a national food policy with a scientific basis, or for a well-informed housewife to plan her family's meals scientifically.

The Question of Quantity

The first problem to be solved is the total quantity of food required. A normal person needs no telling whether he is eating enough: hunger is the guide. There is some individual variation, especially in relation to weight, but on the whole the amount needed depends on the type and quantity of the work done. In this respect our bodies can quite legitimately be compared with a railway locomotive burning coal, or an automobile petrol, in proportion to distance travelled or to speed. The energy value of food is measured in Calories. (A Calorie is the amount of heat needed to raise one kilogram of water from 15 to 16° C.) An adult of average weight lying in bed, and taking no exercise at all, needs about 1700 Calories a day to prevent loss of weight. This is the basic quantity needed to keep us going at the lowest level of activity. An hour's light work, such as typing or sewing, adds about 75 Calories to the basic need. An hour's house-work or slow walking may add between 75 and 150. A man like a coal-miner, doing very hard physical work, requires 300 Calories or more for each hour, and in times of shortage men doing heavy work may receive extra rations of such foods as bread and cheese.

Chemically there are three types of foodstuff that supply us with energy. (A fourth, ethyl alcohol, contained in wine, has been reckoned to provide Frenchmen and Italians each with an average of about 100 Calories a day, but most nations are less fortunate.) First there are the *carbohydrates*, of which the most important are starch (the main con-stituent of cereals and potatoes), and sugar. In practice, whether most people have enough to eat depends on whether they have enough starch. Wheat, rye, and rice (the first two largely in the form of bread) supply, in an average year, enough Calories for more than half the population of the world. Barley, maize, oats, and millet are also eaten in large amounts.

The second type of foodstuff, *protein*, provides, weight for weight, roughly as much energy as carbohydrate. But it is much less important for most people as a source of energy. The main sources of animal protein are meat, fish, cheese, and eggs; milk too is important. Plant protein is eaten main-ly in pulses and whole cereals. An adult can do with very little protein indeed, but he can, if necessary, manage on a diet of which almost all the solid is protein: this is what men who depend on hunting have to do. We need, too, very little of the third main type of fodstuff, the *fats*, provided we have plenty of palatable carbohydrate. Fat however pro-vides about twice as much energy per pound as protein or carbohydrate and is therefore a more concentrated form of energy food. Today, in 1954, there is a world shortage of fats. Apart from the fact that this is one aspect of the general shortage of food, fat shortage affects us in two important ways: first, it may reduce our intake of the fat-soluble vitamins, A and D, which we discuss below; second, it makes it more difficult to prepare palatable meals. The traditional sources of fat in the West are butter and cheese, and meat, but vegetable fats are becoming more important. They have long been in general use in, for instance, large parts of India.

Carbohydrate, fat, and protein are needed, not only as energy-givers, but for the growth and maintenance of the body tissues. In this respect protein is of especial importance. It is possible for children to suffer protein deficiency where there is no over-all food shortage. The term 'protein deficiency' is, however, imprecise. There are many proteins and each has a different chemical composition and so a different nutritive value. It has, therefore, become customary to distinguish 'second-class' plant protein from 'first-class' animal protein. This is a very crude classification: some animal proteins, notably gelatin, hardly deserve to be called first-class on any scheme; and the value of plant proteins – which we get mainly from whole wheat, peas, beans, and lentils – depends partly on what other protein is being eaten. There are two important practical points. First, growing children, and pregnant and nursing mothers, have a special need for protein, and so should have first call on proteinous foods of animal origin: milk, meat and fish, cheese and eggs. (Men doing heavy work have no special, physiological need for protein. They may however be dissatisfied with meatless meals in a country such as England, with a long tradition of a heavy consumption of beef, mutton, and pork or bacon. Moreover, meat contains substances which stimulate appetite, and so increase the amount of food eaten. The justification for extra cheese for heavy workers is that it provides, owing to its high fat content, a considerable amount of energy in a form easily put in a sandwich.) Second, if children and mothers throughout the world are to have adequate diets there must be an enormous increase in milk production. Milk, as everyone knows, is the

most complete of all single foods, and it is an excellent
source of protein of high nutritive value.

'Minerals' and Vitamins

There are certain other obvious dietary necessities. Bones and
teeth are made largely of calcium phosphate, and so calcium and phosphorus are both required. Milk and cheese
are excellent sources of both. In Britain today the most widespread nutritional deficiency is of calcium. Iron is another
chemical element easily identifiable in the body, and particularly in the blood: lack of it causes one type of anaemia.
Infants and young women are especially liable to be short
of it, and after calcium it is the dietary component of which
we are most likely to be deficient. Meat, fruit, vegetables,
and whole flour are important sources. Iodine, as we saw
in chapter 2, is also an essential element. Even sodium
chloride, the common salt of our tables, is a serious problem
in many countries, particularly in the tropics where the heat
causes much salt loss in sweat. In the past it has been an
expensive (and heavily taxed) commodity even in Western
Europe.

Carbohydrates, fats, and proteins, the 'minerals' mentioned in the last paragraph and water: these are obvious
necessities. However, if a diet consisting only of these
materials in a pure form is given to animals such as young
mice, the animals stop growing, sicken and die. On the
other hand if a small amount of milk is added the animals
survive and grow. Milk makes this difference because it
contains several further substances which are essential for
life: these, the *vitamins*, are present, and are needed, only
in very small amounts.

The table on page 244 lists the most important vitamins,
the effects of deficiencies, and the principal foods in which
the vitamins occur. Most large human populations show a
high incidence of serious vitamin deficiency diseases. In some
of the densely populated areas of Asia beri-beri is common
because the principal food is rice without the husk: this

The Main Types of Foodstuff

NEEDED IN LARGE AMOUNTS **USED AS FUEL**		
	MAIN SOURCES	SPECIAL FUNCTION IN BODY
PROTEIN	Meat, fish, eggs, milk, cheese ; peas, beans, lentils, wheat	Especially important in growth ; also a source of energy
CARBOHYDRATE	Cereals and cereal products ; sugar ; potatoes	Main source of energy for most of world's population
FAT	Meat, butter, cheese, margarine	Twice the fuel value per unit weight of carbohydrate or protein ; contains fat-soluble vitamins
'MINERALS': NEEDED IN SMALLER AMOUNTS		
CALCIUM PHOSPHORUS (as phosphate)	Milk, cheese	Make up a large part of the constituents of bone and teeth
IRON	Vegetables, fruit, whole wheat	Contained in haemo-globin (the red pigment of blood)
IODINE	Most foods	Contained in the thyroid hormone

All these elements are found in every cell of the body, as well as in the tissues mentioned

The Main Types of Foodstuff – continued

VITAMINS: NEEDED IN VERY SMALL AMOUNTS			
	MAIN SOURCES	GROSS LACK CAUSES:	MINOR LACK CAUSES:
A	Fish-liver; milk, butter, eggs; green vegetables	Keratomalacia; xerophthalmia	Night-blindness (one kind); less growth in young
D	Fish-liver; milk, butter, eggs; (sun on skin)	Rickets (children); osteo-malacia (adults)	Inadequate bone growth
B_1 (THIAMIN)	Whole wheat; wheat germ; meat; eggs; yeast	Beri-beri	Nervous disorder; fatigue
RIBOFLAVIN	As B_1	Degeneration of cornea of eye	Inflammation of lips and mouth
NICOTINIC ACID	As B_1	Pellagra	Nutritional diarrhoea
C (ASCORBIC ACID)	Citrous fruits, tomatoes; other fresh fruit and vegetables	Scurvy	Anaemia; slow healing of wounds

There are other vitamins, most of them of less practical importance.

supplies starch without B vitamins, and beri-beri is due mainly to extreme vitamin B_1 deficiency. In beri-beri the heart is affected, there are muscular spasms and weakness, and unless suitable food is given death results. Another disease with a high incidence in India is xerophthalmia, due to vitamin A deficiency; the eyes are affected, and the disease is a common cause of blindness; it is often fatal. A third disease, pellagra, is common in the south of the U.S.A., especially among the Negroes, and in south-eastern Europe. It is due to lack of another of the B vitamins. The skin becomes scaly and sores develop; once again, it may be fatal.

The two other outstanding deficiency diseases, scurvy (vitamin C deficiency), and rickets (vitamin D deficiency), are more likely to occur in northern climates. Vitamin C is found particularly in certain fruits, notably oranges and lemons, and in fresh vegetables. Scurvy has in the past been common in western European towns in late winter. It is fatal in extreme cases, notably among infants. At one time it was called 'the London disease'. England, indeed, in spite of its thriving agriculture, has a bad reputation for deficiency conditions. Rickets used to be called 'the English disease', and certainly until well after the first world war gross rickets was widespread among the children of workers in the large towns. Today the value of fish liver oils has become known to almost everyone, and serious rickets is uncommon, though some degree of calcium deficiency is still general among our children. It is rarer in sunnier climates because vitamin D is formed in the skin by the action of sunlight.

A result of the knowledge of vitamins acquired during the twentieth century has been to increase the demand for certain foods. Fruits that supply vitamin C have entered more and more into world trade, and their production has increased. The other important water-soluble vitamins, those of the B group, occur particularly in whole wheat, whole rice, oatmeal and potatoes, and emphasis has come to be placed more on these than on the more purified forms of carbohydrate such as white flour and sugar. This is of especial importance because the amount of B vitamins required varies with the amount of carbohydrate eaten. As for the fat soluble vitamins, vitamin A (or a substance that becomes vitamin A in the body) is fairly easily obtained from green vegetables and from carrots, although this has not prevented a good deal of mild vitamin A deficiency among the poor in England. And both A and D are found in liver, the fat of meat, fat fish such as herrings, eggs, and butter. They are also now added in small quantities to margarine in the United Kingdom.

Beyond all these foods in importance is milk. Every essential nutrient, with the possible exception of vitamin C, is found in useful amounts in cows' milk, and anybody over the age of a few months can digest it.

What People Eat

In the period between the wars much discussion about food dealt with vitamins and perhaps minerals, and the general need for improving the *quality* of diets. In the next section we shall see the reason for this. But today, as we have seen, the Food and Agriculture Organization of the United Nations is primarily concerned with the quantity of food in the world. This problem is not a new one: it is not only a result of war followed by world-wide drought. In the 1930s Europe, with a population just over one-third that of Asia, consumed appreciably more cereals and more than six times as much meat as the whole of the peoples of Asia. This is a measure of the inadequacy of the food available to more than half the world's population living in Asia. If similar figures were available for dairy products there is no doubt that the disparity would be found to be even greater. Yet, as we shall see, diet even in some of the better-fed European countries was grossly deficient for large sections of the population.

Let us consider the position in the 1930s in some of the main countries. The areas of greatest deficiency, according to a report by F.A.O., were Central America and most of Asia. But parts of South America and of Africa, on which there is less information, were probably as bad. Some useful dietary surveys have been carried out in *India*. (In this book 'India' is a geographical expression, and includes Pakistan.) For the majority of the population rice is the staple food, though some eat other cereals as well, and in the north, notably the Punjab, wheat and millet are eaten. On the whole the rice eaters had little or no fresh fruit or green vegetables; about 50 per cent of families had milk, but usually only in very small amounts; few ate meat, and little

Nutrition by Nations. Only the inhabitants of the areas shown black have, on the whole, enough to eat (though the diet of the poor in these lands may be deficient in vitamins and salts). Nutrition in China is, however, rapidly improving of that. So the energy value of the food was inadequate, and animal protein was very low. We have already seen that there is a marked incidence of gross vitamin deficiency diseases. The complaint was sometimes made by Europeans that 'the natives' are idle and bad workers. The food position was part of the explanation; the next chapter gives another part. In 1933 the Director-General of the Indian Medical Service estimated that 40 per cent of Indian villages had populations too high for the existing food supply. Even when the weather is favourable periods of scarcity are reckoned to occur for 20 per cent of villages in every ten years; but if the rains fail, there is famine. It is reckoned that India needs 50 per cent more food than is now (1949) available, to feed its present population adequately. The experiments already described illustrate the effect that a better diet can have on the health and physique of Indians.

On *China* we have less information, but what there is suggests a situation similar to that in India. Again there was little consumption of meat or of dairy products. There was much severe deficiency of the B vitamins and of vitamin A. The famines of China are as notorious as those of India and may well have killed more people (100m. has been suggested) during the past hundred years; but China has until now lacked a government capable of collecting accurate figures about them. Today the situation is changing rapidly, and China is beginning to be able to export certain foodstuffs.

Absence of statistics cannot be complained of if we turn to the British colonies in *Africa*. An extensive survey, published by the Colonial Office in 1938, showed that in these vast areas too the majority of the people suffer near-starvation on diets of poor quality. The Africans for the most part in the past had effective forms of agriculture or stock-raising, together with appropriate tribal customs, which varied a great deal from place to place. Much of this social organization has been overthrown, and the Africans in many areas have been obliged by economic pressure to leave villages to the women and children and to work for the Europeans in plantations, mines, and other establishments. The primitive agriculture has consequently been disrupted, but nothing satisfactory has replaced it.

So far we have considered colonial or semi-colonial peoples. But even in the agricultural lands of *south-eastern Europe*, in Rumania, Bulgaria, Yugoslavia, and Hungary, diets were very bad, especially in winter. In Hungary even the energy-value of the peasants' food seems to have been deficient.

Diet in the West

It might be expected that, while the industrially backward countries had underfed populations, the relatively rich countries of the west would have no difficulty in getting an adequate supply of good food. An examination of the situation in England and the United States shows that this was far from true.

Until the beginning of the nineteenth century the problem in England was to produce enough food. Most people grew their own, and if the harvest was good all was well. This had been the position for centuries among the peasantry. Chaucer's widow in the *Nonnes Preestes Tale* did not have much variety:

> No winne dranke she, neyther white ne red:
> Hire bord was served most with white and black.
> Milk and broun bread, in which she found no lack,
> Seinde bacon, and sometime an ey or twey.

But a diet based on milk, rye or wholemeal bread, bacon, and eggs is not likely to lead to serious deficiency, except perhaps of vitamin C. Little sugar was eaten, but there was a good supply of vegetables, at least in summer. A bad aspect of this state of affairs was that it led to occasional famines when crops failed.

Industrialism led to a great change. The industrialists wanted cheap food for the working people in the towns, since without it they could not get hands for the factories. The landowners, on whose estates food was produced,

Starvation and Malnutrition. Food in four countries before the second world war. A comparison of two wealthy, food-producing countries with two poor ones

wanted food prices kept up. At the beginning of the nine-teenth century there was a duty on imported wheat, and the 4-lb. loaf cost fourteen pence. Wages were one or two shillings a day. In 1846 the factory workers and industrialists achieved the repeal of the Corn Laws: the import duty came off, and by 1900 the 4-lb. loaf cost sixpence. During the nineteenth century, as we shall see in chapter 15, the popu-lation of England and Wales doubled, and from being agricultural became predominantly urban and industrial, living largely on cheap imported cereal foods, sugar, and potatoes. Wheat was eaten mainly as white flour, and the annual consumption of sugar rose from a few pounds per head to nearly one hundredweight. Agriculture declined and the consumption of dairy products, vegetables, fruit, and oatmeal fell. Rickets and scurvy became common. At the beginning of the century the minimum recruiting height for the army was 5 feet 6 inches; by the end it had had to be reduced to 5 feet. It was the high proportion of recruits rejected as unfit for service in the Boer war, at the turn of the century, that eventually led to the introduction of school meals.

But it was not until the 1930s that knowledge of nutrition made possible the setting up of dietary standards. Given a standard it then became possible, by investigation of the diets of large numbers of families, to determine the extent and character of the still prevailing malnutrition. It must be admitted that standards vary, and that there is even now no final agreement on the necessary amounts of certain essentials: we know that nobody can do without vitamin C, for instance, but we cannot lay down precisely, with reasonable certainty, the minimum any person, or even any class of persons, must have in order to avoid all ill effects. It is easy to see the effects of gross deficiencies, but far from easy to relate less obvious symptoms, such as an apparently excessive susceptibility to some infections, to shortage of a particular vitamin. One difficulty is that individuals almost certainly vary genetically in their vitamin needs. Tooth decay is unquestionably influenced by diet; but one child may have excellent teeth, while another on the same diet may have extensive decay. And complexities do not end there. In one investigation it was found impossible to induce certain volunteers to show signs of vitamin B_1 deficiency: although deprived of the vitamin they continued to excrete it in their urine, and it seemed that they were synthesizing it in their bodies. Further experiments gave the explanation. A drug was fed to them in sufficient amounts to kill most of

VI

V

IV

III

II

I

FRUIT   MILK   EGGS   MEAT

Food and Income. Estimates of weekly consumption of certain nutritionally important (and expensive) foods from Orr's survey of nutrition
in England in 1935. They illustrate the relationship between income and
nutrition, and help to account for the lower average height and inferior
physique of the children of the poor. Group I is the poorest 10 per cent,
group VI the richest 10 per cent; each other group represents 20 per cent
of the population

the bacteria in their intestines. (Our intestines always contain harmless bacteria.) When this had been done the
excretion of B_1 stopped; it was the bacteria which had been
producing it. Thus our liability to vitamin B_1 deficiency
depends in part on the bacteria we harbour.

Despite these difficulties nutrition surveys have given
valuable information. Those carried out before the war
illustrate the state of nutrition attained in a period of relative stability. The relationship between income and nutritional level was clearly shown in Orr's famous report *Food,
Health and Income*, published in 1935. The diagram above
shows that, on the standard chosen, the food of at least half
of the population of England and Wales was seriously deficient. The malnourished 50 per cent belonged to the lower
income groups, and since the poorer people had, on the
average, larger families than those better off, it was reckoned
that about 75 per cent of the children of England and
Wales were inadequately fed. Later surveys confirmed Orr's
general findings. Within each income group there is wide

variation from the average: some individuals or families do very much better, and others correspondingly worse. This individual variation has been very clearly shown in American work. But this does not invalidate the conclusions drawn from the surveys.

Orr's results, and those of later workers, show what, in fact, people do eat. If every housewife were a skilled dietician, had unlimited time and patience, access to the cheapest markets, and adequate skill and cooking facilities, the nutritional level would doubtless be higher. This however is an academic point, except that it suggests the need for a long-term policy of education and of improvement in kitchen equipment. However, the malnutrition of the poor cannot be attributed to ignorance: Orr's figures show that, even with the maximum of knowledge and skill, 20 per cent of the population, with then existing wages and prices, could not have afforded a satisfactory diet. His comment was as follows:

It has been suggested that the standard adopted, viz. what is needed to enable people to attain their inherited capacity for health and physical fitness, is so high that it is impracticable. One writer terms it 'utopian'. In animal husbandry, an optimum standard, far from being utopian, is regarded as good practice. Every intelligent stock farmer in rearing animals tries to get a minimum diet for maximum health and physical fitness. A suggestion that he should use a lower standard would be regarded as absurd. If children of the three lower groups were reared for profit like young farm stock, giving them a diet below the requirements for health would be financially unsound. Unfortunately, the health and physical fitness of the rising generation are not marketable commodities which can be assessed in terms of money.

England and Wales were not exceptional in their nutritional status among industrial countries. Germany, for instance, in the period immediately before 1933, was slightly worse. The Germans drank more milk, on the whole, than the English, but ate much less butter and less meat. The exceptional countries were four which produce food of animal origin for export: Australia, New Zealand, Holland,

and Denmark. In all these the nutritional level of the whole population (except the Australian aborigines) was high, and required relatively little improvement.

The position in the United States, the wealthiest country in terms of national income in proportion to population, was probably slightly better than that of England. But it was not good. The United States Department of Agriculture Yearbook for 1939 contains the following passage:

> If the total quantities of food produced in this country were distributed in proportion to need, a fairly satisfactory diet would be provided for every individual. As it is, the national dietary level appears high because of the high consumption of certain foods by some families. Urban families with limited funds for food and rural families with limited opportunities for home production tend to lay emphasis on the kind of foods that satisfy obvious hunger cheaply and to neglect those that satisfy also the 'hidden nutritional hungers' – for vitamins and minerals – described by science.

The point is put in another way elsewhere in the same volume, where it is calculated that to raise consumption of all groups to the level of the most favoured it would be necessary to increase the production of milk by 20 per cent, of butter by 15, tomatoes and citrus fruits 70, leafy and yellow vegetables 100, and eggs 35 per cent. The similarity to England holds too in the relationship between poverty and malnutrition. In 1936 about 32 per cent of families and single individuals in the U.S. had incomes under 750 dollars a year, and it was reckoned that none of these could afford satisfactory diets at the prices then prevailing. Extensive studies made since the second world war show that malnutrition and even deficiency diseases remain wide-spread. Children and pregnant women suffer in particular.

The Effects of Better Food

Reports of widespread malnutrition in advanced countries were at first received with a good deal of scepticism, but they have been confirmed, not only by the results of further surveys, but also by study of the effects of improving diets. The effects are most clearly seen in children and in women before and after childbirth. In a study of a village colony for boys, some of the boys were allowed an extra ration of milk each day, while others remained on the usual diet. The average annual gain in weight of boys in the milk group was 6·98 lb.; that of the boys receiving the normal diet, 3·85 lb. To quote Marrack:

The experiment was kept going for three years, although many of the original boys left; the milk group maintained their advantage throughout. What is perhaps more striking than these figures is the fact that the slowest-growing boys of the milk group grew faster than the fastest-growing boys of the basic group.

Apart from the gain in weight and height, the boys who received the extra milk improved in their general condition. They lost the tendency to chilblains during the winter months, which was almost universal among the boys eating the basal diet; their skins became softer and smoother; they were more high-spirited. A casual visitor entering the dining-hall would never fail to recognize the table at which the boys who received the extra ration of milk sat, as these boys were obviously more fit than the others. Furthermore, during the winter 1923–4 they were completely free from illness, although among the other boys the sickness rate had been somewhat higher than usual owing to influenza and a limited outbreak of measles and scarlet fever.

Other, similar experiments have since been done both in Britain and the United States, with similar results. These results are paralleled in both countries by two well established facts: that the children of the poor are smaller, weaker, and suffer more disease than those of the rich; and that there has been a steady improvement during the twentieth century in all classes.

The clearest index of improvement is the increase in average weight and height of children of all ages. To quote Marrack again:

In some thirty years the average height of a London school boy at any age from five to thirteen has increased by over two inches, and the average weight by from 5 lb. at five years to 11 lb. at twelve years; the weight of the older girls has increased by over 13 lb. This improvement has not been confined to London.

Thus the effects of the dietary collapse of the nineteenth century have been partly reversed in the twentieth. Similar changes have been observed both in Canada and the United States.

The improvement cannot be attributed wholly to better nutrition. We shall see in the next chapter that the amount of infectious disease has been much reduced, and this is only partly due to better food and consequent higher resistance. Smaller families and child-welfare clinics have both led to better care of children. A number of other changes may have contributed. Nevertheless we need not doubt that food has played a major part. We shall see below that even during the second world war the improvement continued.

Growth in height and weight is generally used in assessing physical condition. This is primarily because both height and weight can be measured accurately and quickly. However, it is further justified by the fact that other qualities vary with physical growth. Children who grow most rapidly also, on the average, have higher resistance to infection and are better at all kinds of school activity, both physical and intellectual. This does not signify that small people are inferior, but only that, on the whole, growth in the ordinary sense goes with the growth of intellect and ability.

When we come to study the effect of diet on pregnant women the simplest criteria to use are the proportions of deaths in childbirth, stillbirths, and deaths of the children in the first month of life. This has been done in several investigations in Britain and Canada. In one, carried out in South Wales in 1934, when there was much unemployment among the miners, over 27,000 women were studied, some of whom were given extra food. Here are figures obtained in one year.

		Attended clinic only	*Clinic + food*
Maternal death rate	per 1,000	11·29	4·77
Stillbirth rate + neonatal mortality	live births	84·0	59·0

The extra food included a small amount of protein, together with calcium, phosphorus, iron, vitamin A, and B vitamins. This supplement, although it markedly influenced death rates, still left the total diet of the women far below any recommended standard.

To sum up the two preceding sections we may quote the *World Food Survey* published by the Food and Agriculture Organization in 1946:

Calculations based on the prewar populations of the individual countries show that in the years before the war –

In areas containing over half the world's population food supplies at the retail level (not actual intake) were sufficient to furnish an average of less than 2250 calories per caput daily.

Food supplies furnishing an average of more than 2750 calories per caput daily were available in areas containing somewhat less than a third of the world's population. The remaining areas, containing about one-sixth of the world's population, had food supplies that were between these high and low levels . . .

The high-calorie areas include most of the Western world, all of North America, and much of Europe. Oceania and the Union of Socialist Soviet Republics also belong to this group, but it includes only three countries in South America.

The medium-calorie areas include most of Asia, a part of the Middle East, all of Central America, and probably parts of South America and Africa which were not covered by this survey.

But averages do not tell the whole story. They conceal many sharp differences. Whatever the average calorie intake of a country, some people obtain considerably more than the average while a large number have less. Even in the countries with the most liberal food supplies and the highest calorie intake, it is well known that a considerable part of the population is not well nourished. There are wide local variations in food supply which are not brought out by average figures for the whole population.

Poverty is the chief cause of malnutrition. In the course of preparing this survey prewar calorie consumption was compared with national incomes per person as far as these are known. It is interesting to observe that all the countries in which the supply of calories per caput was less than 2250 a day were countries in which the average per caput income was less than U.S. $100 a year. At the other end of the scale there were 365 million people living in countries in which the average supply of calories exceeded 2900 a person a day. Of these, 342 million were in countries in which the average income exceeded U.S. $200 a person a year.

Thus for the world as a whole it can be said, 'Tell me what you earn and I will tell you how you eat.' There are exceptions, but in general well-to-do countries fare well nutritionally, poor countries fare badly, and the poorest groups within these countries fare the worst.

Food Distribution

The F.A.O., in the same publication, gives a table showing world food needs in 1960. The figures in this table are the percentage increases in the production of the various types of food, required to raise nutrition throughout the world to a fairly satisfactory level. They are calculated on the assumption of a 25 per cent increase in world population.

Here are the figures:

Commodity	Increase per cent
Cereals	21
Roots and tubers	27
Sugar	12
Fats	34
Pulses	80
Fruit and vegetables	163
Meat	46
Milk	100

There is, in 1954, no evidence that even half these increases will have been achieved by 1960, although world food production is certainly rising. The only thing on which we can congratulate ourselves is that, for the first time, the world's food needs have at least been roughly assessed.

Feeding people well depends not only on production but also on satisfactory methods of distribution. The first country to attempt the planned production and distribution of food in peace time was the Soviet Union. The problem was mainly one of a peasant population with adequate cereals except in times of famine, but inadequate meat, vegetables,

and dairy produce. Farms were too small for economic production, and methods of cultivation were primitive. The
total area under cultivation also was too small. By 1939
75 per cent of agricultural land was in the hands of co-
operatives and much of the remainder consisted of state
farms. The cultivated area has been much increased, and
the extra land used for growing vegetables and animal
food. From 1933 livestock greatly increased: cattle, in
particular, by 646 per cent in five years. By 1935 it was
possible to abolish rationing, and in 1947 it was again
found unnecessary. But food distribution remains planned.
A League of Nations report, published in 1936, referred
especially to the development of communal restaurants
and factory canteens; even the collective farms had mobile
kitchens bringing meals to the workers in the fields. Special
attention was given to the diet of children, and in particular
to the supply of free meals in schools. This probably
accounts for the rapid increase in children's height and
weight observed after the revolution. In Leningrad, as
early as the period 1925–32, the 13-year averages for boys
increased by 3 inches and 11 pounds respectively, and for
girls by 1·5 inches and 9 pounds.

The Soviet Union provides an instance of planning for a
vast agricultural country with a population which was
initially largely illiterate. The Soviet experience has therefore much to tell us of the possibilities for the other great
peasant and undeveloped areas. On the other hand the
experience of the United Kingdom during the second world
war shows what can be done in a densely populated industrial country. Despite the lowered food imports, which were
not fully balanced by increased home production, the
nutritional level for the country as a whole was raised. In
1943, for instance, although average fat consumption had
fallen, protein consumption had increased; and in both
vitamins and minerals there had been improvement, although the adequacy of the amounts of vitamins A, B_1, B_2,
and C was doubtful. The improvement depended on three
things: the rationing of most essential foods at controlled

K

prices; the availability of adequate energy food in the form
of unrationed bread and potatoes, also at controlled prices;
and full employment and consequently higher incomes for
the poor. (For a time after the war, however, both bread
and potatoes had to be rationed, though at a high level.)
Both agricultural production at home, and the import of
foods, were determined largely by the known nutritional
needs of the population. There were several similarities to
the Russian scheme, including the organization of communal meals at low prices; special supplements for children
and mothers; and extra rations for some classes of workers.
It was also recognized that rationing and other measures
would be less effective if people did not understand them,
or made wrong use of the foods available. Attempts were
therefore made to improve public knowledge of food values.
Habits had to be changed: such valuable foods as dried egg
and dried milk were unfamiliar; many people were unaccustomed to eating cheese, which was one of the most
valuable of the rationed foods; and campaigns had to be
run to induce mothers to make use of the vitamin supplements supplied for their children and themselves.

These two examples illustrate the complex of biochemical,
economic, and social problems involved in making a national
food policy. Despite the complexity it is now possible to
define with precision all the main steps to be taken to feed
any given community. This in itself is an enormous advance.
At present, if we survey the whole world, the knowledge is
being applied only piecemeal, and indeed can be only so
applied in many countries until food production is increased. Nevertheless, provided that man applies himself to
peaceful ends during the rest of the twentieth century he
can reasonably look forward to a well-fed world at the end
of it: the result will be an unprecedented state of health and
well-being for every nation.

LIFE AND DEATH

Death be not proud, though some have called thee
Mighty and dreadfull; for, thou art not soe.

JOHN DONNE

THROUGHOUT human history the two great causes of premature death have been famine and infectious disease. The
casualties due directly to war have been trifling by comparison, at least until the middle of the twentieth century. The
conquest of infection remains second only to feeding people,
among the twentieth-century objectives of applied science.

The problem arises from the crowded populations of
civilization. Primitive peoples untouched by advanced cultures seem to have few serious epidemics or endemic infections, though individuals rarely reach more than middle age.
This is inferred from study of their skeletons, and from the
reports of the civilized men who first reach them. Once
regular contact with advanced communities is established
there is a complete change: since primitive groups have not
before been exposed to the disease-causing microbes of
civilization they are highly susceptible to them; this is at
least partly because the first experience they have of them is
a sudden, heavy infection: there is little possibility of getting
a mild or undetectable attack from a light infection, such as
often occurs in most communities. It is also probable that
isolated groups, not having been selected for resistance to
these diseases, are genetically more susceptible than larger
communities. The inhabitants of Tierra del Fuego, in less
than a century, were reduced in numbers from about
60,000 to 200, largely through infection with smallpox,
measles, and tuberculosis.

These three diseases are mainly airborne, and so depend for their spread directly on the crowding of people together. But the density of civilized populations also gives opportunities for other noxious organisms. Water supplies may be infected; sewage and other household waste may harbour the germs of disease or the animals that carry them; food itself, in its journey from the farm to the consumer, may become infected, and is liable, like waste, to maintain populations of germ-bearing pests such as flies and rats, as well as the human population for which it is intended.

The 'Sanitary Idea'

None of this was properly understood anywhere until the middle of the nineteenth century, when the germ theory of disease was established. Although a relationship between disease and filth had long been suspected, the connexion was not proved. It was believed that 'foul airs' or miasmas were the agents of disease, and the name of *malaria* (bad air) remains a memorial to this view. Microscopists had demonstrated the presence of bacteria and other microbes in a variety of places, including decaying material, but it was thought that these organisms grew directly from the stuff they lived on. The foundation of bacteriology was the demonstration that microbes do not appear 'spontaneously' in any medium, however suitable for their growth; they appear only if the medium has been exposed to infection from elsewhere: microbes, like larger organisms, grow only from other, similar bodies. Thus it came to be realized that filth caused disease on account of microbes which grow in it and which can also live in men's bodies.

Infection from these sources is far from being the cause of all disease. (In the last chapter we had examples of deficiency diseases which are in no way infectious; and in chapter 3 we referred to abnormal conditions which are fixed genetically, and are virtually independent of environmental effects.) Moreover, most microbes are harmless. But many of the worst killers of children and of men and women in their prime turned out to be infections preventible by sanitary measures.

The need for these measures had never been so great as in the new industrial towns of the nineteenth century. The squalor and degradation of the working population in English towns is fully described in a series of official reports published during the 1840s. Chadwick, the inventor of the expression the 'sanitary idea', wrote:

Such is the absence of civic economy in some of our towns that their condition in respect to cleanliness is almost as bad as that of an encamped horde, or an undisciplined soldiery.

He describes army standing orders for camp sanitation, and goes on:

The towns whose populations never change their encampment have no such care, and whilst the houses, streets, courts, lanes, and streams are polluted and rendered pestilential, the civic officers have generally contented themselves with the most barbarous expedients, or sit still amidst the pollution, with the resignation of Turkish fatalists, under the supposed destiny of the prevalent ignorance, sloth and filth.

Similarly the Frenchman, Blanqui, describes how in 1849, in the industrial town of Lille, 3000 families lived in unventilated, insanitary cellars.

Improvement required the setting up of a national public health organization in each country, and effective public health departments for each local government authority. This was a big task, both administratively and technically. Engineers, sanitary inspectors, dustmen and sewermen, as well as doctors, had to be recruited, trained, and paid. It is only recently that, even in England, all houses in towns have had a reliable piped water supply free from infection; (the poorer houses often have even now only one tap, and in the country much water still comes from wells, some quite shallow and easily infected); but today most urban areas have, not only enough water for drinking, cooking, washing, and cleaning, but also a bacteriological service to keep watch on the quality of the water supplied. A necessary complement to a good water supply is an efficient system of drains and sewers. In 1840 household waste of all kinds was put in cesspools (Windsor Castle had 250 of them), or human excrement was collected in heaps for sale as manure; refuse collection was unorganized and sporadic, where it existed at all. The new working-class houses whose occupiers suffered these conditions were flimsy, airless, ill-lit, and commonly built in terraces back-to-back, with only a narrow alley in front. Some of these houses are still in use.

Although the first attempts to improve the hygiene of cities were made even before the elements of bacteriology were understood, the squalor remained almost untouched for most of the century; the efforts of the wealthy taxpayers who did not wish to spend money on the poor, of the water companies, of some sections of the medical profession and of other vested interests prevented progress for several decades. Nevertheless, by the first decade of the twentieth century the application of the sanitary idea had wrought a vast change in mortality and morbidity from some major diseases, not only in England but also in the main countries of western Europe, and in the United States. The extent and limits of this advance can be shown if we consider the main epidemic diseases of human populations.

Pestilence

Throughout the world the worst *water-borne* diseases are cholera, typhoid, and various forms of dysentery. Today cholera is called a 'tropical disease', but there were four major outbreaks in western Europe during the nineteenth century. Epidemics are nearly always due to infection of drinking water; in one famous instance a single infected well near Piccadilly Circus, in London, caused 485 deaths in ten days. Cholera is no longer a disease of western Europe, but as this chapter is being written a serious epidemic is reported in Egypt, and it is continually present in the densely populated tropical lands. Much the same applies to typhoid fever or more generally to the enteric fevers of which typhoid is

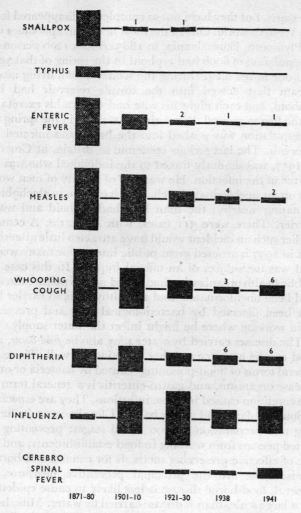

Mortality. Deaths from eight diseases, per 100,000 persons per year, in England and Wales. The first group of diseases has been almost wiped out, the second has become much less serious. The third represents new problems which have arisen in the twentieth century the worst, but they have not so completely disappeared from the Western world. One of the most notorious epidemics was in Plymouth, Pennsylvania, in 1885. About 1200 persons in a population of 8000 had typhoid in the spring of that year, and one in ten died. During the winter a man living near a stream that flowed into the town's reservoir had had typhoid, and each night his wife had thrown his excreta on to the frozen ground. When the thaw came in the spring the accumulation was washed into the brook and infected the reservoir. The last serious epidemic in Britain, at Croydon in 1937, was similarly traced to the individual who was the source of the infection. He was one of a party of men working on an unchlorinated well, who had been in the habit of urinating nearby; the man had had typhoid and was a carrier. There were 311 cases, with 42 deaths. A century earlier such an incident would have attracted little attention, but in 1937 it aroused great public interest for many weeks, and was the subject of an official inquiry. In this case the public health organization had failed at two points: the well had been unchlorinated, and a healthy typhoid carrier had not been detected by bacteriological tests and prevented from working where he might infect the water supply.

The diseases carried by water may also be *food-borne*, and food can be a source of other infections as well. There are several forms of 'food-poisoning' caused by bacteria or other disease organisms, and gastro-enteritis is a general term for the condition caused by these infections. They are especially serious in infants and young babies. Cleanliness in the handling and preparation of food at all stages; preventing infected persons from working in food establishments; and the use of effective preserving methods for canned and bottled foods: these are the principal preventive measures. In general, food-borne disease is less likely to cause epidemics on a large scale, than is disease carried by water. Milk, however, occupies a special place among foods: it is distributed in bulk to very large numbers of people in towns, and it is as good a food for some bacteria as it is for men. Infected milk can cause epidemics of typhoid, dysentery, tonsillitis,

Mortality. Changes in total mortality, and in death rates from some respiratory infections, per 100,000 living, per year, in advanced communities. The upper figure refers to tuberculosis alone and undulant fever. Even worse, it is the source of one type of tuberculosis. The heat treatment, or pasteurization, of milk, which is now compulsory in some advanced communities, can prevent the transmission of all these infections.

Food may be infected, not only by man himself, but by various *animals*: flies provide the most familiar example, and are still a menace in the western world as carriers of germs of enteritis and food poisoning. However, the discovery of specific insecticides, of which DDT is the most familiar, promises the elimination of flies in communities in which they are used on a large enough scale.

But rat fleas, lice, and mosquitoes take pride of place among animal carriers of disease. All these infect man directly and not through food or water. Rat fleas are the source of plague, the Black Death of the middle ages. The plague bacillus is primarily a parasite in the bodies of various species of wild rodents, varying from ground squirrels in central Asia to rabbits in California. In these animals it causes little harm, and it certainly does not give rise to epidemics with a high mortality. It is transmitted from one individual to another by fleas, and rats become infected in the same way. Rat populations too may maintain a comparatively mild plague infection. Human infection occurs where there are many infected rats, and the rats have comparatively large numbers of fleas. These conditions hold today in large parts of India and, at least until very recently, in China, and there are plague reservoirs also in North and South Africa, and in North America. Thus plague in man is a by-product of a disease of rodents. We know for certain of three world outbreaks, or pandemics, of plague, though it is likely that others occurred before them. A pandemic begins suddenly, spreading over a large area, such as Europe, within a few years; at this stage the proportion of the population getting plague is high – perhaps 10 per cent – and the mortality among those infected varies between about 50 and 100 per cent; the highest mortality occurs when the bubonic form gives place to pneumonic plague, when the lungs are involved and bacilli are coughed into the air. For a century or more after the first outbreak plague continues intermittently and with diminishing intensity. Finally in large areas it disappears completely.

We cannot explain this sequence. The first fully authenticated pandemic, the 'plague of Justinian', began in the sixth century, and we have no detailed knowledge of what happened. The second was the Black Death which began in the fourteenth century, and reached France and England in 1349. The initial mortality, though high, was probably less disastrous than the steady drain of lives and health that followed during the next hundred years. This was a period of falling population and collapsing economy in Western Europe, and plague made a major contribution to that state of affairs. The last flare-up in England was the 'great plague of London' of 1664. The third pandemic is still going on as this book is written. It began in China, probably in the 1870s, spread rapidly to India, and then to the main ports of Africa and Asia Minor. Europe largely escaped. England had a few cases during the period 1910–21, and rodents in an area in East Anglia were infected at that time.

Plague is far from being a simple problem of public health, and we cannot attribute Europe's escape simply to improved hygiene and precautions against rats at the ports, though they doubtless played some part. With our present knowledge the remedy for plague is prevention by killing rats and their fleas, and by reducing filth that encourages them; protection can also be given by inoculation. We have still to get full understanding of the complex biological relationships between the plague-ridden rodent populations, their fleas and ourselves.

While plague is a problem of the rats that live in our houses, and of public cleanliness, epidemic typhus fever is a problem of the lice that live on our bodies and of personal cleanliness. This, the worst form of typhus, has destroyed armies and altered the course of wars. The great outbreaks occur when unwashed people are crowded together, and the lice can move rapidly from one to another. In earlier times alternative names for typhus were jail fever and hospital fever. The habit of washing which has become so widespread in the Western world in modern times has made perhaps a contribution to disease prevention comparable with the control of the water supply. A Lancashire miner, in 1842, was asked how often the coaldrawers washed their bodies. He is reported to have replied:

None of the drawers ever wash their bodies. I never wash my body; I let my shirt rub the dirt off. I wash my neck and ears and face, of course.

Even more to the point is the cheerful mention in the diary of Samuel Pepys, a First Lord of the Admiralty, of the presence of twenty lice in his hair one evening – 'more than I have had this many a long day. And so with great content to bed.'

The diseases so far discussed are called 'tropical' in Britain, because they have been largely banished from the temperate zone. The main mosquito-borne infections have a more permanent claim to the name, since they are almost confined to the tropics and sub-tropics. It is true that malaria can occur as far north as Archangel, and that one form of it turned up regularly in the London hospitals and even in the south of Scotland as recently as the 1860s. But ague, as it was called, was never such a menace in the north as it has been, and still is, in hotter climates. In large parts of the most densely populated countries malaria is almost universal, and it is the world's leading cause of infectious illness and death. A conservative estimate of its total incidence suggests that a quarter of the world's population suffer from it. In India the number of people treated for malaria each year is of the order of ten million, but it is certain that this is only a small proportion of the total infected. Malaria differs from the acute infections (such as plague and typhus) in being, very often, a chronic disease. An acute disease either kills in a few days or weeks, or subsides; a chronic infection may persist for years, and perhaps for a lifetime. People with chronic malaria are weak and lethargic, and the uninformed and uninfected European, seeing them, is led to believe that all 'natives' are naturally lazy. We have seen that the effects of chronic undernutrition may encourage him in this mistaken view.

The principal means of preventing endemic malaria is destruction of mosquitoes of the genus *Anopheles*. This is a formidable task requiring a large organization of trained persons. Methods include the draining of marshes and streams, where the mosquitoes breed; poisoning the water; and the introduction of plants or fishes that prevent breeding. What is done depends partly on the species of *Anopheles*. Mosquito teams applying these methods have already had considerable success in countries as diverse as India, Italy, Panama, and Brazil. In Central and South America, and in West Africa, they are called on to operate also against *Aëdes aegypti*, the mosquito that carries yellow fever. It was the destruction both of *Anopheles* and *Aëdes* that finally made possible the building of the Panama Canal. Today, epidemic yellow fever, which used to occur in the Americas with dramatic and terrifying results, has been eliminated. But endemic yellow fever remains: like plague, it is dependent on a complex set of animal vectors, including mosquitoes (not *Aëdes*) and various species of monkey. As such, both in tropical Africa and in South America, it is still a potential threat.

All these diseases can be prevented, and in some places have been prevented, by the application of a rather wide interpretation of the sanitary idea. They represent the easiest targets for public health authorities. This is because they depend on other animal species besides ourselves, whereas most infectious diseases are carried from man to man. This is the case with the group of *air-borne* infections, which are in principle at least a more difficult problem. (It is true that diseases such as plague and typhus can be air-borne, but they are not so as a rule.) It is an extraordinary fact that the worst of them, smallpox, had been shown to be preventable more than half a century before the germ theory of disease was established, since the technique of vaccination was invented before the end of the eighteenth century. At that

DEATHS

444

2875

IMMUNIZED

5%

59000

60%

CASES

18000

1935-9   40   41   42   43   44   45   46
AVERAGE

Diphtheria in England and Wales. Widespread immunization of children in the first year has gone far to defeat this disease

time few people in Europe escaped having smallpox at some time in their lives, and about one in twelve of infected persons died. Most survivors were disfigured for life by the pockmarks, and some were blinded. Today deaths from smallpox are rare in the West, partly as a result of vaccination.

The other outstanding success against air-borne infection is that of immunization against diphtheria: in the countries where it has been carried out on a majority of children it has been reduced to an almost negligible danger. In England and Wales at the beginning of the century 65 in every 100,000 children under 15 died of diphtheria. Between the wars, when the numbers of children immunized were relatively low, the figure was steady at about 29. During the 1940s the proportion of children immunized was greatly increased as a result of publicity campaigns by the government and local health authorities, and in 1947 the death-rate was down to 2 per 100,000. Even this could be improved on, given a sustained effort to get every child immunized at the age of one year.

The almost complete disappearance of diseases such as typhus, typhoid, and smallpox in some countries is a triumph of applied science. It has involved the use not only of biological science, but also of engineering, chemistry, and other disciplines. Just as with food production, so with the control of disease we find it necessary to consider ecologically an involved nexus of living things; and, just as with food production, the task is one for the whole community and not only for specialists.

This knowledge is applicable, not only in the areas with good public health services, most of which are in the temperate zone, but also in the tropical lands, with their immense populations, where the great epidemic diseases remain as potent as ever. There is a notion that the tropics must be unhealthy, both to people unaccustomed to them and also to the native inhabitants, but there is no valid evidence to support this view. The temperate zone also was 'unhealthy' until public health measures brought improvement. The 'white man's grave' of West Africa was so called for reasons that need no longer apply today: in particular it is a home of malaria, which is now preventible. Certain diseases occur mainly or solely in hot countries, just as others, such as rickets, belong mainly to the lands in which there is little sunlight for part of the year. Perhaps, if the Africans had colonized large areas of the temperate zone, northern Europe would have been called 'the black man's grave', although it is in fact possible for Africans to live there in good health.

The tropical countries remain graveyards by comparison with advanced countries, at least for their native inhabitants, mainly because the known principles of public health have not yet been generally applied in them. Throughout the tropics the vitality of the people is sapped, not only by malaria and other diseases already mentioned, but by many others, of which hookworm is probably the most widespread. There are two types of hookworm: both are passed out of the bowel with the faeces, and re-enter a human being through the skin. The people who get it in large numbers are those who live in communities with inadequate sanitation and who do not wear shoes. Hookworm is rarely fatal, but it is chronically enfeebling. We do not know how many millions of people are infected with hookworm, but we do know that there are whole communities, for instance in the West Indies, living a depressed existence on account of it.

Resistance

The great epidemic diseases can be avoided by rather simple and easily understood methods designed to block the routes by which the disease germs enter the body. For public health purposes the question is: are people liable to be infected, say, with the cholera germ? If so, we must expect them to get cholera; if not, all is well. But, in general, infectious disease is not merely a result of the entry of a disease germ into the body: the body itself must be susceptible to the germ or, in other words, its resistance must be inadequate. It is a familiar fact that one attack of a particular disease may confer immunity, at least for a time. The immunity is a result of a change in the composition of the blood, and in some instances such a change can be induced by 'inoculation' which gives rise to little or no discomfort. But the problem of resistance is far wider than this: we have already seen that *nutrition* is an important factor; the *psychological state* of a person may affect his resistance to some infections; and a number of other environmental factors, including *housing* and, in some trades, *working conditions*, may be of vital importance. Once again, we see that disease is a social problem, influenced by all the conditions in which people live.

All these effects can be illustrated from one disease, tuberculosis. In each year nearly 2000 English and Welsh children die of tuberculosis, but the worst sufferers are young adults: about 1 in 20 of all deaths in England and Wales are due to tubercle, and the majority occur between the ages of fifteen and forty-five; in a quarter of all cases the disease is first diagnosed between fifteen and twenty-five. In most European countries after the second world war (just as after the first) the position is far worse than in England. Even in the United States tuberculosis is third on the list of causes of

Tuberculosis: The Influence of Income. Relative death rates from tuberculosis in five economic classes. Class 5, the poorest, come off worst

death, coming after diseases of heart and blood vessels, and cancer. Apart from the principal diseases of infancy and childhood tubercle has a special importance compared with the other main causes of death: it kills people in their prime, whereas cancer and the disorders of the vascular system, scourges though they are, are largely problems of the later years of life.

The history of tuberculosis in modern times shows how the disease is a product of economic circumstances.

> Youth grows pale, and spectre thin, and dies

wrote Keats in the spring of 1819. This was an accurate description of what was happening at that time, not only to poets and their friends, but to the enfeebled, disease-ridden young men and women of the new manufacturing towns. As early as 1796 a Manchester commission had reported:

Children and others who work in the large cotton factories are peculiarly disposed to be affected by the contagion of fever, and ... it is rapidly propagated, not only among those who are crowded together in the same departments, but in the families and neighbourhoods to which they belong.

Such warnings were ignored. As Dubos, the distinguished bacteriologist, has written:

The passion for financial gains made acquisitive men blind to the fact that they were part of the same social body as the unfortunates who operated their machines. Tuberculosis was, in effect, the social disease of the nineteenth century, perhaps the first penalty that capitalistic society had to pay for the ruthless exploitation of labor.

In chapter 2 we saw that there is genetical variation in the liability to tuberculosis, but that there are several environmental factors which have a far more important influence in practice. Of these, working conditions that promote the development of tubercle are notorious: miners and others working where there is much silica dust in the air are especially liable to the disease, and prevention takes the form of various measures to reduce the amount of dust. There is also ample evidence that poor ventilation, in factories for example, increases the amount of tuberculosis. The same applies in the home, but overcrowding there is also likely to cause a greater amount of air-borne infection from one member of a family to another. The connexion between nutritional deficiency and resistance to tubercle has not been fully worked out, and remains uncertain. As for mental state, it is well enough known that some illness, not caused by germs, such as gastric ulcer, is associated with anxiety and suppressed emotional tension (acting in a susceptible person), and that mental upset can cause symptoms of illness in any part of the body. Sometimes the effect is to reduce the resistance of an organ of the body to disease germs. This certainly applies to some tuberculosis patients, and for them psychological and physical treatment may have to be combined.

With the doubtful exception of psychological disturbance

(such as 'worry') all the environmental factors which promote tuberculosis press more heavily on the poor than on
the rich. The picture is not, however, even for the poor,
uniformly black. Since 1875 in England and Wales there
has been steady improvement, apart from two brief checks
due to war, in all classes. Moreover there is now a means of
inoculating people against tuberculosis, and so immuniz-
ing them. This is expected to be particularly valuable for
workers, such as nurses, whose occupation exposes them to
exceptional risks.

The problems of public health are therefore far more complex than might be supposed from a superficial study of the
achievements against a few epidemic diseases. The prevention of disease involves not only bacteriology and sanitary
engineering, but also a host of other branches of knowledge,
from psychology to economics. The attack on tuberculosis
alone calls for better housing and a rise in the general
standard of life, and for better ventilation in factories, which
is again in part an economic problem; for early diagnosis a
greater development of mass radiography is required, and,
for adequate treatment, more beds in sanatoria and more
nurses, doctors, and other trained persons. And this does not
exhaust the list.

To illustrate further the problems of public health we may
take other examples of the effects of housing and working
conditions. An outstanding example is measles. If the population of England and Wales is divided into five groups,
according to income level, it is found that the proportion
of children who contract measles is roughly the same in each
group; but the proportion of children *dying* from measles in
the lowest group is 19 times that of the highest. Whooping
cough – which is the main killer of children between one and
five years – shows a similar contrast. The difference between
the social classes is, for these two diseases, entirely due to the
bad housing of the poor and the difficulties that go with it.
Crowding makes it more likely that very young babies will
get these diseases; resistance is lower in the first year of life
than later, hence many babies are killed. We have no such

scientific standard for housing as we have for nutrition, but we can say that housing which makes it impossible for a baby to be put to sleep apart from the rest of the family is inadequate.

Another condition which has been proved to be affected by housing is rheumatic heart disease in children. In Britain it is probable that between twenty and thirty thousand people die of this disease each year, and it is responsible for nearly all the deaths from heart disease before the age of forty; among youths and young adults its place is second to that of tuberculosis. In one investigation a number of working-class families were first classified by their economic position; this is not the same as classifying them by total income, since a couple with one child and £5 a week are much better off than a family of seven with the same income. An arbitrary 'poverty line' was then chosen, below which, it was assumed, a family could not maintain a standard of living adequate for health. Seventeen per cent of the families studied fell below this line, and among them the frequency of rheumatic heart disease was 39 per cent above the average. On the other hand, 22 per cent had at least double the chosen minimum income, and among them the frequency of the disease was 23 per cent below the average. One immediate conclusion could be drawn from these results: to get a satisfactory reduction in the rate of heart disease in children a standard of life well above the chosen minimum would be necessary. It is by objective standards such as this that minimum wages, family allowances, and other factors influencing the standard of living, should be judged. Further analysis of the figures showed that the higher incidence of the disease among the poorest families was due mainly to overcrowding: other consequences of poverty, such as inferior diet, could not be shown to have any effect in this instance.

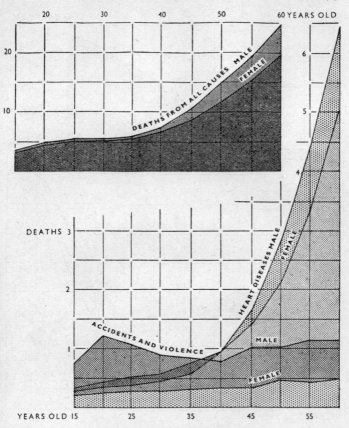

Mortality. The principal causes of death in England and Wales, expressed as deaths per 1000 living (continued on the next page)

Problematic Viruses

Diseases such as tuberculosis and rheumatic heart disease can be overcome only by a general change in the way of life of the poor. The problem is not primarily one of finding specific remedies, even though such remedies can sometimes be of value once the disease is diagnosed and the patient got

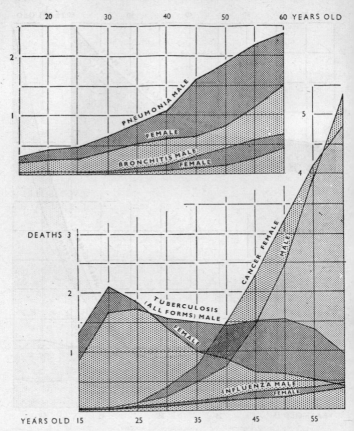

Mortality. The principal causes of death in England and Wales, expressed as deaths per 1000 living (continued from previous page)

into a suitable hospital. The prevention of these diseases is as much a social and economic task as it is medical or scientific. There remains, however, a group of common infectious diseases which are still a problem to the bacteriologist and epidemiologist. They are all caused by viruses, organisms smaller than bacteria and correspondingly more difficult to study.

Of this group acute *poliomyelitis* is the most dreaded, although if we consider its total incidence we find that its importance has perhaps been exaggerated: in Britain, motor traffic presents at all times greater danger to life and limb than polio even in its worst epidemics. Its commonly used name, infantile paralysis, is based on the fact that when the disease first became important, in the late nineteenth century, a majority of cases were in children under five, and the most conspicuous sign was paralysis. More recently, however, the main incidence has been among children of from five to ten years, and in epidemics today an appreciable proportion of adults become seriously infected; moreover, only a minority of those infected show any paralysis. The most remarkable feature of poliomyelitis is that it is a disease of advanced communities: epidemics occur in just those countries which have the best public health organizations and the highest level of hygiene. This is not because the virus is not present in the undeveloped countries: during the second world war soldiers from advanced countries suffered severely from poliomyelitis on being posted, for instance, to Asiatic countries. Yet the local inhabitants remained unaffected.

It is probable that in lands where hygiene is poor nearly every child suffers a mild, non-paralytic infection at a very early age, while it is still being fed by its mother and partly protected by substances in the milk, and that this sets up a natural resistance. Infected persons are found to pass polio virus in their faeces. Most children with infected faeces present only minor signs such as slight fever, or symptoms such as backache. In Western countries, presumably, a proportion of children escape early infection, and so are susceptible, later on, to the acute form of the disease. Even then, it is believed, most of those infected show no serious effects: only a minority, in whom the virus invades a particular part of the nervous system, show any paralysis. In Britain more than 50 per cent of adults contain substances in their blood which indicate a previous infection by the virus, though they give no record of the actual disease.

The great problems are, how the infection is spread, and how to prevent it. We have seen that the virus is passed out with the faeces: there are detectable amounts of the virus in the sewage of a city during an epidemic, though not at other times. This suggests the desirability of ordinary hygienic precautions. But it is almost certain that the virus is also air-borne; it follows that crowds, especially in badly venti-lated places, are to be avoided – another commonplace principle. There is evidence that fatigue increases the likeli-hood of severe infection, and so parents are recommended to avoid over-tiredness in their children during epidemics. Finally, it is fully established that the operation of removing the tonsils greatly increases the danger of infection, and as far as possible surgeons avoid carrying it out if there is a poliomyelitis epidemic.

None of these precautions can prevent epidemics, though it is thought that personal hygiene of a high standard can be valuable. Prevention, now, may be made possible by the use of vaccines, made from virus grown in tissue culture. Owing to the small number of people who ever develop severe poliomyelitis, tests of such vaccines have to be made on vast numbers. In one American inquiry nearly a million children have been inoculated. As this book goes to press the pros-pects of effective immunization are promising.

The other virus diseases to be mentioned here are so commonplace as to be quite unfrightening; yet they cause far more ill health and inconvenience, even suffering, than poliomyelitis. They include the common cold, a number of more severe infections without a definite name, and epidemic influenza. In one investigation of the work of general medical practitioners it was found that about one-third of all ailments treated in patients over sixteen belonged to this group. All are primarily due to infection with viruses, but how many different viruses are involved, and what decides the degree of illness in each infected person, are still unsolved problems.

Colds themselves may be due to more than one microbe, but research has been hampered by the fact that the common laboratory animals do not get colds; chimpanzees do, but they are very expensive to keep: today research is done on human volunteers. In the United States the average number of colds a year for an adult is about 2·5, most of them in the colder half of the year. During each winter there are epidemic periods when the incidence of colds is particularly high. The susceptibility of individuals to colds varies very greatly and, what is less well known, any one person may vary a great deal from year to year in his liability to catch colds. There is good evidence that psychological state is an important factor in a person's response to infection, and this may be the explanation for the apparently favourable effect of some anti-cold vaccines: none of the vaccines so far used has proved effective under rigorous test. It is probable that low temperatures are not important in causing colds, but that variation of temperature is: in one experiment a group of medical students were kept for a fortnight in conditions of constant temperature and humidity; every effort was made to give them colds by contact with infected persons or material, but all failed.

Efforts have been made by manufacturers to persuade physicians and the public that certain drugs, called the 'anti-histamines', cure colds. These drugs do relieve the symptoms of hay-fever, and similar conditions. In an experiment, large numbers of people with colds (but no hay-fever) were given anti-histamines, and a control group, also with colds, were given a dummy medicine, without being told that it was a dummy. Many members of *both* groups reported that their colds were cured, but not more in one group than another. The anti-histamines were concluded not to be cold cures. This investigation illustrates well the nature of the scientific tests required to assess claims of cure or prevention.

Rather more serious than colds is the group of infections commonly called influenza but different in character from true epidemic influenza. There is no accepted name for this group: the U.S. army name is curd (common undifferentiated respiratory disease), but the U.S. navy talks of cat fever (acute catarrhal fever). Some of these fevers may be due to the same viruses as colds, others to one of the true influenza viruses, but it appears to be certain that most are due to neither. It has been suggested that some are due to mild infection with the poliomyelitis virus.

Finally we come to *epidemic influenza*. This differs from colds and curd in producing mainly general toxic symptoms, such as headache and muscular pains; there is less local effect on the nose, and less coughing. In a typical epidemic, from 10 to 20 per cent of the population in a particular area develop the disease, during a period of four to six weeks. Deaths due to influenza are confined to infants and old people. There are two viruses involved, called A and B, but epidemics due to virus B are relatively rare. Serious outbreaks of influenza A occur at intervals of two to four years: an epidemic seems to confer general immunity on a population for at least the following winter, sometimes for longer. What happens to the virus between epidemics is unknown, but it is possible that a few people can remain carriers for many months. There is no specific treatment for influenza.

In 1918–19 there was a unique pandemic, or world epidemic, of influenza, which is generally supposed to have been due to virus A although no direct evidence exists on this point. The most remarkable feature of the outbreak was the high mortality, especially among young adults. It is believed that the world mortality was 25m. There is no explanation for the pandemic, and no reason to expect that it will ever be repeated.

All these diseases are transmitted through the air, probably by 'droplet infection' in which the fine spray given out with each cough or sneeze is the main source of infection. Research on air sprays, which might kill the viruses in crowded buildings and vehicles, promises to give useful results. Dust particles may play a part in spreading infection, and the application of a light mineral oil, spindle oil, to the floors of public buildings reduces the amount of dust in the air and may have a preventive effect.

A potentially important line of study is provided by the

very difficult problem of immunity to these diseases. It is a general rule that newcomers to an established community, for instance recruits entering an army camp, show a much higher incidence of respiratory disease than those who have been there six months or more. Similarly, isolated groups, such as the crews of ships exploring remote waters, or small island communities, may be quite free from colds, curd, and influenza, yet show an explosive epidemic as soon as contact with members of other communities is made. It seems likely that in most groups there is a constant interchange of the local viruses and a consequent setting up of a temporary immunity; so long as this immunity is regularly reinforced by repeated infection, there will be freedom from the various diseases the viruses may cause. This does not however account for the fact that people do get respiratory diseases: no doubt the factors involved in the failure of immunity include the appearance of a new strain of virus in the neighbourhood, and a lowering of resistance in particular individuals.

True influenza confers a high degree of immunity to the virus which caused it, but this lasts only two or three months. Vaccines which confer a similar immunity artificially have already been made, and are now being used among people, such as doctors and nurses, for whom immunity is especially important. Whether we can hope that they will finally prevent influenza epidemics altogether, as diphtheria immunization can prevent diphtheria, is uncertain.

The story of these virus infections is therefore incomplete and unsatisfying. It would have been easier to omit it altogether, and to have restricted this chapter to the diseases of which the scientific account is fairly complete. But to do so would have been misleading: although the most obviously urgent need in the field of public health is the application of existing knowledge, especially in the backward lands, there is still work for the research microbiologist. The public are called upon to support this research in various ways, notably by paying for it, and they need to know something of the problems which face the scientists.

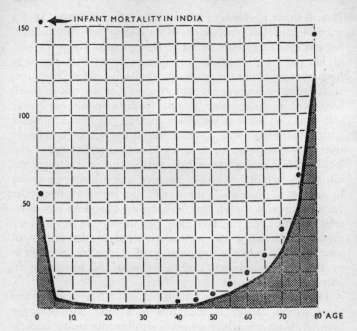

Mortality at Different Ages in England and Wales. The dangerous ages in the Western world today are the first year and after sixty; female mortality is shown by the shaded area; male mortality is higher than female. Where the difference is significant the male mortality is indicated by dots. The infant mortality in India is shown for comparison. The figures show deaths per thousand living per year

Health is Purchasable

The special health problems of the advanced countries can be studied from another point of view. Today, in the West, most people die when they are either very young, or over fifty: the great reduction in mortality has most affected the intermediate ages. This is why diseases which occur mainly in elderly people, in particular cancer and disorders of the heart and blood vessels, now loom so large in medical practice; the proportion of men and women over fifty is far

higher than ever before. The study of the problems of ageing, or gerontology, is only in its earliest stages, and little
can usefully be said about it here. There is however much to
be said about the health of children in their earliest years –
a contemporary problem which deserves just as much
attention.

We have seen that the health and physical and mental
development of each individual is strongly influenced by the
economic position of his parents. Nutritional level depends,
in most countries, largely on income; and nutrition affects,
not only growth directly, but also susceptibility to many
diseases. At the same time poverty involves bad housing,
and so evokes a further group of diseases.

The combined effects of the various consequences of
poverty in the advanced countries are clearly shown in the
figures for diseases of children. The figure opposite shows
that, of all ages below seventy, the first year of life has the
highest death rate. The death rate in the first year is called
the infant mortality, or IM. It does not include still-births.
The IM for England and Wales in 1938 was 53, signifying
that 53 infants died out of every 1000 born alive. For the
whole world this was rather low. The highest accurately
recorded in peacetime was that of Malta, where it was 243
in 1937; during the decade immediately before the second
world war almost one in every four Maltese babies died in
the first year of life. (Since then the Maltese IM has been
reduced to about 116.) The highest figure for a large country was 241 for Chile; the lowest, 31, was for New Zealand,
though the Maori section of the population was less well off
than the whites in this respect. In Europe, Iceland with 33
and Holland with 38 did best, and Rumania with 178 had
the highest figure.

Until about 1900 the IM for England and Wales was
much like that of Rumania or India today, but in the first
forty years of the twentieth century it fell by about 66 per
cent. However, there remains, even within Britain, much
variation in IM between different towns. A few small towns
have an IM of less than 30, while in some larger ones, such

Mortality. Changes in infant mortality in England and Wales, compared with death rates at ages 1–2 and 2–3. Infant mortality lags behind. There has however been further improvement in the post-war 'welfare state'

as Liverpool and Edinburgh, it approaches 100. This difference between different places has been shown to be quite independent of latitude: the fact that the south of England does better than the north is evidently not because it is warmer or drier, but because a smaller proportion of the inhabitants are in the lower income groups. The figure

Infant Mortality. IM by social class of father in England and Wales. Class 1, the 'professional and managerial' group, is the richest, class 5 is the poorest

above illustrates the difference between the economic classes: the child of an unskilled labourer is more than twice as likely to die in the first year, as the child of a professional man. In later years the differences between the classes become still greater; no doubt this is because the inferior environment of the poor has a cumulative effect on the health of the growing child.

It has been claimed that improvement in the survival rate of working-class children is undesirable because large numbers of the 'unfit' – of weaklings – are consequently kept alive; there are then many who are unable to make an adequate contribution to maintaining themselves as useful members of society. This view is held in particular by those who believe the working-class to be genetically inferior. If this belief were true a fall in IM would be followed by a corresponding rise in mortality at later ages: relatively many of the weaklings would show their unfitness by dying before they reached old age. But no such effect is found. A lowered IM is always accompanied by lowered mortality in later years. Moreover, as death rates fall, so do sickness rates: that is indeed one reason why death rates are so much

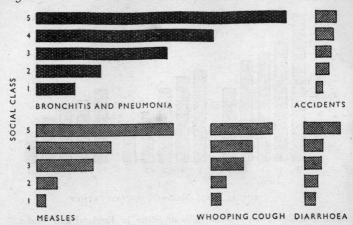

Infant Mortality. IM from five causes, by social group. Class 5 is the poorest

studied, since they provide a convenient index of health in general. Further evidence against the genetic inferiority of the poor is the fact that *congenital* malformations causing death in infancy are of roughly equal frequency in all classes; and these conditions are largely of genetic origin and little affected by environment.

The improvement in IM in the Western countries undoubtedly reflects the better nutrition, housing, sanitation, and medical care. It is shown in all classes, and it might be thought that differences between the different economic levels are of secondary importance. After all, the IM of the lowest income group in 1931, in England and Wales, was the same as that of the highest group in 1911. But a statistical study of IM by social class in England and Wales has shown that class differences are not only not diminishing: they are increasing. In 1911 a child in the lowest income group was three times as likely to die between the ages of six and twelve months as a child in the highest group; in 1931 it was *five times as likely to die* as a child in the highest group. The same point can be illustrated for the period since 1931. In 1931–2 the ten English county boroughs with the highest IM had

an IM 22 per cent higher than the average for the whole
country; in 1944-5 their IM was 30 per cent higher than
the average. Thus although the improvement has affected
all classes, it has affected least those most in need of improvement.

'Mental' Health

Preventing infection is, with certain exceptions, a matter of
applying existing knowledge. The same cannot be said of
preventing (or curing) disorders of behaviour. Yet no survey
of public health, however brief, is adequate if it ignores the
psychological aspect. We have already seen that emotional
factors are important in causing or exacerbating disease.
In Britain, surveys have shown that at least one in three

Mortality. The second year: deaths among children aged 1-2, per
100,000 legitimate live births.

L

of doctors' surgery patients are suffering from conditions largely or entirely of nervous origin. These conditions need as much attention, and sympathy, as those due to microbes or to a fractured bone, but unfortunately psychological medicine is still far behind bacteriology or orthopaedics.

One general advance, however, has been the recognition of the nervous or emotional influences which act on *all* parts of the body. We saw in chapter 6 that, in the past, it has been usual to speak of human beings as if they consisted of two separate entities, a 'mind' and a 'body'; whereas in scientific psychology today it is commonly found convenient to speak of each individual as a single whole, in whom all parts interact. The same attitude is beginning to influence medicine. Hence we have the 'psychosomatic' approach to medicine, in which emphasis is put on the emotional or nervous causes of certain illnesses, such as ulcers, asthma, and many others, in which quite specific failures of certain organs (stomach, lungs, and so on) are evident. Unfortunately, the term 'psychosomatic' in itself perpetuates the mind-body distinction, since it is derived from Greek words meaning 'soul' or 'spirit', and 'body', respectively. More strictly, the contemporary trend might be described as simply 'somatic'. Emotional changes, which we know in ourselves as feelings, are regarded as a function of the nervous system, influenced both by the internal state of the rest of the body and by what we see or hear.

There is no sharp division between the so-called psychosomatic conditions and the psychoneuroses which have been so much discussed ever since Sigmund Freud published his theories on their causes. The psychoneuroses cover a vast field of abnormal behaviour, from a failure of function such as the hysterical paralysis of a limb, to a compulsion to wash the hands every half-hour. (Lady Macbeth is a portrayal of a disorder, due to repressed feelings of guilt, of this sort.) Owing, no doubt, to the publicity which psychoanalysis has received, they are generally thought of as illnesses which have to be dealt with by prolonged treatment of the individual sufferer. But, while treatment by psychoanalysis has thrown light on the causes of neurosis, its curative value is still not adequately assessed; and in any case, the number of people who can be analysed, even by the most abbreviated methods, is small compared with the numbers of those suffering from nervous disorder. In fact, the only way of dealing effectively with such common conditions as chronic severe anxiety, sexual inadequacy and other emotional maladjustments, is to prevent them. It is this which makes psychological medicine a vital part of public health.

On how to prevent these disorders there is much to learn. But one essential is to create a society in which all parents can bring up their children in security and with confidence in the future. In chapter 6 some extreme examples of the effects of lack of normal maternal care were given; but, short of such severe deprivation, gross poverty, malnutrition, fear of war or of unemployment, and loneliness due to an inadequate community life, can all provoke or make worse psychological instability and maladjustment. Both 'material' and 'psychological' factors are important in causing disorders of behaviour, as we might expect if the somatic approach to psychology is a sound one.

Nor does this apply only to the neuroses. True madness, or psychosis, also varies in its incidence according to the conditions in which people are living. In chapter 9 we saw that delinquency is influenced in this way. The same applies to the most prevalent of the psychoses, schizophrenia, and probably to other psychoses as well. This fact would be of relatively small importance if the psychoses were rare diseases. But they are not. In Britain today, in 1954, *one half* of all the hospital beds in use are occupied by patients with psychological disorders, and two-fifths of all beds by schizophrenes. These people are therefore a severe burden on the community, and with their relatives represent an immense total of unhappiness.

The Meaning of 'Statistics'

This chapter, more than most, is full of numbers and percentages. It is therefore perhaps appropriate to quote a passage from a recent publication of the British Ministry of Health:

Statistics may be dull things and are much abused by cynics, but they have provided the starting point for many of the advances in preventive and curative medicine and they will continue to do so.

A topical and instructive example is that of primary carcinoma of the lung. This form of lung cancer has been increasing dramatically: in the period 1911 to 1919 the annual death rate due to it in England and Wales was about 250 persons; in 1952, 11,981 men and 2237 women died of it. Other countries have shown similar increases. It is clear that this increase is not merely due to better diagnosis. Research in Britain, the United States, and elsewhere has now established a statistical correlation between smoking, especially the heavy smoking of cigarettes, and lung cancer. Since this type of cancer is responsible for one in four of all cancer deaths in men, and for one in twenty of *all* male deaths, the matter is one of serious concern for large numbers of people, in fact for the whole community. At least two governments, those of Britain and the U.S.S.R., have issued warnings of some kind against the habit of heavy smoking among young people, though in Britain at least there is no evidence, in 1954, that the warnings have been heeded. It has of course long been known that smoking can lead to an increase in respiratory infections, shortness of wind and chronic pharyngitis. Unfortunately, nicotine is a drug of addiction; smoking is also a social ritual; and the tobacco companies are wealthy and are able to maintain expensive advertising campaigns, regardless of the effects of their products on consumers.

Both in the United States and Britain tobacco firms have,

however, offered large sums for research on the physiological effects of smoking. It has recently been claimed that
the tar produced by burning tobacco can induce skin
cancers in mice, and there can be little doubt that the
research now going on, stimulated by the original statistical
observations, will reveal much of interest and importance.
Only experiment can finally validate the inferences drawn
from numerical studies.

Certain other features of the statistical evidence are worth
noting. Lung cancer is not wholly dependent on smoking for
its development: some, though relatively very few, non-
smokers develop it. Further, there are proportionally higher
numbers of lung cancers among town-dwellers than country-
folk. The most plausible explanation for this is that atmo-
spheric pollution by smoke (or by petrol fumes) is responsible, though there is no direct evidence for this. (The
occasional disastrous mortality, due to 'smog', in large
cities, is of course nothing to do with cancer.) However,
since nobody is addicted to fog, and nobody makes a profit
by selling it (though some save money by failing to abate it),
it might be expected that strenuous efforts would be made to
get rid of it, without the additional incentive of cancer
prevention.

Other examples of the importance of 'statistics' have been
given earlier in this chapter. To determine some of the main
causes of rheumatic heart disease it was necessary to study
sample groups of families, and to relate the incidence of the
disease to various factors, including economic status and
overcrowding. The techniques of sampling, and of correlat-
ing one group of facts with another, come under a particular
branch of mathematics, statistical analysis. A statistician,
when he uses his special methods of analysis, is taking the
results of counting something – perhaps the number of persons suffering from a particular disease – and working out
the significance of the results of the counting.

There is no more justification for criticizing the statistician
than there would be for criticizing a farmer who reported
that he owned 40 dairy cows, and that 30 of them (or 75 per

cent) were in milk. A possible reason why many nevertheless feel a distrust of 'statistics' – which generally means a distrust of general statements about large numbers of people or things – is that they are necessarily impersonal. For the statistician as such the latest group of deaths from some disease are, so to speak, just another buzz and click on the calculating machine. What is needed is to relate the results of his calculations to individual experience. It is one thing to read of the tens of millions of sufferers from chronic malaria, quite another to appreciate the suffering of these many persons, condemned throughout their lives to a debilitated existence in poverty and squalor. In discussing a community with a high infant mortality it is necessary to understand what the figures mean for the individual mothers who have to watch their babies die after a few days of vomiting and diarrhoea.

A book of this sort can do little more than report the facts of starvation or disease in general terms: the task of conveying what the facts signify, in terms of individual suffering or the relief of suffering, must be left to the journalist or the novelist writing of particular persons and incidents. One lesson of this chapter is the immense power of modern bacteriology to prevent a great number of the worst diseases. Although there are some serious gaps, our knowledge of the causes and means of prevention of infectious disease is remarkably complete. Cholera, the dysenteries, typhoid, typhus, and smallpox not only can be, but in some countries have been, almost completely wiped out. Even malaria and yellow fever have been brought under control in some areas. Full application of existing knowledge could reduce tuberculosis and the main causes of death in infancy to a very small fraction of the present total. But the knowledge cannot be applied simply by the passage of laws or by government regulations. Just as food production and nutritional standards can be raised only as part of a general process of economic improvement, so the prevention of infectious disease requires vast expenditure on public health services, and education of the whole community to take advantage of them. In the long run such expenditure justifies itself not only by the increase in health and happiness, but also by the release for productive purposes of human energy which would otherwise be drained away by disease. Knowledge of these facts is especially necessary today, both to enable ordinary people to play their part in promoting their own health and that of their children, and to reinforce the demand that the greatest possible exertion should be devoted to this end.

POPULATION

> Be fruitful, and multiply, and replenish the earth, and sub-
> due it: and have dominion over the fish of the sea, and over
> the fowl of the air, and over every living thing that moveth
> upon the earth.
>
> GENESIS

DESPITE the famine and disease which have always killed
men, and which continue to kill them, human populations
have enormously increased since man first appeared. And,
as we know, they are still increasing. Among animals in
general man is relatively infertile: women bear as a rule
only one child at a time, and the interval between children
is seldom less than a year; often it is much more even in the
absence of deliberate contraception. Nevertheless human
reproductive potential can maintain a high rate of population increase, in the absence of a corresponding mortality
or of birth control. In the most favourable conditions a large
human population can double itself in about seventeen
years. Even in times of food shortage reproduction may
continue at a high rate, and so make the shortage worse,
until famine occurs and numbers are reduced by starvation.

The first great increase in human numbers, as we saw in
chapter 11, arose from the invention of agriculture: before
that, food scarcity had severely limited human populations.
In the agricultural period of the past seven thousand years
food has still often been a limiting factor, but epidemic
disease has also played a part in restraining population
growth. Today, some populations are still increasing, while
others remain roughly stationary. They may be facing, in
the first place, famine and a greater incidence of infection;
in the second, economic difficulties due to an increasing

proportion of old people. In this chapter we shall consider how the various factors influencing population size actually work, and what changes are going on in the populations of various countries.

Death Rates

The death rate is the number of persons dying in one year, in each 1000 of population. We find three kinds of influences affecting death rates. First, the direct causes of death may become more, or less, effective: measles, for instance, seems to have become more virulent in the past fifty years, and scarlet fever less virulent. But changes of this sort have only a minor importance. Second, death rates are influenced by changes in the resistance to the causes of death: resistance in this sense may be within the individual, as when a poor diet leads to lowered resistance, or outside – for instance sanitary measures which prevent infection. The third factor is the age-composition of a population. If a population has relatively many old people its death rate will be higher than that of a population of normal composition: some English south-coast towns, for instance, have very high death rates because many of their inhabitants have come to them on retirement at sixty or later.

The death rates referred to above are called *crude* death rates, but when the rates of two countries are compared we use *standardized* death rates: that is, we allow for differences in age composition. Recently the crude death rate in Sweden was 12 per thousand, while that of Australia was between 8 and 9; but when the rates were standardized they were found to be almost identical. So, insofar as the death rate is a measure of health, Sweden and Australia had equally good health. The reason for the lower crude rate for Australia was the presence of immigrants in the prime of life, among whom the death rate is lower than for other age groups.

In large parts of the world, but especially in the west, death rates have fallen strikingly since 1800. The most obvious cause has been improvement in the health services. Recently the rise in nutritional standards also has contributed. Other social changes have played a part: since about 1750 the availability of cheap cotton clothing, which can be washed, has made cleanliness easier and so has reduced infection. There are also political influences: wars and internal disorder tend to increase death rates, not only directly but even more by the social disruption they bring about. The political factor has probably been important in China, for instance, where the Manchu dynasty kept civil war in check from 1644 until the present century; during this period the Chinese population increased a good deal.

One way in which mortalities can be compared is by taking the *expectation of life at birth* for different places and different times. In England and Wales in 1841 it was just over 40 years for men; in 1891 it was 44, and in 1931 nearly 59; by 1951 it was over 66 years; for women the figures are slightly higher. In India, between the two world wars, it was about 25. In colonial Africa it is very low, and has even fallen during this century. In these undeveloped countries mortality is much as it was in the ancient world: the mummy cases of Roman Egypt suggest that the upper class Egyptians two thousand years ago had an expectation of life at birth of between 25 and 30 years; there is evidence that in Rome it was only 20, but in some Roman provinces it was probably about 35. The last figure is close to some of those computed for the Middle Ages: in Breslau in 1690, for instance, it is believed to have been about 33·5.

These figures do not signify that most Indians, for example, die at about twenty-five: very large numbers die in the first few months of life, and most of the remainder pass the age of thirty: the expectation of life is, in fact, only an average, and can be misleading unless the death rates at different ages are kept in mind. This is illustrated in the figure on page 286.

European Population. Estimates showing the recent striking increase in population, compared with the relatively steady state during the previous millennium

Birth Rates

The decline in death rates has been followed in some countries by a decline in birth rates. For most of the world's population, however, birth rates are near the maximum allowed by human fecundity. (Fecundity is the reproductive *capacity*, whereas fertility is the amount of reproduction actually achieved.) In Japan, China, India, Java, and Egypt, in Carr-Saunders' words, 'marriage is early and universal, and when marriage has been consummated no steps are taken to limit the size of the family'. The decline in birth rates has occurred on the whole in the countries where death rates have fallen most, and in particular where child mortality has been much reduced. Had there been no decline, the populations in these countries would have increased enormously in the past century, and most parents would be faced with the upbringing of between five and twenty children. In Britain in the mid-Victorian period each couple had on an average about six children born alive. The corresponding figure by 1925–9 was 2·2.

The crude birth rate is affected by three main factors. First, as with death rates, it is influenced by the age distribution of the population: births are almost confined to women between the ages of fifteen and fifty, and the birth rate depends on the proportion of such women in the population. The age distribution within the child-bearing range may also have some effect, since women are most fertile in their twenties. A second factor is marriage: there will be fewer births the more women remain unmarried, or the more marriage is delayed. This has probably been important both in Europe and in the United States. In the U.S.A. the birth rate is reckoned to have fallen from 55 in 1800 to 20 in 1930; yet the proportion of women of child-bearing age rose during that period. Part of the explanation is an increase in the proportion of single persons, which was particularly marked in the census of 1890. Similarly, in Britain, age of marriage rose after 1871. By 1911 more people were marrying at ages twenty-five to twenty-nine than at twenty to twenty-four. (Very recently, however, this trend has been reversed, and now, in the 1950s, the commonest age of marriage for women is twenty-one.)

But the decline of fertility in the West cannot be attributed only, or even mainly, to less marriage. The decline has been so great that the obvious explanations have seemed to be inadequate, and some fancy ones have been put forward. For example, vitamin E deficiency is known to reduce reproductive capacity in some mammals, and it has been suggested that if we ate more vitamin E we might get more babies; but there is no evidence that we lack vitamin E: it is present in most foods. Then cleanliness has been accused of some responsibility in two ways. First, soap tends to kill human sperm and is indeed a good deal more spermicidal than some of the chemical contraceptives that have been widely used; it has therefore been suggested that soap in the vagina may have reduced fertility. But again there is no evidence. On the other hand there is some experimental basis for the second theory. Human sperm are killed at temperatures only a little above that of the scrotum in which the testicles are suspended, and it has been shown that the application of hot water to the scrotum reduces the number of live sperm produced in subsequent ejaculations. It is therefore possible that hot baths before retiring may tend to reduce male fertility. An entirely different suggestion attributes lowered fertility to less coitus resulting from an increase in alternative sources of enjoyment. However, it is difficult to measure the extent to which people are enjoying life, and there is no adequate evidence that enjoyment does lessen sexual activity.

The most obvious and probably the principal cause of the falling birth rates is the increasing practice of contraception. Carr-Saunders has summarized the evidence. He points out that the decline of the birth rate in most countries coincided with outbursts of birth-control propaganda, and goes on:

In almost every country the decline began in the upper economic class and spread downwards in such a fashion that there has come into being a marked negative correlation between social status and fertility.* This is compatible with the spread of contraception if it is supposed that the better-off people first acquired these new practices. It is in general true that fashions spread downwards; moreover, contraceptive appliances are costly, and therefore not easily accessible to the poor.

Further evidence comes from the fertility of groups of different religious faiths. In Holland and Canada, Protestant groups can be compared with Catholic, among whom birth control (except by means of the 'safe' period) is forbidden. Catholics have a much higher fertility. The relatively low fertility of the nominally Catholic populations of France and Austria is held to be due to the decline of religious belief in those countries: certainly in Austria the birth rate in the country districts, where the Church is powerful, is higher than among the more sophisticated townsfolk. Special studies support these conclusions. Carr-Saunders refers to the work of Methorst, who investigated 21,307 families in Holland.

He discovered that, when no child had died, there was less

* But see page 315.

than twelve months interval between the birth of children in only 1·4 per cent of the cases, but that when a child had died, another birth took place within twelve months in no less than 19·7 per cent. The only possible explanation is that, when a child has died, the parents seek to replace it and abandon ... birth-control for a time. Again, ... Stevenson showed that, whereas in general the fertility of young wives sank from the age of twenty onwards, the fertility of young wives of the professional class rose until they were over twenty-five. Owing to the late age at which professional men begin to earn a living, there are strong motives for using birth-control among very young professional couples when first married; that they do so is the only possible explanation of this curious anomaly.

Actually, there is an alternative explanation for Methorst's results. The chances of conception are, for physiological reasons, reduced while a mother is suckling a child, and so the early loss of an infant increases the likelihood of a fresh conception. In some primitive societies it is usual for a child to be fed at the breast until three or more years old, and this practice seems to have a use in preventing an excessive birth rate.

An American investigation gives direct evidence on family planning in one group. White Protestant couples of good education were studied in Indianapolis; all had been married for twelve to fifteen years. Thirty per cent of these couples had planned every pregnancy: that is, pregnancy occurred only when contraception was stopped with the object of having a child. Among another 14 per cent, at least the last child had been planned, and so the total number of children had been deliberately chosen. A further 30 per cent had the wanted number of children, but had not planned the last child and would have preferred to have it later. Thus in this inquiry 74 per cent of the couples had the number of children they wanted; and it was further found that most of the remainder had only one more than the desired number.

To sum up, the evidence as a whole leaves little doubt about the part played by deliberate birth control in reducing fertility. Later we shall discuss the reasons for the increasing use of birth control.

Growing Populations

If we turn from birth and death rates to the population changes they bring about, we find that the main feature of the world population is its tendency to increase. If present trends continue world population by the end of the century will be near 4000m. – an increase of more than 50 per cent in fifty years. It is true that we do not know, even now, exactly what the world population is, but we have estimates of tolerable accuracy covering the last three centuries. In this period there has been what Carr-Saunders has called 'an unparalleled outburst of population'. The total number of human beings has increased nearly four times. The increase has taken place in all continents, though it has been greatest among Europeans who have increased seven times; only they have overflowed in large numbers, especially to North America, and there are now 200m. outside Europe.

The 2400m. human beings are very unevenly distributed throughout the world. Europe, with 520m., is densely populated, and parts of Asia, with its total of more than half that of the world, also have dense populations. The Americas are more thinly occupied: North America has 155m. and Central and South America about 20m. and 85m. respectively. The population of Africa is estimated to be 145m., a relatively small figure for a large continent. (These figures are slightly more up-to-date than those of the table.) The densely settled areas are southern China, India, Europe, and eastern North America. These areas all have fertile soil, adequate rainfall, navigable rivers, and coal and iron, and are well placed for trade.

The current increase in world population is not due to a uniform increase going on in all countries. It is due largely to the growth of the populations of India and Indonesia. Some smaller nations, such as Egypt and Ceylon, are also growing rapidly, and even Europe had 21m. more people in 1947 than in 1939; this was due mainly to increases in S.E. Europe. The United States, strangely enough, also has

ESTIMATED WORLD POPULATION AND DISTRIBUTION BY CONTINENTS: 1800–1939

	1800	1850	1900	1913	1939
	POPULATION IN MILLIONS				
WORLD	919	1091	1527	1723	2080
Asia	600	664	839	923	1097
Europe	188	266	390	468	542
Africa	100	100	141	135	157
N. and Central America . .	15	39	110	134	184
South America . . .	14	20	41	56	89
Oceania	2	2	6	8	11
	PERCENTAGE DISTRIBUTION				
WORLD	100·0	100·0	100·0	100·0	100·0
Asia	65·3	60·9	54·9	53·6	52·7
Europe	20·5	24·4	25·5	27·2	26·1
Africa	10·9	9·2	9·2	7·8	7·5
N. and Central America .	1·6	3·6	7·2	7·8	8·8
South America . . .	1·5	1·8	2·7	3·2	4·3
Oceania	0·2	0·2	0·4	0·5	0·5

Many of the figures in this table are necessarily only approximations, especially the earlier ones. China in particular, which now probably accounts for one-fifth to one-fourth of the world's population, has not yet had any adequate census: even today (1954) estimates of the Chinese population are based on nothing better than sample censuses of relatively small areas, but a full census is now planned. The latest estimate is 500m.

Although the total increase in the population of Asia in the past 150 years has been about 500m. its relative increase has been less than that of any other continent except Africa. Potential increase in both these continents has been checked by famine and pestilence. The enormous relative expansion in North and Central America, and to a less extent in South America, has been due to the emigration of Europeans who have subsequently rapidly increased in numbers. Correspondingly, the percentage of Asians and Africans in the world total has diminished. There is no question of 'whites' being swamped by other groups

a quite rapidly increasing population. Of all these India has the largest population. Since the first world war India has shown a steady reduction in mortality, and

Population Growth 1937–47. Areas of most rapid increase are shown black

this will become more marked if the health services proposed since the second world war are made to work. During the twenty years from 1921 the population of India increased by 83m., and this rate of increase could, according to an official report published in 1946, easily be doubled if the health services were improved without a corresponding reduction in fertility. And there is no present indication of a decline in fertility: it is true that as early as 1924 the birth rate among the Brahmins living in Madras was no higher than that of the Europeans, but Brahmins belong to a very small, privileged section of the community, and drastic social changes would be required in India before their example could be followed by a majority of the population. The following estimated birth and death rates for India illustrate the position.

	birth rate	death rate
1881–91	49	41
1891–1901	46	44
1901–11	49	43
1911–21	48	47
1921–31	46	36
1931–41	45	31

If these trends continue we may expect the present Indian population of about 400m. to become 730m. in thirty years, that is, by about 1980. For the whole of this number to be adequately fed, food production in India will have to be nearly three times as great as it is now.

There is a similar situation in Indonesia. In Java, for instance, the population was about 4·5m. in 1815, 28·4m. in 1928, and about 50m. in 1945.

These are countries in which neither birth nor death rates have come under secure control. The same applied to China until recently, though now conditions are changing very rapidly; and it still applies to many of the South American countries. But in these, as far as we know, death rates are not falling as in India and Indonesia: they remain high, and in step with the high birth rates. Consequently

200 PER SQ MILE   40 PER SQ MILE   2 PER SQ MILE

Population Densities

the tendency to increase in numbers remains only latent. China, which is believed to have a population of the order of 500m., may show, for a time, a rapid population growth when health services, such as were introduced into Western Europe in the nineteenth century, become widespread. Up to now the Chinese population has shown violent fluctuations due to famines and epidemics, without any steady trend up or down.

There is one further large population which is still increasing rapidly, that of the U.S.S.R. It differs from all those so far mentioned, except the United States, in having both death and birth rates declining. It has been estimated that the birth rate in 1927 was 45·0, whereas by 1938 it had fallen to 38·3. The death rate had however shown a greater fall, from 26·0 to 17·8.

Declining Populations?

Although their death rates are low, western Europe and the British Dominions have nearly stationary populations. In these countries birth rates have fallen enough at least to balance the much lowered death rates; if this were not the case the peoples of these countries would have a standard of living more like that of the backward peoples. The decline of fertility in the West, and among European populations generally, has led to a good deal of discussion of what has been called 'race suicide', the 'invention of sterility' and so on. Since about 1930 the main population problem has been represented as the 'twilight of parenthood' or the 'parents' revolt'. It might be thought that the attainment of a stationary population when the death rate had been so much reduced would be a source of satisfaction. That it has been instead a source of alarm is due to the fear that the populations of the countries listed in the table on page 313 would fall rapidly: the apparent stability was thought to be illusory.

The prediction that European populations must decline depended on the study of the *net reproduction rates* of these populations. The net reproduction rate measures the extent to which a population is replacing itself. The need for a special means of measuring replacement can be illustrated by an example. Suppose an area, say an island, were newly settled entirely by men and women of between twenty and thirty-five. The number of births per 100 persons in such a population would be exceptionally high, since every individual would be in the reproductive phase. There would also be a very low death rate, and so the population would increase rapidly. The rate of increase would, however, fall off as some of the original population grew old, and as the proportion of children increased. It might indeed turn out that, despite the initially high increase, the birth rate had not been high enough to maintain the population indefinitely at a steady level. For stability each mother must be replaced by another mother. This does not signify that each family should, on the average, consist of one daughter and one son: there is mortality to be allowed for, and the fact that some women never have any children. It is calculated that, in western Europe, for replacement to be assured, each couple who produce children should have, on the average, nearly four. Given this, the net reproduction rate would be approximately 1·0 – the figure that represents a fertility rate just high enough to keep the population constant.

The table on page 313 shows that a number of countries have or had net reproduction rates of less than one. France, indeed, where the net reproduction rate has been below unity since the beginning of the century, has already begun its population decline (if we ignore the effects of immigration). An important question is whether there will be a decline elsewhere. Certainly, if the trends of the 1930s had continued for long the decline in some countries would be startling. The population of the United Kingdom today (1954) is about 50m. Ignoring the effects of emigration and immigration, and assuming the maintenance of pre-war trends, it would be about 31m. in 1975 and 4·5m. in 2035. Figures such as these must not be regarded as prophecies:

they show only what would happen if the rates of a particular period continued unchanged. The likelihood of the maintenance of particular trends cannot be accurately assessed, because of the many influences which affect the birth rate. The way in which net reproduction rates may mislead can be illustrated by a calculation made in 1935, that the population of England and Wales would be 40·14m. in 1947 if the prevailing trends continued. The actual population in 1947 was 43·02m. Moreover, the calculations made in 1935 suggested that by 1945 the population would be decreasing at the rate of 125,000 a year; but in fact, the excess of births over deaths in the first half of 1947 alone was 176,000. A recent prediction, made in the report of the Royal Commission on Population, is that a further slow increase in the population of England and Wales must be expected, and that this may continue for a generation.

The rise in fertility during the 1940s has been common to a number of very diverse European countries, including Eire, Czechoslovakia, France, and the Scandinavian nations. Various explanations have been suggested, including full employment, and better health among the young men and women who became mature during this period. There is little direct evidence on what factors have actually been most important.

Although we cannot predict future populations with any precision, we can get some idea of the motives which have led people to limit their families. Above we saw that birth control, rather than any increase in sterility, has been the probable means of family limitation, and it might be thought that the decline in fertility has been simply due to the spread of knowledge of contraceptive methods. But many inquiries have shown that the most used method even today is *coitus interruptus*, in which the semen is not discharged until the penis is withdrawn; and this method (frowned on by psychologists) must have been known for as long as the connexion between coitus and conception has been understood. The spread of knowledge of contraceptive

Countries with Net Reproduction Rates Near Unity

COUNTRY	YEAR	N.R.R.
U.S.A.	1937	0·965
	1942	1·189
United Kingdom	1937	0·785
	1944	0·990
France	1939	0·9
Belgium	1939	0·859
	1941	0·672
Denmark	1937	0·947
	1943	1·140
Germany	1940	0·976
Austria	1939	1·00
Hungary	1938	1·00
Czechoslovakia	1929–32	0·94
Norway	1939	0·856
Sweden	1941	0·843
Switzerland	1938	0·779
	1943	1·054
Australia	1937	0·981
	1943	1·163
New Zealand	1937	0·999
	1942	1·208
Estonia	1938	0·79
Finland	1938	0·96
Latvia	1939	0·99

methods has probably contributed, as we saw earlier, but it seems unlikely that it was the primary cause.

The most obvious motive for family limitation is the burden imposed on women by a large family. J. S. Mill wrote:

The family is rarely a large one by the woman's desire, because upon her weighs, besides all the physical suffering and a full share in all privations, the unbearable domestic toil which grows from a large number of children.

But this was written at a time when, nevertheless, families remained large. Children were, until very recently, an economic asset to their parents. Apart from their ability to work when still very young, they would probably be their parents' only support in old age. This seems to have been the origin of the practice, still kept up in some parts even of England, of a young couple awaiting the pregnancy of the woman before marrying. Today the economic motive for having a large family is much reduced: the lowered death rate makes it unnecessary to ensure the survival of one or two by having a large number; and old-age pensions and other social services reduce the likelihood of complete destitution even for the childless. Most parents reduce the size of their families but do not voluntarily remain completely childless: the aim seems to be to have perhaps two or three children, but not more. (This disposes of such explanations as 'fear of war' for family limitation.) Alvar Myrdal, in her analysis of the family in Sweden, emphasizes the probable importance of the higher standards of child care now expected, and of the heavy financial cost of maintaining these standards. In a recent survey in Britain the average age of mothers at the birth of a first child was found to be twenty-six in the most fertile income group, and even higher in other groups. The delay is evidently due to waiting until a certain income level or degree of security has been achieved.

From this point of view it may seem an anomaly that the decline of the birth rate begins among those with higher incomes, that is, among those who could presumably best afford a large family. A possible explanation is that, since family limitation was contrary to established convention, it was, in Alvar Myrdal's words,

only to be expected that those social groups that were most mobile and already most emancipated from the static scales of values should first start consciously to consider their childbearing. Thus family limitation is not a function of families being richer. All the instances generally quoted of 'the richer the family, the fewer the children' relate only to a transition period, when the upper classes have temporary precedence in utilizing methods of family limitation.

This explanation, though speculative, is supported by the fact that the reproductive decline has, by the middle of the century, spread to all economic classes. In fact, in Sweden, the tendency is now said to be for the richer families to have the larger numbers of children.

It seems likely, therefore, that, in the countries with net reproduction rates of approximately unity, family size is becoming stabilized in all classes at a low level. Various attempts have been made to prevent or to arrest this decline in fertility. In France, the country with the lowest net reproduction rate, a much-discussed system of family allowances was introduced during the first world war, and made the subject of a law in 1932. The allowances have been estimated to cover about a half of the cost of each child. They did not prevent the continued decline in fertility, though they may have reduced it. Much the same applies to Italy, where there were a bachelor tax, and a higher income tax rate on bachelors and the childless, as well as family allowances. In Germany under the Nazis a number of minor measures were introduced, including marriage loans: there was a temporary increase in births, but no evidence of any long-term effect. In the United Kingdom small allowances for second and subsequent children were introduced in 1945. Two years later a report on child-bearing in Britain, based on a nation-wide inquiry, commented as follows:

The costs of childbearing are so high that they are likely to deter many mothers, of all classes, from having children. It is not

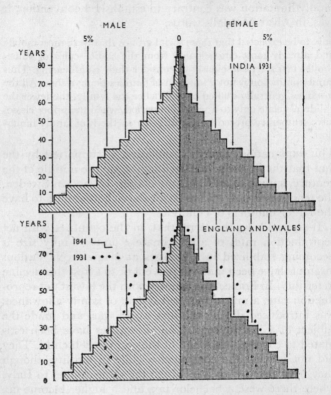

Age and Population. Age pyramids for India (1931) and England and Wales (1841 and 1931). Each population is shown as a series of slabs one on top of the other: each slab represents an age group of five years, e.g. all the people between 30 and 35 years; the oldest are at the top. The width of each slab shows the percentage of the population made up by that age group. In 1841 England and Wales had an age distribution rather like that of India in recent times, with a high proportion of very young people; the 'pyramid' for England and Wales in 1931 shows the temporary effect of a heavy decline in birth rate. The eventual expected shape is an approximate rectangle (indicating little deaths in early or middle life) with a tapering top representing death among those over 60 unlikely that, in many working-class families, this expenditure has to be met by borrowing or drawing upon savings. A substantial reduction in the costs of having a child is only likely to be achieved by lowering the price of baby clothes and equipment.

We may ask whether it will not be necessary also to reduce the rents of larger houses and to increase their number, and to make the bringing up of children, at a high standard of care, easier, by increasing services such as home helps and nursery schools. Security of employment may also turn out to be important. In 1949 the Report of the Royal Commission on Population commented on the 'economic and other handicaps of parenthood' of the period from 1910 onwards:

It remained true throughout the period that for most families the addition of children involved a substantial reduction of the family's standard of living, that the greater the number of children the smaller the chances of each child (and of the parents) of advancing in the competitive struggle and the greater the chances of falling back, and that some of the non-monetary costs of parenthood – the discomforts and risks of pregnancy and childbirth, additions to domestic work, restrictions on freedom, demands on nervous energy – increased more than proportionately with the size of the family. This is true despite the solid gains in human welfare that were achieved since the middle of the 19th century. Indeed, in the process of social advance, the position of parents and of members of larger families relative to others grew worse. The standard of living of the mass of the people rose, leisure increased . . . but the gap between parents and non-parents widened.

It is remarkable that the government which has adopted the most drastic population policy is that of the U.S.S.R., a country with a net reproduction rate still far above unity. In 1926 the rate was 1·72, and it has evidently not fallen greatly since then. Today, in 1954, the population of the U.S.S.R. is probably less than 200m., but at its present rate of increase it will reach about 300m. by the end of the century. The proportion of young people will be far higher, and of old people far lower, than in the countries of western Europe. Nevertheless, in 1944 a law was passed 'On increasing state aid to expectant mothers, mothers of large families, and unmarried mothers, protection of motherhood and childhood. . . .' The new measures included various grants and allowances for children, the expansion of privileges for expectant and nursing mothers, and taxes on single men and women and persons with small families. Various orders and awards were also instituted for mothers with large numbers of children, such as are given in most countries for rather different forms of public service.

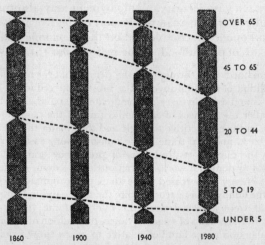

OVER 65

45 TO 65

20 TO 44

5 TO 19

UNDER 5

1860   1900   1940   1980

Ageing Population. The effect of the decline in birth and death rates on the proportion of people in different age groups in the U.S.A. The figures or 1980 are estimates from trends in the 1940s

Future Populations

If the Soviet government is successful in maintaining a satisfactory reproduction rate, its population policy will have important implications for other countries. It has already been strongly urged that its example should be followed in Australia, to prevent an expected decline in the Australian population. Every population may be regarded as having a place in a sequence of changes in which the ratio of births to deaths alters in an orderly manner. A country's population policy must depend on its position in the sequence.

The *demographic cycle*, as it is called, has five phases. The *first phase* is one in which both birth and death rates are very high: in times of peace and abundance the population rises; famine, pestilence, and war at other times cause decreases. There is no steady trend up or down. China is the only large country which has until very recently remained in this phase. In the *second phase* better social organization leads to a fall in the death rate, while the birth rate remains high; the population increases, though not rapidly. India, Indonesia, most of South and Central America, and the whole of Africa except Abyssinia and South Africa, are in this phase. In the *third phase* the death rate declines still further, and although the birth rate also tends to fall the rate of population increase is high. The U.S.S.R., Japan, and the countries of southern and eastern Europe are in this phase. With the *fourth phase* approximate stability is reached with both birth and death rates low. The net reproduction rate is about unity; not only does the population show no marked trend up or down, but, unlike a population in the first phase, it also escapes violent fluctuation. Countries in this phase are shown in the table on page 313. Finally we come to the *fifth phase*, in which the fall in the birth rate is so great that the population, despite a low death rate, declines steadily: this is largely hypothetical, since only one country, France, has ever reached it, and today the French population has returned to the fourth phase.

These phases provide only a rough classification, and one that conceals much interesting detail. For instance, as we saw, the U.S.A., the principal home of writers about the 'menace of population growth in Asia', has (in the 1950s) a higher rate of increase than India. This is made possible by a low death rate.

It will be noticed that the U.S.S.R. is only in the third phase, but that the attempt is already being made there to avoid the fifth, and to ensure for some time a steady population increase despite greater industrialism and a rising standard of life. This policy is based on the view that scientific and technical advances in food production can more than balance the needs of the growing population. A further implication is that there is nothing inevitable in the population cycle: the more we know about population changes, the less we need acquiesce in them if we do not like them.

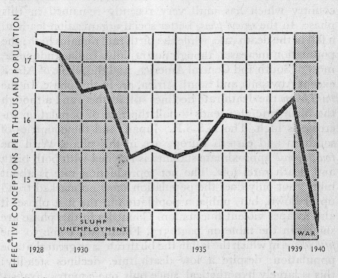

World Affairs and Fertility. Influence of world events on effective conception rate in England and Wales. The diagram is based on the number of live births

In countries with a low fertility, the birth rate at least is very much influenced by what is going on in the world. To be exact, it is the conception rate that has to be studied: birth rates are affected by what was going on rather more than nine months earlier. In Britain the slump and unemployment of 1929–33 were accompanied by a steep decline in the conception rate in 1931–3; after this there was a rise which ended in 1939. The first four months of war showed a steep decline, followed by a much less steep fall in the period of military inactivity. There was another steep decline after the fall of France. Facts of this sort suggest that reproduction could be rapidly influenced also by a policy deliberately designed to change fertility.

If this is so there is no reason to regard the fall in the birth rate in the western countries as anything but fortunate. Certainly a return to the large families of earlier times would not be regarded as tolerable. In the world as a whole the most formidable population problem remains that of countries in which fertility is still uncontrolled, and where numbers are increasing rapidly or are likely to increase with improved conditions. Part of the answer to this, as we saw in chapter 12, must be a tremendous effort to increase food production. Another part of the answer is suggested by F. W. Notestein, an American authority:

The matter cannot be rigidly proved, but the writer is profoundly convinced that only a society in which the individual (child or adult) has a reasonable chance for survival in healthy life will develop that interest in the dignity and material well-being of the individual essential to the reduction of fertility. He therefore firmly believes in directly fostering public health *as part of the program required to reduce growth potential.*

To sum up, in the past famine and epidemic disease have limited populations, and in times of plenty man was at the mercy of his own fecundity. Today we know how to produce much more food and to prevent much disease; we are also beginning to learn how to control reproduction. For most of the world the question is, when will the knowledge be put to use?

HUMAN NATURE

The philosophers have only *interpreted* the world in various
ways; the point however is to *change* it.

KARL MARX

THIS book describes some of the contributions that biological knowledge can make to contemporary problems. It
has been written, and will be read, at a time of social up-
heaval, and it has not been designed as a detached, dis-
interested account of man, such as a biologist might give of
a dung beetle or an earthworm.

In the first chapter biology was described as knowledge
that has come largely from man's efforts to produce food
and to prevent disease. This view of science, as a product of
society as a whole, is in contradiction to the one which
represents science as the product of a few inspired minds,
functioning in isolation and studying 'nature' or 'truth' for
its own sake. It is true that scientific advance depends to
an important extent on the work of a few people, with a
special talent for discovery and interpretation. But the work
of such people is often very closely and obviously related
to the human needs of their own time and country. Pasteur, for example, was one of the greatest of experimental
biologists; all his major contributions to knowledge had an
immediate application, though at the same time he and his
colleagues made an advance in theoretical biology that was
of the first importance. Pasteur is most famous for helping
to found the science of bacteriology, and for showing the
way to prevent a good deal of human disease; but a great
part of his work was inspired, directly or indirectly, by the
needs of French agriculture and the wine industry, and he
gave them valuable help.

Not all scientific work is related so closely and obviously to immediate needs. The other leading figure of nineteenth century biology was Charles Darwin, and it might seem that his theory of evolution had nothing to do with his social background. But close examination of his work, and of the times he lived in, makes it clear that he was not functioning in an intellectual vacuum. The theory of the origin of species by natural selection was arrived at, not only by Darwin, but also simultaneously by Alfred Russel Wallace working independently. Simultaneous discovery by independent workers is a common feature of the development of science, and it is almost invariably true that, whenever a major advance is made, it is the product of the work of a number of scientists, working more or less independently on similar lines. This at once suggests that scientific advance is part of a general historical process, and is not due to the fortuitous appearance of isolated geniuses. In the case of Darwin and the theory of evolution, it is a striking fact that the idea of organic evolution – which had been put forward by various biologists for a century before Darwin – came to be accepted at a time of especially rapid social change.

Both Darwin and Wallace were led to think of natural selection as the main cause of evolution by reading the work of Malthus (referred to in chapter 12) on human populations. One of the implications of Malthus' theories was that it was useless to try to raise the living standards of the poor, since they would then only breed more rapidly and so exhaust the food supply. This outlook fitted well with the attitude of the rising capitalists of the nineteenth century: their attitude was, every man for himself and the most enterprising will come to the top and rightly earn the greatest power and wealth. There is a close analogy between this theory of how human society should work and the theory of natural selection, or 'survival of the fittest', which Darwin and Wallace applied to organisms in general. Natural selection has indeed been invoked as a support for the policy of 'devil take the hindmost' among human beings, although the fallacy in the argument is obvious enough: it is that,

M

even if natural selection operates throughout the organic world, it does not at all follow that it operates in human society; and, even if it did, we need not acquiesce in its doing so. Most people will agree that a cut-throat struggle between individuals is unlikely to be anything but destructive of organized society.

One further fact (out of many) may serve to bring home the way in which Darwinism reflected the ideas of the times: some years before Darwin's major work, *On the Origin of Species*, was published, Herbert Spencer put forward a theory of the survival of the fittest, as he called it, to support the prevailing views on human social relations. Thus a theory similar to Darwin's had already been advanced in the field of sociology.

To say that Darwin's work reflected the contemporary state of society, or was influenced by it, is not to detract from Darwin's achievement. His work was enormous in quantity and outstanding in content. Scientists are not remote and isolated individuals: they grow up in a particular environment like anybody else, they have parents who usually hold views which belong to their own times, and teachers who give conventional instruction. They are part of the society in which they live. Darwin and Pasteur exemplify a general rule in the relations of science to society.

Progress in the application of technical knowledge depends on the use made of the abilities of especially gifted persons, such as Pasteur and Darwin, together with those of many less able men and women. These abilities include the passion for inquiry which is sometimes represented as the main driving force of scientific advance. It is one force, but its scope is limited by the extent to which those who possess it are allowed to give vent to it. Today this depends on two things. First, a child with potential scientific ability can use it only if parents or government pay for a lengthy education. Second, if his particular gifts are directed towards one line of inquiry, say, the study of moulds, he will still be unable to apply them fully, unless it is thought by the government (or by some other body with funds) that the study of moulds deserves support. This particular example is taken because penicillin, one of the most valuable of chemical agents for preventing or curing infections, is produced by a mould; and it happens that in Britain the study of moulds and other fungi has been, and is, seriously neglected. If this were not the case use might have been made of penicillin soon after it was originally discovered in London in 1929, instead of more than a decade later. This would have involved the employment of a number of botanists, chemists, and medical scientists whose talents during that period may in fact have been not so profitably used.

Biological science today, in fact, is still, as it was in earlier times, largely a product of the efforts of men to get what they want. This is true even though there are a few men and women who are able to study it without any practical end in view, and not consciously influenced by the society in which they live.

Whatever the motives or motivation of scientists, most people will wish to know what direct use their work is for everyday purposes. The most fundamental contribution of biology to the study of man is a general law which has been exemplified in almost every chapter. Every individual is the product of a complex development, in which the effects of the genes and of outside influences are continually inter-acting: neither heredity nor environment can be said to be the more important, though one may have more influence than the other in causing variation in particular characters. If we are considering differences – physical or behavioural – between 'races', classes, or the sexes, this interaction has to be allowed for.

When it is allowed for we find that 'human nature' is much more varied and changeable than has commonly been supposed. 'Races' are found to be both exceedingly hetero-geneous genetically, and capable of very rapid changes from generation to generation: that is, they include people with all sorts of potentialities, and the expression of these potentialities varies with social organization. In palaeolithic society there was little opportunity for the expression of many of the qualities we most admire today, except courage, some manual dexterity, and, in certain periods, skill in the visual arts; the appropriate genes must have been available, but an environment in which they could have full effect had not been evolved. All we know at present suggests that any human group, in an appropriate environment, is capable of producing individuals with a high level of technical skill, artistic ability, and social sense.

Just as there is no monopoly of virtue among races, so economic or social classes are found to be of very mixed heredity; they are indeed even less permanent and less sharply marked off from each other than the racial groups, and ability is lost if the children of any group are forbidden access to education, or to particular trades or professions, on account of the poverty or social status of their parents. In most societies, moreover, the female sex as a whole occupies, quite unjustly, an inferior social position.

Although heredity and environment are of equivalent importance in determining the course of individual development, they are not of equal importance when we come to action. There is at present little to be done to alter human genetic constitutions (though it is a different matter with domestic animals): if we find a group of persons of poor physique, low intellectual ability or criminal tendencies we must seek to alter the environment in which the group has developed. The outstanding contributions of biology to the improvement of our environment have been the increase of food supplies, the knowledge of nutrition, and the demonstration of the origin and method of prevention of many diseases.

The emphasis on environment as alterable, while heredity is regarded as practically fixed, may seem to conflict with the second great biological principle which we have applied to man. Just as each individual is a product of heredity and environment, so mankind as a whole is a product of evolution. And evolution depends on the survival of some genetic constitutions and the disappearance of others. But the genetic changes in populations occur on a quite different time scale from that of the changes in human society, if we except those in domestic animals under controlled breeding. *Homo sapiens* has barely had time to show even slight evolutionary change in the biological sense in the whole of the 70,000 years during which he is known for certain to have existed; yet in less than ten thousand years he has evolved socially from savagery to civilization, and civilization itself has taken on a series of progressively more complex forms. Today social change has become even more rapid and more drastic, as a result of the application of scientific knowledge and methods to the solution of a limited range of problems. Apart from food and sanitation these problems have been mostly those of power, transport and communications, and of the mass production of goods, such as clothes, which had formerly been made individually by craftsmen or in the home.

But now it is realized that scientific methods can be applied to a much wider range of problems. For instance, we no longer have to take for granted traditional building methods: in the words of one report, 'At present, ... we drag more than 100 tons of material to the site of every house, when less than 5 tons would produce a house that would be much warmer and take less coal to heat it.' Inside the house the kitchen can be designed so that it fully meets the convenience of those who work in it, cooking can be done with little or no destruction of food content, and food can be kept without suffering decay or infection with disease germs. Similarly, in the factory, the methods of operational research can be applied to minimize fatigue, danger of injury, and loss of time; and this is not only a matter of such obvious things as ventilation and lighting, but may extend to the colour of the paint and whether workers should listen to music while they work.

Advances of this sort often depend on research requiring the help of laymen in large numbers. And once the research has been done the intelligent collaboration of the public is even more necessary. Diphtheria immunization is a notable example of what has already been achieved. Science is still often regarded as something remote – the property of a select few whose knowledge the majority of people cannot hope to share and whose outlook ordinary men would not think of adopting. The barriers are today being broken down as the rôle and scope of scientific knowledge become more obvious to non-scientists, and as the scientists themselves become increasingly involved in the social and political turmoil.

The business of making the whole of society scientific has begun in a few countries with the acquisition of a general understanding of the nature of infectious disease; and, in the physical sciences, with the development of popular knowledge of, for instance, electricity. But there is still nowhere a widespread understanding of scientific method, even among those with a superior education, and there will probably be none until children have the opportunity to practise it in school. At present, education remains in the pre-scientific phase: we are told what we ought to think, instead of having to discover things for ourselves and to exercise our powers of criticism. It is likely that parents who have recently co-operated in the mass testing of vaccines have learnt more of scientific method in doing so than they did throughout their schooling. In one group of tests, in which the parents of seven English boroughs co-operated, new whooping-cough vaccines were on trial: some thousands of infants were injected, one half with a vaccine and the remainder, the 'control' group, with a mixture outwardly similar but not containing the material under test. Neither the parents nor the doctors who administered the vaccines knew which was which: all injections were numbered, and the key was kept by the Medical Research Council. Two years after injection each child was observed again, and a comparison made of the incidence of whooping-cough in the various groups: if an experimental group shows a much lower incidence than the control, that is evidence for the effectiveness of the vaccine given. It is now reported that one vaccine in particular shows great promise. The investigation illustrates the need for working with large numbers, and the need for controls and for other rigorous precautions. When this sort of thing is generally understood it will no longer be possible for a responsible adult to take a patent medicine for some complaint, and to attribute his eventual recovery to the medicine, without any other evidence of its efficacy.

Just as scientific advance leads to questioning of conventions about, say, housing and food, so it may also prevent us from taking moral ideas for granted. Waddington has said:

The contribution which science has to make to ethics, . . . merely by revealing facts which were previously unknown or commonly overlooked, is very much greater than is usually admitted. The adoption of methods of thought which are commonplaces in science would bring before the bar of ethical judgement whole groups of phenomena which do not appear there now. For instance, our ethical notions are fundamentally based on a system of individual responsibility for individual acts. The principle of statistical correlation between two sets of events, although accepted in scientific practice, is not usually felt to be ethically completely valid. If a man hits a baby on the head with a hammer, we prosecute him for cruelty or murder; but if he sells dirty milk and the infant sickness or death rate goes up, we merely fine him for contravening the health laws. And the ethical point is taken even less seriously when the responsibility, as well as the results of the crime, falls on a statistical assemblage. The whole community of England and Wales kills 8000 babies a year by failing to bring its infant mortality rate down to the level reached by Oslo as early as 1931, which would be perfectly feasible; but few people seem to think this a crime.

While for many such ideas are quite new, for some they may already seem nothing but common sense. Science itself has indeed been defined as organized common sense. But getting general agreement on new attitudes is not simply a matter of the steady spread of knowledge, as education becomes more widespread and more fitted to contemporary needs. There is no walk-over for common sense. It is not only ignorance or even conservatism that has to be overcome: there is also active opposition.

There are plenty of examples from the subject matter of this book. Lies about race differences are promulgated by those who wish to use subject groups as a source of cheap labour, or for a background for wars of conquest. Class differences are said to be inherited and fixed, by those who profit from the existence of a privileged class with economic and political power over the rest. Food and patent medicine manufacturers advertise their products with misleading statements about their chemical composition and lies about the working of the body and the causes of disease. This propaganda has full scope in at least the advertisement columns of the daily newspapers; moreover the newspaper proprietors often depend financially on the advertisers and cannot as a rule afford to expose them even if they wish to do so. Education can rarely provide an antidote: teachers are as much victims of the prevailing propaganda as parents and pupils, and usually do little more than reflect the ideas of the community to which they belong.

The full application of the modern knowledge of human biology, as of science in general, is impossible while there remain powerful groups with vested interests in ignorance and unscientific ideas. Throughout human history there are instances of drastic changes in social organization accompanying technical advances. The transition from primitive communism to government by priest-kings over populations of slaves and peasants followed the development of agriculture. In the West states based on slavery collapsed and gave place to serfdom in a feudal society at the same time as new techniques in agriculture and other production came to be used. Feudalism in turn was replaced by capitalism when the physical sciences were applied to industrial production. In the same way, today, the application of science for human good demands further social change. The need for change, however obvious, is always denied, not only by those whose special interests might be upset, but also by those ruled by the principle that 'nothing should ever be done for the first time'. The latter are, perhaps, the more numerous.

The application of biology calls for changes in at least two ways. In the first place food production by modern methods depends on very large-scale planning and organization; it cannot be done by peasants working small plots independently, and in a chronic state of indebtedness to money-lenders or banks. Even in the United States, where farms are large, the problems of soil erosion have obliged the farmers and other producers in some large areas to accept communal enterprise. The problem of food production today is, in fact, a problem for society as a whole, and not for the family or village or the individual landowner. This is an example of the economic implications of applied biology. There are many others. In the second place, the application of scientific knowledge to food production and disease prevention requires an educated people in which all adults are capable of taking an active part in these social enterprises. We could not hope for such a population anywhere if in each country there were large groups of people genetically so far inferior that they could not profit from a modern education. We have seen that there is no evidence for the existence of such inferior groups; yet even now, in the world as a whole, only a minority have access to learning. (All the readers of this book belong to this minority.) These facts lead to the second major social implication of the application of biology, or indeed of science in general: we cannot make use of science properly while small privileged minorities have a monopoly of knowledge. To get the full benefit of existing knowledge we must be rid of the social or economic divisions into classes as they exist in most countries today. We shall then destroy at the same time the smaller groups, mentioned above, whose positive interest it is to promote ignorance.

We may take an example of the effects of such a change from the most obvious place in which to look for instances of conflict between classes, big industry. Large employers of labour often have experts to advise them on methods of reducing the human work involved in production, and they employ such methods as 'time and motion study' which

M*

have, or can have, a sound scientific basis. These methods are often in Britain and the United States strongly opposed by the trade unions, on grounds such as the excessive speed-up which they impose on the workers. Yet it is clear that scientific method could be used to make it easier and pleasanter for workers to perform their tasks, provided it were applied with regard to their interests.

We are far from applying science fully to humanitarian ends today. Lord Boyd Orr, on the eve of his retirement from the position of Director-General of the Food and Agriculture Organization, said:

If the food problem is not solved there will be chaos in the world in the next fifty years. The nations of the world are insane, they are spending one-third of their national incomes preparing for the next war. They are applying their energies to building up a war machine instead of applying the world's steel and industrial production to conserving the resources of the land. That is the only basis of civilization.

Two years after the end of the second world war, of £110m. spent by Britain in a year on scientific research and development, £67m. was devoted to war science; and the proportion in the United States was almost exactly the same. Since then in both countries the proportion has risen. Until scientific work is planned for peace, and not for war, we can hardly hope to make much progress towards a prosperous, egalitarian world society.

It must not be thought that the society to which we look forward is a vision of a scientific utopia peopled by robots. It is the tedious, automatic tasks that can most easily be done by the machines, and the more this happens the greater will be the demand for individual enterprise and ability. A part of mankind has already been liberated from the toil from sunrise to sunset which has been the lot of most men and women since agriculture began; but many of those so freed have been forced to work as long hours in worse conditions in industry, and to live in conditions of unprecedented squalor in industrial towns. Today, however, we have the technical knowledge needed to free men from slavery to production.

To make the fullest use of the liberty so acquired men and women must first have the basic essentials of food, good health, and shelter. But they must also have access to the refinements of civilized life, and here too scientific knowledge has a fundamental contribution to make. Apart from the fact that science is itself an integral part of the culture of today, it makes possible the diffusion of knowledge of all kinds. The printing press promoted the spread of literacy and the production of written works for popular use. The development of various forms of democracy also depended on it. Today radio and the cinema are taking us, or are at least capable of taking us, several steps further.

Applied science, in fact, can not only increase our material wealth, but also give us greater access to learning and the arts. Human biology can further this process by giving information both on human *abilities* and human *needs*. Chapters 8 to 10 have given some idea of what we already know of the diversity of human abilities. As for needs, chapters 12 to 14 have shown not only how knowledge of nutrition and health protection has accumulated, but also how appropriate action has been taken in some countries.

It is indeed only in action that the full implications of human biology can be learnt. Many will grasp the fallacies of race theory more easily by working with men and women of different colour, than by reading books about it. Members of a privileged class will appreciate the abilities to be found among the unprivileged majority by working with them on some joint enterprise. The facts of nutrition or infectious disease are brought home to many for the first time when they are faced with the upbringing of their children. Certainly the small families of the West are more readily understood when one has become a parent.

Use and understanding go together. The attempt to reach some limited objective, such as a piped water supply or adequate sanitation in one's village, can make real the knowledge passively acquired in school or by reading; it may also create a demand for more knowledge, which can be satisfied only by further reading. But the reading, if it is to be more than the casual acquisition of knowledge by a dilettante, must be an adjunct to action. This book tells a number of unfinished stories. The stories are being continued by the men and women who are working to apply the knowledge that we have.

ACKNOWLEDGEMENTS

FOR the first edition I had the benefit of many stimulating discussions with Dr M. L. Johnson and Michael Abercrombie; they also read and criticized the whole of the manuscript. Professor W. E. Le Gros Clark, F.R.S., kindly discussed a number of problems that arose in the writing of the book, and provided up-to-date information and material. Richard Palmer read the whole book in draft, Dr John Humphrey the chapter on disease, and Dr J. S. Weiner the chapters on human evolution and on 'race'. I am very grateful to all of these for their expert advice.

For this edition I have added a chapter on behaviour, and re-written many sections of the original chapters. I have also taken the opportunity to correct a number of errors, and to insert some new ones. In the former process I have been greatly helped by advice and criticism from many friends and colleagues, especially: Dr A. R. Hill, Dr Charles Lack, John McLeish, Professor L. S. Penrose, F.R.S., Professor G. Pontecorvo, F.R.S., Professor R. W. Russell, Dr G. I. M. Swyer, Dr J. C. Trevor.

Special acknowledgement is due to Edward Walton, who has redrawn, and in most instances redesigned, almost all the charts and diagrams, including a number of new ones.

S. A. B.

Acknowledgement is due also as follows for permission to use illustrations either in the original or in a modified form:

Text Figures: p. 19: *Genetics in Relation to Agriculture* by E. B. Babcock and R. E. Clausen (McGraw Hill); p. 71: *From Head to Foot* by A. Novikoff (Lawrence and Wishart, London; International Publishers, N.Y.); pp. 85, 86, 90, 92, 93, 98: *Mankind so Far* by W. Howells (Sigma, London; Doubleday, N.Y.); p. 110: *Doubt and Certainty in Science*, by J. Z. Young (Clarendon); p. 177: *Introduction to Modern Genetics* by C. H. Waddington (Allen and Unwin); p. 198: *Man the Tool-Maker* by K. P. Oakley (British Museum); pp. 213, 224, 307, 309: *Our Undeveloped World* by L. D. Stamp (Faber); pp. 230, 301: *The World's Food* by M. K. Bennett (Harper); p. 267: *The White Plague* by R. and J. Dubos (Gollancz); pp. 288, 289: *J. Hyg. Camb.* (1945), B. Woolf and M. Waterhouse (Cambridge).

Plates: 1: *Albinism in Man* by K. Pearson, E. Nettleship and C. H. Usher (Cambridge); 2, 3: *Genetica* (1928), J. P. Lotsy and W. A. Goddijn (Nijhoff); 4: Zoological Society, London; 5, 6, 8, 9, 11, 13: Pitt Rivers Museum, Oxford; 7: American Museum of Natural History; 10: Alexander Lipschutz; 12: *The Tissues of the Body* by W. E. Le Gros Clark (Clarendon); 14: *An Eskimo Brain* by A. Hrdlička (Knickerbocker); 15: Anthropology Laboratory, Oxford, photograph by D. F. Roberts; 16: Australian Museum, Sydney; 17, 18: *Trees*, photographs by R. St Barbe Baker; 22, 23: S. M. Manton; 24-32: World Health Organization.

BIBLIOGRAPHY

CHAPTERS 2 and 3

FORD, E. B. *The Study of Heredity*, Oxford University Press, 1937. An introduction to general genetics.

KALMUS, H. *Variation and Heredity*, Routledge, London, 1957. A volume in the Survey of Human Biology, reviewing the topical problems of human genetics and the applications of genetics to human affairs.

WADDINGTON, C. H. *An Introduction to Modern Genetics*, Allen & Unwin, London, 1939. A textbook for students covering systematic genetics, evolutionary theory, chromosomes and the gene, applied and human genetics.

CHAPTER 4

CORNER, G. W. *Ourselves Unborn*, Princeton University Press, 1942. Readable lectures covering human evolution as well as development.

SWYER, G. I. M. *Reproduction and Sex*, Routledge, London, 1954. A volume in the Survey of Human Biology, dealing with the physiology of reproduction and child-bearing, and with sexual behaviour.

CHAPTERS 5 and 6

CLARK, W. E. LE GROS. *History of the Primates*, British Museum, London, 1950. An up-to-date, lucid, and straightforward account by an authority on human evolution.

FRY, M. *Child Care and the Growth of Love*, Penguin Books, Harmondsworth, 1953. A popular version of John Bowlby's important report on the effects of maternal deprivation.

HOWELLS, W. *Mankind So Far*, Doubleday, New York and Sigma, London, 1945. A full and entertaining account of human evolution, written before the recent important discoveries in Africa.

YOUNG, J. Z. *Doubt and Certainty in Science*, Clarendon Press, Oxford, 1950. Broadcast lectures with additions, mainly on the human brain.

ZANGWILL, O. L. *An Introduction to Modern Psychology*, Methuen, London, 1950. A short but lucid and comprehensive introduction, with good documentation.

CHAPTERS 7 and 8

BENEDICT, R. *Race and Racism*, Routledge, London, 1942. A short, readable book by a social anthropologist.

HALDANE, J. B. S. *Heredity and Politics*, Allen & Unwin, London, 1938. Brilliant lectures on 'nature and nurture', eugenics and 'race'.

KLINEBERG, O. *Race Differences*, Harper, New York, 1935. A comprehensive but concise survey of the facts of physical, intellectual, and social differences between human groups.

CHAPTER 9

BLACKBURN, J. *The Framework of Human Behaviour*, Routledge, London, 1947. A discussion of sex, race, national and class differences by a social psychologist.

TYLER, L. E. *The Psychology of Human Differences*, Appleton-Century, New York, 1947. A textbook for students.

CHAPTER 10

MYRDAL, A., & KLEIN, V. *Women's Two Roles*, Routledge, London, 1956. Women in present-day society.

SCHEINFELD, A. *Women and Men*, Harcourt, New York, 1943. Comprehensive, simply written.

SELTMAN, C. *Women in Antiquity*. Thames and Hudson, 1956. Written by a scholar in a lively style, with much that has a bearing on our own times.

CHAPTER 11

CHILDE, G. *Man Makes Himself*, Watts, London, 1941. Short review of the origin of agriculture and cities by a distinguished archaeologist.

CHILDE, G. *What Happened in History*, Penguin Books, Harmondsworth, 1942. A stimulating review of the main developments in human history.

CLARK, G. *Savagery to Civilization*, Cobbett, London, 1946. Short and clearly written.

CURWEN, C. *Plough and Pasture*, Cobbett, London, 1947. Concise history of major agricultural developments.

LILLEY, S. *Men, Machines and History*, Cobbett, London, 1948. History of invention in relation to social change.

OAKLEY, K. P. *Man the Tool-Maker*, British Museum, London, 1952. A review of the cultures of fossil men and of savages generally.

CHAPTERS 12 and 13

CASTRO, J. DE. *Geography of Hunger*, Gollancz, London, 1950. A long, brilliant and controversial book on the world's food problem, by a Brazilian authority.

CLARK, F. LE GROS, & PIRIE, N. (ed.). *4,000 Million Mouths*, Oxford University Press, 1950. A series of lucid and authoritative essays, showing how the problems of producing more food can be solved.

DRUMMOND, J., & WILBRAHAM, A. *The Englishman's Food*, Cape, London, 1939. A history, full of fascinating detail.

ELTON, C. *Animal Ecology*, Sidgwick & Jackson, London, 1947. An outstanding, short textbook.

MCCARRISON, R., & SINCLAIR, H. M. *Nutrition and National Health*, Faber, London, 1953. A famous series of lectures, with a recently added chapter by the director of the Oxford Nutritional Research Unit.

ORR, J. B. *Food, Health and Income*, Macmillan, London, 1936. The most famous of all nutrition surveys.

CHAPTER 14

DUBOS, R. & J. *The White Plague*, Gollancz, London, 1953. A brilliantly written account of tuberculosis, for the general reader, with much interesting historical information.

LEFF, S. *Social Medicine*, Routledge, London, 1953. A volume in the Survey of Human Biology, giving an up-to-date account, for the general reader, of medicine as a social endeavour.

TITMUSS, R. M. *Birth, Poverty and Wealth*, Hamilton, London, 1943. Infant mortality, stillbirth rates, etc., in relation to economic facts.

WINSLOW, C.-E. A. *The Cost of Sickness and the Price of Health*, W.H.O., Geneva, 1951. A valuable survey of what can be done to combat disease, and the cost of failing to do so.

CHAPTER 15

CARR-SAUNDERS, A. M. *World Population*, Oxford University Press, 1936. Population problems, and population trends throughout the world.

MYRDAL, A. *Nation and Family*, Routledge, London, 1945. General discussion of declining fertility in Europe, and detailed account of Swedish experience.

THOMPSON, W. *Plenty of People*, Jacques Cattell Press, Lancaster, Penn., 1944. Short, popular, comprehensive review of population problems.

CHAPTER 16

BERNAL, J. D. *Science in History*, Watts, London, 1954. An account of the growth of science, in all its aspects, from the prehistoric to the present, and of the relations of science to other aspects of social organization. There is a full discussion of the present status of science and scientists, including a critique of the social sciences.

BERNAL, J. D. *Social Function of Science*, Routledge, London, 1952. The outstanding work on this subject.

DUNHAM, B. *Man against Myth*, Muller, London, 1948. Debunking of misconceptions about human biology and other important topics, by a philosopher; entertainingly written.

WADDINGTON, C. H. *The Scientific Attitude*, Penguin Books, Harmondsworth, 1941. The nature of scientific thought, and the relations of science to art and politics.

INDEX

References to line-drawings in the text are indicated by printing in bold type the numbers of the pages on which they occur

341

THE HUMAN MACHINE

Sir Adolphe Abrahams

A 373

This book, the first volume of the Pelican Medical Series, is based on analysis and description of the human body, and its structure and functions, in terms of inanimate machinery. It has been found possible to examine such details as the construction of the chassis of a motor-car, the engine, the fuel, lubrication, ignition, heat regulation, and, apart from purely vital processes, to find reasonable analogies. Such topics as repairs and periodical overhauls in man and motor are compared. And the lessons learnt from the care a man pays to his motor-car may encourage him to apply the same attention to his body that he is accustomed to treat with comparative neglect. Consideration of the principles of locomotion leads to the study of muscular exercise in general, its place in daily life, its physiology, its applications according to age, sex, physical capability, and inclination. The various interpretations of 'fitness' are examined, with the principles of athletic training, where the traditional fetishes are viewed in the light of modern scientific knowledge.

Such matters as athletic records and professionalism in sport, which nowadays receive widespread interest and encourage critical scrutiny and debate, are also included.

CINE-BIOLOGY

J. V. Durden, Mary Field, and F. Percy Smith

A 85

Many people who are not interested in biological text-books have had their interest excited by the glimpses of strange forms of animal and plant life on the earth and in the sea provided by *Secrets of Life* and other nature films. This book is an attempt to explain and describe more fully than film caption and comments can do, something of the life of some of the fascinating creatures about which films have been made. The examples chosen are all taken from the invertebrates – animals without backbones – who form the vast majority of living species. A large selection of photographs – essential in a book of this kind – illustrates the text, which has been kept free from technicalities.

In this story of some of Nature's creations an attempt has been made to get a true perspective of their significance, in the universal scheme, by the amalgamation of three points of view. There is the expert biologist, *J. Valentine Durden,* contributing the facts as discovered by science; the naturalist photographer, *F. Percy Smith,* who lived with animals and made pets of them; and *Mary Field,* who acted as the non-technical author of the book and was responsible for any human touches which may have crept in.